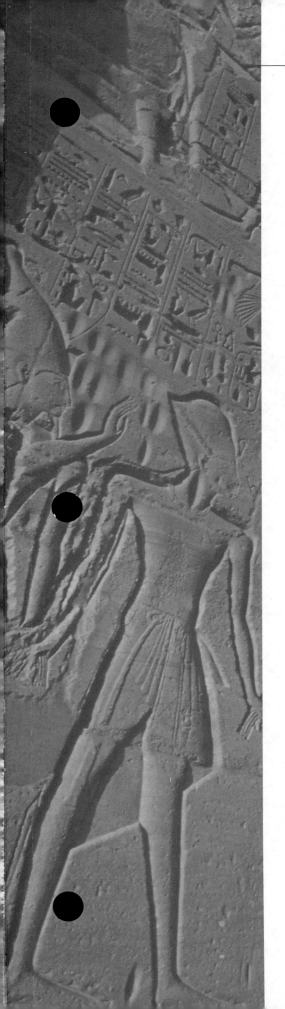

History Alive!®
The Ancient World

TCi™

Chief Executive Officer: Bert Bower

Chief Operating Officer: Amy Larson

Director of Curriculum: Liz Russell

Managing Editor: Laura Alavosus

Editorial Project Manager: Nancy Rogier

Project Editor: Pat Sills

Copyeditor: Susan Arnold

Editorial Associates: Anna Embree, Sarah Sudano

Production Manager: Lynn Sanchez

Art Director: John F. Kelly

Senior Graphic Designer: Christy Uyeno

Graphic Designers: Sarah Wildfang, Don Taka, Victoria Philp

Photo Edit Manager: Margee Robinson

Photo Editor: Diane Austin

Production Project Manager: Eric Houts

Art Editor: Mary Swab

Audio Director: Katy Haun

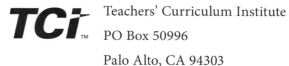

Teachers' Curriculum Institute

PO Box 50996

Palo Alto, CA 94303

Customer Service: 800-497-6138

www.teachtci.com

ISBN 978-1-58371-905-3

2 3 4 5 6 7 8 9 10 -MLI- 14 13 12 11

Program Director

Bert Bower

Program Author

Diane Hart

Creative Development Manager

Kelly Shafsky

Contributing Writers

John Bergez

Mark Falstein

Diane Hart

Marisa A. Howard

Amy Joseph

Curriculum Developers

Joyce Bartky

April Bennett

Nicole Boylan

Terry Coburn

Julie Cremin

Erin Fry

Amy George

Anne Maloney

Steve Seely

Nathan Wellborne

Reading Specialist

Kate Kinsella, Ed.D.
*Reading and TESOL Specialist
San Francisco State University*

Teacher Consultants

Melissa Aubuchon
*Indian Trail Middle School
Plainfield, Illinois*

Anthony Braxton
*Cruickshank Middle School
Merced, California*

Amy George
*Weston Middle School
Weston, Massachusetts*

Randi Gibson
*Stanford Middle School
Long Beach, California*

Lisa Macurak
*New Windsor Middle School
New Windsor, Maryland*

Sherry Owens
*Lubbock Independent School District
Lubbock, Texas*

Acknowledgments

Scholars

Dr. Anthony Bulloch
University of California, Berkeley

Dr. Mark W. Chavalas
*University of Wisconsin,
La Crosse*

Dr. Eun Mi Cho
*California State University
Sacramento*

Dr. Steve Farmer
Palo Alto, California

Dr. Bruce Grelle
California State University Chico

Dr. David N. Keightley
University of California, Berkeley

Dr. Brij Khare
*California State University
San Bernardino*

Dr. Gary Miles
*University of California,
Santa Cruz*

Dr. Daniel Veidlinger
California State University Chico

Dr. Jed Wyrick
California State University Chico

Dr. Joel Zimbelman
California State University Chico

Assessment Consultants

Denny Chandler
*Curriculum and Assessment
Specialist
Cold Spring, Kentucky*

Julie Weiss
*Curriculum and Assessment
Specialist
Elliot, Maine*

Assessment Consultant

Melanie Pinkert
*Music Faculty
Montgomery College, Maryland*

Cartographer

Mapping Specialists
Madison, Wisconsin

Internet Consultant

Amy George
Weston, Massachusetts

Diverse Needs Consultants

Erin Fry
Glendora, California

Colleen Guccione
Naperville, Illinois

Cathy Hix
*Swanson Middle School
Arlington, Virginia*

**Unit 3
Ancient India**

**Unit 5
Ancient Greece**

**Unit 6
Ancient Rome**

Directions for Interpreting Cave Art

Follow these steps to discover what cave paintings and artifacts may reveal about the lives of early humans.

1. When instructed, go to one of the "cave" stations.

2. Carefully examine the photograph at the station and match it to one of the images in your Interactive Student Notebook.

3. Complete the section of the Reading Notes that corresponds to the photograph.

4. Have your teacher check your work.

5. Repeat the steps above until you have examined all the photographs.

Chapter 1 Assessment

Mastering the Content

Fill in the circle next to the best answer.

1. People who study the past are most like
   ○ A. artists.
   ○ B. builders.
   ○ C. detectives.
   ○ D. teachers.

2. What important discovery did four teenagers make at Lascaux, France, in 1940?
   ○ A. clay sculptures of an army of soldiers
   ○ B. a cave filled with paintings of animals
   ○ C. the stone wall of an ancient storage shed
   ○ D. a wooden stick used for throwing a spear

3. Which of these activities would an archaeologist most likely do?
   ○ A. make maps
   ○ B. examine objects
   ○ C. read old newspapers
   ○ D. study Earth's features

4. An object made or used by people in the past is called
   ○ A. an artifact.
   ○ B. a document.
   ○ C. a ritual.
   ○ D. a theory.

5. Why do historians read diaries and letters from the past?
   ○ A. to agree on plans for the future
   ○ B. to compare their ideas of history
   ○ C. to learn to speak an ancient language
   ○ D. to find out what happened and why

6. Which of these is a human-made feature that a geographer might study?
   ○ A. a cave
   ○ B. a road
   ○ C. a spear
   ○ D. a volcano

7. A prehistoric object is one that comes from a time
   ○ A. before history was written.
   ○ B. before people lived in cities.
   ○ C. before humans hunted animals.
   ○ D. before electricity was discovered.

8. What is the evidence that prehistoric cave artists built wood structures (scaffolding) to stand on?
   ○ A. Many trees grew in the area.
   ○ B. The ancient planks are still there.
   ○ C. Pictures of the scaffolding have been found.
   ○ D. Some paintings are too high to be reached from the floor.

9. If ancient paintings were found in a cave, which of these questions would be the hardest to answer?

○ A. Why did people paint in caves?
○ B. How did people make the paint?
○ C. What did people paint pictures of?
○ D. What did people use for paintbrushes?

10. Which clue to the past has been found near the artwork displayed in parts of caves?

○ A. maps of the land nearby
○ B. masks in the shape of birds
○ C. prayer books for ceremonies
○ D. lamps for burning animal fat

11. About how long ago were the objects and art described in this chapter created?

○ A. about 500–800 years ago
○ B. about 2,000–3,000 years ago
○ C. about 10,000–18,000 years ago
○ D. about 2 to 3 million years ago

12. Why are ancient handprints found on cave walls very small?

○ A. The cave ceilings were very low.
○ B. The prints were made by children.
○ C. People long ago were not as big as people today.
○ D. The smallest members of the group stayed home to paint.

13. What does this ancient spear thrower, with its detailed carving, indicate about the person who may have used it?

○ A. This person was a hunter.
○ B. This person was very strong.
○ C. This person prayed to animals.
○ D. This person was a skilled painter.

14. Which question about the past does cave art **most** help to answer?

○ A. What did the people look like?
○ B. What animals lived in the area?
○ C. What language did people speak?
○ D. What did geometric shapes mean?

15. What do scientists think may have been the reason why ancient artists made paint by grinding different minerals and mixing the powder with fat or oil?

○ A. to find out which paint would last longest
○ B. to make different colors of paint for their art
○ C. to make the paint dry in different lengths of time
○ D. to use the paint in ceremonies for hunting different animals

Name_____ Date_____

Applying Social Studies Skills

Use the picture, the paragraphs below it, and your knowledge of history to answer the questions. Write the word or phrase in the space provided.

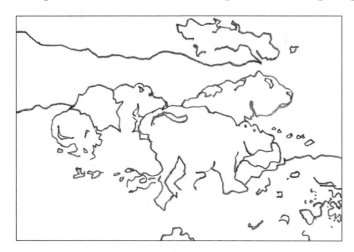

In October 1912, three brothers found these clay sculptures of bison in the Tuc d'Audoubert cave in southern France. The cave was formed by an underground river. The room with the bison is deep inside the cave, where, even today, it is hard to get to. Footprints of children have been found nearby.

Each of the two bison is about two feet long, twelve and a half inches high, and three to four inches thick. Lines made by a tool or a fingernail represent the bisons' fur. The clay of their bodies is cracked. Scientists believe that the cracks may have happened soon after the bison were made, while the clay was drying.

16. What material was used to make the bison?

17. You can see cracks in the picture of the bison. What do scientists believe explains these cracks?

18. What information about the bison sculptures would most interest a geographer?

19. What is the most likely reason these sculptures were unknown to scientists before 1912?

Exploring the Essential Question

How do social scientists interpret the past?

Follow the directions to complete the item below.

20. Suppose that you are the host for a TV news show. A site where people lived long ago was recently discovered in South America. Your next program is a discussion about this discovery. You have invited three experts as guests on your show:

    • an archaeologist
    • a historian
    • a geographer

    Write one interview question to ask each of your three guests. Remember that a good interview question cannot be answered with a simple "yes" or "no" response. A good interview question encourages the guest to talk about the subject in a way that fits his or her specialty.

    a. Interview question to ask the archaeologist:

    b. Interview question to ask the historian:

    c. Interview question to ask the geographer:

Early Hominid Act-It-Out Directions

You will work in a group to bring to life a character in an image of early hominids. Your teacher will assign a character to your group. Complete these steps to prepare for the act-it-out:

Step 1 Assume the role of the character that your teacher has assigned to your group. Discuss the questions below. Make sure everyone in your group can answer all the questions.

- What are you doing?

- In what parts of the world do your people live?

- What things have you done or made that may help you survive?

- How have these things improved your life?

Step 2 Select someone from your group to play the part of your assigned character in the image.

Step 3 Brainstorm body postures and facial expressions that the actor can use to make the character as realistic as possible.

Step 4 Find or make simple props for the actor to use during the act-it-out.

Chapter 2 Assessment

Mastering the Content

Fill in the circle next to the best answer.

1. If your profession is to study the development and culture of early hominids, then you are most likely
   ○ A. a historian.
   ○ B. a geographer.
   ○ C. an archaeologist.
   ○ D. an anthropologist.

2. What could Lucy do that gorillas could **not** do as easily?
   ○ A. use her hands to defend her children
   ○ B. make tools such as a sharp knife
   ○ C. form a group to hunt for animals
   ○ D. build fires to cook meat for her family

3. Which statement about *Homo habilis* describes a capability that helped their group survive?
   ○ A. They knew how to make tools.
   ○ B. They came before Neanderthals.
   ○ C. They lived 1.5 million years ago.
   ○ D. They had ape and human features.

4. Which of these helped *Homo habilis* survive against animal attacks?
   ○ A. building shelters
   ○ B. burying their dead
   ○ C. using bows and arrows
   ○ D. living together in groups

Use this map to do the next four items.

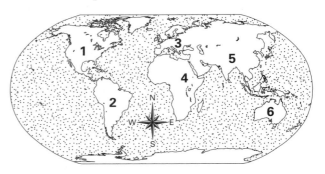

5. Where did the earliest hominids live?
   ○ A. continent 2
   ○ B. continent 4
   ○ C. continent 5
   ○ D. continent 6

6. Which group is believed to be the first to live on continent 3?
   ○ A. *Homo habilis*
   ○ B. *Homo erectus*
   ○ C. *Homo sapiens sapiens*
   ○ D. *Australopithecus afarensis*

7. Which new capability enabled hominids to survive in the colder climate of continent 3?
   ○ A. building fire and shelters
   ○ B. drawing art on cave walls
   ○ C. gathering food from plants
   ○ D. making tools out of bones

8. How do scientists think hominids first migrated to continent 1?
   ○ A. down rivers on bamboo rafts
   ○ B. in boats made out of hollow logs
   ○ C. over land that is now under water
   ○ D. by riding animals that could swim

© Teachers' Curriculum Institute

9. The name *Homo habilis* means
   ○ A. "Upright Man," the biped.
   ○ B. "Handy Man," the toolmaker.
   ○ C. "Wise Man," the language user.
   ○ D. "Artist Man," the cave painter.

10. The bones of a number of hominids were found in one location. Scientists concluded that this type of hominid probably
   ○ A. made tools.
   ○ B. died in wars.
   ○ C. had language.
   ○ D. lived in groups.

11. What trait made *Homo erectus* well suited for traveling?
   ○ A. short, stocky build
   ○ B. ridge above the eyes
   ○ C. long, strong leg bones
   ○ D. round, smooth foreheads

12. *Homo erectus* was the first hominid to use
   ○ A. fire.
   ○ B. hands.
   ○ C. fish hooks.
   ○ D. stone tools.

13. Large brains helped *Homo sapiens neanderthalensis* survive, giving them the ability to
   ○ A. run much faster.
   ○ B. bend farther forward.
   ○ C. design better tools.
   ○ D. plant crops for food.

14. At Neanderthal sites, evidence from burial mounds, showing signs that people cared for the sick and injured, has led scientists to believe that Neanderthals had
   ○ A. creative minds.
   ○ B. a complex religion.
   ○ C. a desire to make art.
   ○ D. a sense of community.

15. What advantage over previous hominid groups did the invention of the spear thrower give to early modern humans?
   ○ A. to cook animals for food
   ○ B. to injure animals with spears
   ○ C. to kill animals from a distance
   ○ D. to hunt animals in organized groups

16. Who made cave paintings. carvings, and musical instruments?
   ○ A. *Homo erectus*
   ○ B. *Homo sapiens sapiens*
   ○ C. *Australopithecus afarensis*
   ○ D. *Homo sapiens neanderthalensis*

Applying Social Studies Skills

Use the passage and your knowledge of history to complete the sentences. Write the word or phrase in the space provided.

Mary Leakey looked for hominid bones with her husband, Louis Leakey. In 1994, she told an interviewer for *Scientific American*,

> *For me it was the sheer instinctive joy of collecting, or indeed one could say treasure hunting: it seemed that this whole area abounded in objects of beauty and great intrinsic interest that could be taken from the ground.*

She found a hominid skull from about 1.8 million years ago. She said,

> *For some reason, that skull caught the imagination. But what it also did . . . it caught the imagination of the National Geographic Society, and as a result they funded us for years.*

One of her most important discoveries was the footprints of three hominids. They were from about 3.6 million years ago. They proved that very early hominids walked on two feet. She told the interviewer,

> *It was not as exciting as some of the other discoveries, because we did not know what we had. Of course, when we realized what they [footprints] were, then it was really exciting.*

She talked about how hard it is to know the meaning of things she found.

> *There is so much we do not know, and the more we do know, the more we realize that early interpretations were completely wrong.*

---

17. Who paid for much of the Leakeys' work?

18. What did Mary Leakey realize about the footprints that made them really exciting?

19. What have new findings shown about the early interpretations of hominid remains?

Exploring the Essential Question

What capabilities helped hominids survive?

Follow the directions to complete the item below.

20. Write a short story about a Neanderthal individual or family. Your story should
    - show how Neanderthal capabilities such as skilled toolmaking, hunting in an organized group, and caring for each other help them survive in their environment.
    - establish and develop a plot and setting, and present a point of view that is appropriate to the story.
    - include sensory details and concrete language that develop plot and character.
    - use several different narrative devices such as dialog and suspense.

Creating a Comic Book

Create a comic book about life in the Neolithic Age. Use the characters of Neolithic Nel and Neolithic Nick to tell a story about how ways of life changed over time, from the Paleolithic to the Neolithic Age.

Cover Page

Your comic book needs a colorful cover page with a title and drawings of the main characters, Nel and Nick. Color and add creative touches to *Student Handout 3B: Comic-Book Cover Template*. Or create your own cover page.

Story Pages

The inside of the comic book should have three story pages. Each story page will be related to one of the topics you studied (food supply, shelter, community, jobs, or trade). Select the three topics you think represent the most important changes from the Paleolithic to the Neolithic Age. Write and draw on *Student Handout 3C: Comic-Book Story Page Template*, or create your own story pages.

At the top of each story page, write one or two sentences that describe life during the Paleolithic Age. Complete the rest of the story page to show how the way of life changed in the Neolithic Age and why these changes are important. Follow these steps:

- Cut, color, and glue drawings from *Student Handout 3D: Comic-Book Characters*.
- Write informative speech or thought bubbles for the characters. Two bubbles should explain ways that life changed in the Neolithic Age, and two should explain why these changes are important.
- Add your own drawings of other animals, objects, and scenery.
- Add other details to make your comic book more realistic.

Comic-Book Cover Template

The Amazing Adventures of . . .

Neolithic Nel   **Neolithic Nick**

Comic-Book Story Page Template

Back in Paleolithic times,

Back in Neolithic times,

These changes are important because

Comic-Book Characters

Chapter 3 Assessment

Mastering the Content

Fill in the circle next to the best answer.

1. How did people in the Paleolithic Age get their food?
   - ○ A. by hunting and gathering
   - ○ B. by planting and harvesting
   - ○ C. by herding goats and cattle
   - ○ D. by trading over land and sea

2. What change began the Neolithic Age, about 8000 B.C.E.?
   - ○ A. trading
   - ○ B. hunting
   - ○ C. farming
   - ○ D. building

3. The Neolithic Age ended about 3000 B.C.E., with the discovery of how to
   - ○ A. make metal tools.
   - ○ B. weave linen cloth.
   - ○ C. tame wild animals.
   - ○ D. build brick houses.

4. Why was the Fertile Crescent the site of many early settlements?
   - ○ A. The hills were rich in gold.
   - ○ B. The soil was good for crops.
   - ○ C. The forest was full of animals.
   - ○ D. The caves were deep and warm.

5. What was the greatest benefit to people when early farmers began to raise plants and animals?
   - ○ A. They kept pets for company.
   - ○ B. They could travel more easily.
   - ○ C. They shared most of the work.
   - ○ D. They had a stable food supply.

6. One animal that was domesticated mainly for meat and milk was the
   - ○ A. goat.
   - ○ B. mule.
   - ○ C. camel.
   - ○ D. chicken.

7. Archaeologists have found houses in which the doorways were built high up on the walls. What was the most likely reason for this?
   - ○ A. People grew taller because they had more to eat.
   - ○ B. The land around the houses has sunk over the years.
   - ○ C. People wanted to be safe from wild animals or enemies.
   - ○ D. The lower parts of the walls were covered with paintings.

8. Why did people in the Neolithic Age live together in larger groups, compared with earlier times?
   - ○ A. They found better ways to get along with others.
   - ○ B. They made special goods like baskets and pottery.
   - ○ C. They needed more people for hunting and gathering.
   - ○ D. They could grow enough food to support more people.

9. Which of these was a change that resulted from building permanent shelters?

○ A. new ways of living in smaller family groups

○ B. new ways of cooking food in clay-lined pits

○ C. new ways of protection with bows and arrows

○ D. new ways of making clothing out of animal skins

10. How did dividing up the work help communities produce more to meet their needs?

○ A. Everybody did the same job.

○ B. Most people enjoyed working alone.

○ C. Villagers learned to make stone tools.

○ D. Individuals developed a variety of skills.

11. Archaeologists have found decorated pottery and polished stones. What does this suggest about Neolithic people?

○ A. They mined to get flint.

○ B. They cared about beauty.

○ C. They wanted more to eat.

○ D. They used money to trade.

12. What is the best title for the list in the box?

> - Spinners
> - Weavers
> - Basket Makers
> - Toolmakers

○ A. Trade in Catal Hoyuk

○ B. Education in Catal Hoyuk

○ C. Community in Catal Hoyuk

○ D. Specialization in Catal Hoyuk

13. Why did Neolithic people trade?

○ A. to learn other languages

○ B. to ride across the deserts

○ C. to get resources they lacked

○ D. to show off their good crafts

14. How did trade help Neolithic people make stronger tools?

○ A. They built thick stone walls around their communities.

○ B. They developed sturdy muscles by walking long distances.

○ C. They learned from nearby villages how to work with metal.

○ D. They got special materials such as obsidian from other areas.

15. If you were a Neolithic trader, what would most likely happen as you traveled and traded?

○ A. You would find out how other groups lived.

○ B. You would invent an alphabet and start writing.

○ C. You would become a better hunter by following animals.

○ D. You would make a lot of money and move to a new place.

Applying Social Studies Skills

Use the map and your knowledge of history to complete the sentences.
Write the word or phrase in the space provided.

World Food Crops, About 6000 B.C.E.

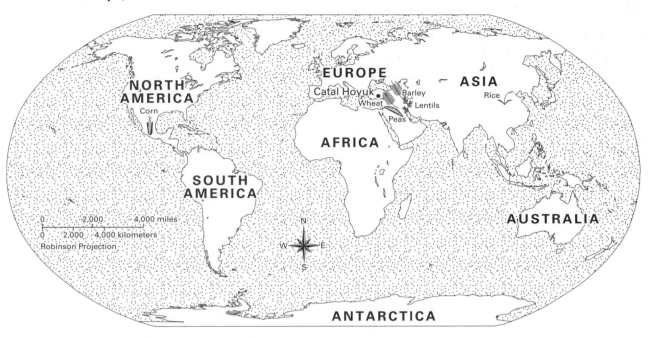

16. What was a Neolithic crop in the Americas?

17. Archaeologists have found clues that early people in eastern Asia grew and ate what crop?

18. As knowledge of planting and harvesting spread from the area of Catal Hoyuk into Europe, what one crop is it likely that European farmers began to grow?

Fill in the circle next to the best answer.

19. Which of these statements does the map best support?

○ A. The same kinds of plants grew wild in every region.

○ B. Travelers carried seeds and knowledge from Asia to the Americas.

○ C. The area with the best climate developed the greatest variety of crops.

○ D. Agriculture developed separately in several different parts of the world.

Exploring the Essential Question

How did the development of agriculture change daily life in the Neolithic Age?

Follow the directions to complete the item below.

20. Look at the map on the previous page. Find Catal Hoyuk.

    Fill in the graphic organizer below to show how the food crops displayed on the map affected daily life in Catal Hoyuk. Write one or two complete sentences in each of the five empty circles. One circle has been filled in as an example.

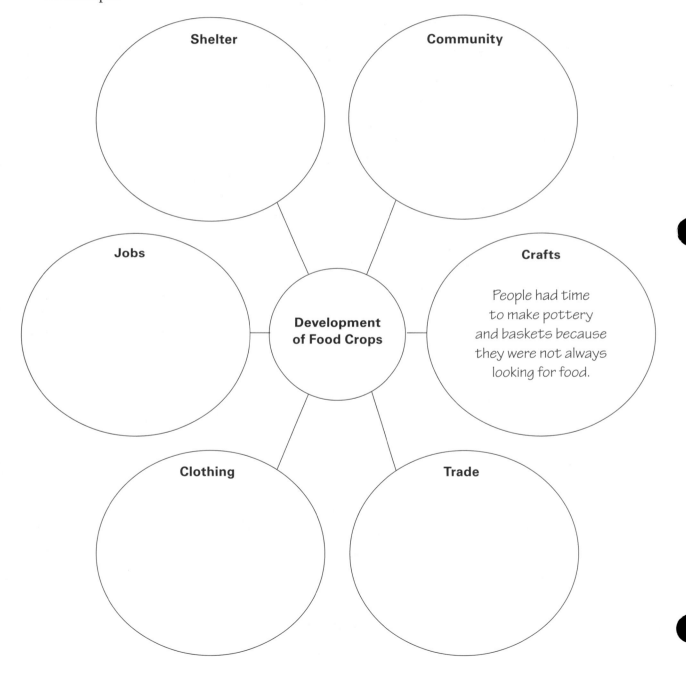

Shelter

Community

Jobs

Development of Food Crops

Crafts

People had time to make pottery and baskets because they were not always looking for food.

Clothing

Trade

Chapter 4 Assessment

Mastering the Content
Fill in the circle next to the best answer.

1. The name of Mesopotamia comes from its location, which was
   ○ A. between two rivers.
   ○ B. in mountain foothills.
   ○ C. near a region of many conflicts.
   ○ D. at the site of the earliest cities.

2. Why were Sumerian communities called city-states?
   ○ A. Each of them kept written records.
   ○ B. They were all part of one great empire.
   ○ C. They all depended on each other for water.
   ○ D. Each of them had its own ruler and farmland.

3. The environment of Sumer was
   ○ A. low and flat, with little rain.
   ○ B. hilly and dry, with many stones.
   ○ C. thickly forested, with heavy storms.
   ○ D. high and cold, with sharp mountain peaks.

4. Which fact allowed Neolithic people to farm in the foothills of the Zagros Mountains?
   ○ A. Goats can live on dry grass.
   ○ B. The region had plenty of rain.
   ○ C. Shallow canals watered the fields.
   ○ D. Harsh climates are good for grains.

5. What development caused food shortages in the Zagros foothills?
   ○ A. overuse of the soil
   ○ B. change in the climate
   ○ C. increase in population
   ○ D. fighting between villages

6. What solution did people in the Zagros foothills find to fix the problem of food shortages?
   ○ A. building terraces
   ○ B. moving to the south
   ○ C. constructing reservoirs
   ○ D. joining villages together

7. One factor that made farming difficult in the area of Sumer was
   ○ A. rocky soil.
   ○ B. steep hillsides.
   ○ C. lack of rainfall.
   ○ D. growth of weeds.

8. Why did the rivers flood in the spring?
   ○ A. Heavy rain fell throughout the area.
   ○ B. Strong winds blew from the Persian Gulf.
   ○ C. Ice that had formed on the rivers broke into bits.
   ○ D. Snow melted in the mountains where the rivers began.

9. What was the chief purpose of dams and reservoirs?

○ A. to allow travel by boat
○ B. to make it easier to fish
○ C. to store water for later use
○ D. to protect villages from attack

10. If you were in ancient Sumer, you might see a levee beside a river. Why was the levee built?

○ A. to load barges
○ B. to irrigate crops
○ C. to prevent floods
○ D. to control workers

11. Why was silt a problem for the people of Sumer?

○ A. It dried up the rivers.
○ B. It crumbled the city walls.
○ C. It ruined the soil for planting.
○ D. It clogged the irrigation canals.

12. Why did the villages of Sumer depend on each other?

○ A. They formed caravans to safely visit the mountains.
○ B. They cooperated to keep the water systems working.
○ C. They exchanged different kinds of natural resources.
○ D. They had to fight off attacks from empires to the east.

13. Using natural resources found in the environment, Sumerians built strong walls with

○ A. bricks made of mud.
○ B. logs with pointed tips.
○ C. reeds cut near the rivers.
○ D. rocks shaped into squares.

14. The people of Sumer constructed moats to

○ A. get crops to grow better.
○ B. protect cities from attack.
○ C. make villagers work together.
○ D. bring drinking water into towns.

15. Which phrase belongs in the empty box?

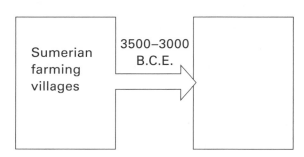

○ A. self-governing cities
○ B. large-scale private estates
○ C. bands of hunters and gatherers
○ D. abandoned archaeological sites

Name_____   Date_____

Applying Social Studies Skills

Use the map and your knowledge of history to answer the questions. Write the
word or phrase in the space provided.

Mesopotamia, About 2500 B.C.E.

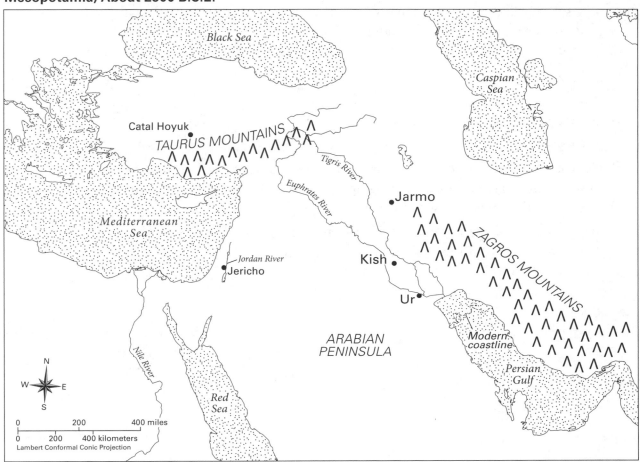

16. What two Mesopotamian city-states are shown on the map?

17. About how many miles long is the Euphrates River according to this map?

18. The Tigris and lower Euphrates rivers flow in a generally_____
    direction until they reach the body of water called the_____.

19. What major physical feature lies between the waters of the Caspian Sea and
    the Persian Gulf?

Exploring the Essential Question

How did geographic challenges lead to the rise of city-states in Mesoptamia?

Follow the directions to complete the item below.

20. In the space below, draw and label a diagram showing features of a Sumerian city-state. Your diagram must include the following:

- a river
- a city wall
- a moat
- an irrigation system
- the location of crops

After you complete your diagram, select three of the features on your diagram that were a Sumerian response to geographic challenges. For each of the three features, briefly explain these points:

- what geographic challenge led to the feature
- how the feature addresses the geographic challenge

Die Template

To create a die, copy this page onto card stock. Cut the template along the solid lines, fold it along the dashed lines, and tape it together to create a cube.

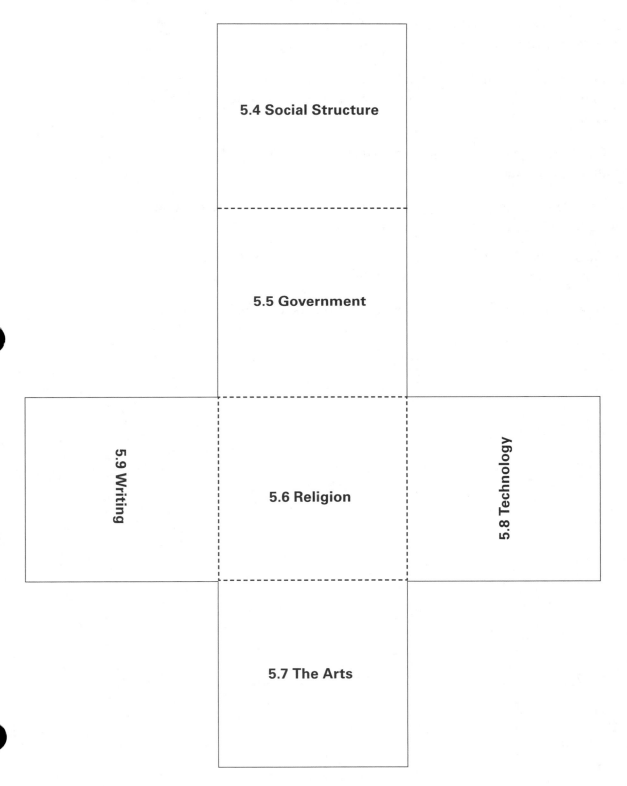

Steps for Analyzing Artifacts

Follow these steps to analyze artifacts from ancient Sumer:

Step 1: Roll one of the dice to determine which characteristic of civilization you will read about. If you have already read this section, roll again.

Step 2: Read the corresponding section in Chapter 5 of *History Alive! The Ancient World*. Complete all but the last activity (list of artifacts) in your Reading Notes for this section.

Step 3: Carefully examine the artifacts posted around the room and read the accompanying archaeologist's notes.

Step 4: Complete the last activity for this section by listing all the artifacts that show evidence in Sumer of the characteristic you just read about.

Step 5: Then choose one of the artifacts and write a sentence explaining how the artifact relates to this characteristic of civilization.

Step 6: Have your teacher check your Reading Notes. Then start over at Step 1.

Chapter 5 Assessment

Mastering the Content

Fill in the circle next to the best answer.

1. A blue stone called lapis lazuli, used on the Standard of Ur, came from far beyond the Zagros Mountains. This shows that the city-states of Sumer engaged in
   - ○ A. trade
   - ○ B. mining
   - ○ C. agriculture
   - ○ D. jewelry-making

2. A society has a stable food supply if
   - ○ A. it gives food to the king.
   - ○ B. it has enough food for its people.
   - ○ C. it buys food from other groups.
   - ○ D. it gets food by hunting and fishing.

3. Which one of these inventions most affected the food supply in Sumer?
   - ○ A. the arch
   - ○ B. the plow
   - ○ C. the wheel
   - ○ D. the chariot

4. Which of these ancient Sumerians most likely lived in a two-story house near the center of the city?
   - ○ A. a skilled metalworker
   - ○ B. a fisherman
   - ○ C. a government official
   - ○ D. a merchant

5. Small, mud-brick houses at the edge of the city were the homes of
   - ○ A. slaves.
   - ○ B. traders.
   - ○ C. potters.
   - ○ D. farmers.

6. Which Sumerian belief about the king helped strengthen the social order?
   - ○ A. He was chosen by the gods.
   - ○ B. He cared most about the poor.
   - ○ C. He consulted with wise advisers.
   - ○ D. He wanted everyone to be happy.

7. Read this list of responsibilities:
   - Lead the army.
   - Enforce the laws.
   - Have temples built.

   Who had these responsibilities?
   - ○ A. the king
   - ○ B. the priests
   - ○ C. the scribes
   - ○ D. the council

8. Why were scribes important in Sumerian government?
   - ○ A. to entertain the rulers
   - ○ B. to write down the laws
   - ○ C. to collect people's taxes
   - ○ D. to teach the royal children

9. The building in the picture was most closely related to which of these features of Sumerian civilization?

Ziggurat

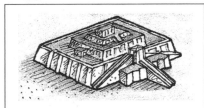

- ○ A. food
- ○ B. writing
- ○ C. religion
- ○ D. government

10. Which evidence shows that the Sumerians lived after the Stone Age?

- ○ A. brick houses
- ○ B. wooden plows
- ○ C. copper jewelry
- ○ D. painted pottery

11. Read this list of Sumerian items:

- • Drums
- • Pipes
- • Lyres

What was the main use of these items?

- ○ A. warfare
- ○ B. irrigation
- ○ C. construction
- ○ D. entertainment

12. Which invention made it possible for Sumerian armies to use chariots?

- ○ A. wheels
- ○ B. swords
- ○ C. sledges
- ○ D. horseshoes

13. Which invention added strength and beauty to Sumerian buildings?

- ○ A. glass
- ○ B. paints
- ○ C. arches
- ○ D. concrete

14. What evidence found by archaeologists shows that Sumerians were not prehistoric?

- ○ A. ziggurats
- ○ B. city walls
- ○ C. stone statues
- ○ D. written records

15. What did Sumerians use to produce cuneiform?

- ○ A. poles pulled by oxen
- ○ B. a wedge-shaped stylus
- ○ C. a net woven from reeds
- ○ D. feathers from large birds

16. Records of the goods people exchanged were made on

- ○ A. metal coins.
- ○ B. clay tablets.
- ○ C. animal hides.
- ○ D. flattened reeds.

Name_____ Date_____

Applying Social Studies Skills

Look at the three scenes below from the Standard of Ur. They show wealthy people at a banquet, workers bringing fish and animals to the banquet, and armies in battle.

Also, remember the seven characteristics of a civilization:

- stable food supply
- social structure
- government
- religion
- arts
- technology
- written language

Use the scenes, the list, and your knowledge of history to answer the questions in the space provided.

17. Which of the seven characteristics of civilization does this image show? Explain your answer.

© Copyright The British Museum

18. Which of the seven characteristics of civilization does this image show? Explain your answer.

© Copyright The British Museum

19. Which of the seven characteristics of civilization does this image show? Explain your answer.

© Copyright The British Museum

Exploring the Essential Question

Why do historians classify ancient Sumer as a civilization?

Follow the directions to complete the item below.

20. Historians call Sumer one of the world's first civilizations. Support this argument. Near each line extending from one of the seven outer circles in this diagram, write one sentence giving specific information—such as a description or an example—about that characteristic in Sumer.

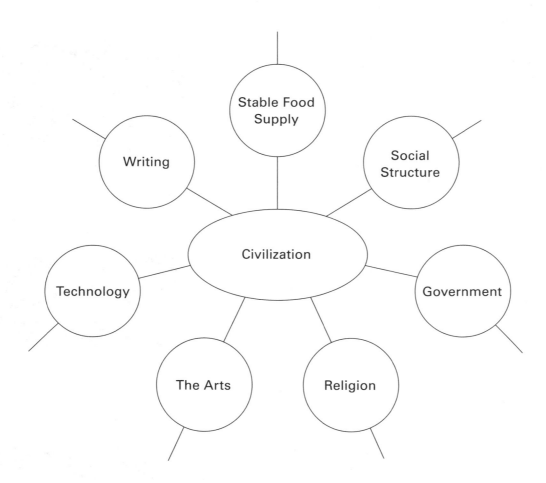

© Teachers' Curriculum Institute

Model Mechanical Diorama

Create a mechanical diorama demonstrating the Sumerian achievement of writing. One person will represent a Sumerian Scribe, and one person will represent a Sumerian Trader.

The Scribe should do the following to prepare:

- Use a pencil as a prop to represent a stylus, and a textbook as a prop to represent a clay tablet.
- Hold the "stylus" as if writing on the "clay tablet." Look deep in thought as you write. Freeze in this position.

The Trader should do the following to prepare:

- Use coins or paper as a prop to represent money.
- Hold the "money" in one hand. Hold the other hand out as if shaking hands with someone you just traded with. Freeze in this position.

When the diorama is ready, do the following:

1. Press the "Start" button on the Scribe's sleeve.
2. The Scribe says,

   "I am a scribe in the city-state of Ur. I write with a stylus, which is a sharpened reed. We do not yet have paper, so I write on wet clay. My written language is called cuneiform. It has over 700 wedged-shaped symbols."

3. The Scribe freezes. The Trader says,

   "Writing is extremely important for Ur. The scribe records the people we trade with and the goods we trade. This encourages business because now there is better record keeping. We also use writing to keep track of taxes people have paid, so the city-state knows how much money it has."

Steps for Creating a Mechanical Diorama

Work with your group to create a mechanical diorama about your Mesopotamian empire. In the mechanical diorama, you will position yourselves like statues. Tape a red "Start" button to the right arm of one member of each of the two pairs in the diorama. These parts of your diorama will "come alive" and speak when members of the audience push the "Start" buttons.

_____ **Step 1: Review the roles.** Your teacher will assign an empire to your group, and a role to you. With your group, read the information below. Make sure everyone understands his or her responsibilities.

Historian: You will lead the group during Step 2 to make sure everyone understands and uses key historical information about your empire.

Set Designer: You will lead the group during Step 3 to create a rough sketch of your mechanical diorama.

Props Manager: You will lead the group during Step 4 to determine the props and costumes for your mechanical diorama.

Director: You will lead the group during Steps 5 and 6 as group members write their scripts and practice their presentations.

_____ **Step 2: Learn about your empire and complete your Reading Notes.** Open your book to Chapter 6 and take turns reading aloud the two sections about your empire. Complete the corresponding Reading Notes in your Interactive Student Notebook. Be certain everyone in the group can describe two important achievements of this empire.

_____ **Step 3: Brainstorm your mechanical diorama and create a rough sketch.**

• Your diorama will bring to life your empire's two achievements that you illustrated and explained in your Reading Notes.

• Everyone in your group must have a part in the diorama. Two group members will bring to life one achievement, and two members will focus on the other achievement.

• Each pair will come to life by making simple movements and giving a short speech. Pairs will use props and costumes to help the audience understand what achievement is being demonstrated and why it is important.

• After you have finished brainstorming, have the Set Designer use a separate sheet of paper to make a rough sketch of what your diorama will look like. Draw and label the pairs in the scene, where they will be positioned, and what achievement each pair will illustrate.

_____ **Step 4: Determine the props and costumes for the mechanical diorama.** Each pair in the diorama must hold props or wear costumes that will help the audience better understand the achievement that that pair represents. On a separate sheet of paper, describe the props and/or costumes for each pair, and list who is responsible for making or finding each item.

_____ **Step 5: Write a script for each person in the mechanical diorama.**

- Each pair in the diorama must take turns moving and speaking when a member of the audience pushes their red "Start" button. Each person should write what he or she will say.

- One person will use 2–4 sentences to explain the achievement. This person speaks first.

- The other person will use 2–4 sentences to explain the importance of the achievement. That person speaks second.

_____ **Step 6: Practice your mechanical diorama.** Be certain all group members know where and how they will be positioned in the diorama. Have each member of the diorama practice how he or she will move and speak after the pair's "Start" button is pushed. Make sure all members of the group have memorized their speeches.

_____ **Step 7: Present your mechanical diorama.**

- Have the first speaker in each pair tape a red circle to his or her right arm. Each member of the diorama should stay motionless until the "Start" button for his or her pair is pushed.

- Then each member of that pair will come to life, perform actions and speak to the audience, and return to a frozen position.

- At the conclusion of your presentation, audience members will take notes about what they have seen. The diorama should remain motionless during this time. If an audience member has a question about information that was presented, then he or she may push a "Start" button again, and that pair in the diorama will come to life and repeat their speeches.

Chapter 6 Assessment

Mastering the Content

Fill in the circle next to the best answer.

1. What was a problem caused by Sumerian city-states' independence from one another?
   ○ A. They were unable to trade crops with one another.
   ○ B. They did not cooperate to build irrigation systems.
   ○ C. They had very few different natural resources available.
   ○ D. They could not defend themselves against stronger groups.

2. The Sumerians were a civilization but **not** an empire. What feature did the Akkadian, Babylonian, and Assyrian empires have that the Sumerians lacked?
   ○ A. One government ruled several groups.
   ○ B. Rulers claimed to get power from the gods.
   ○ C. Many beautiful works of art were produced.
   ○ D. Public works such as irrigation were organized.

3. Which of these leaders of empires came first?
   ○ A. Cyrus
   ○ B. Sargon
   ○ C. Hammurabi
   ○ D. Nebuchadrezzar

4. Which of these did the Akkadians use to gain power over Sumer?
   ○ A. military strategy
   ○ B. economic wealth
   ○ C. religious teachings
   ○ D. complex technology

5. How did the Akkadians get the resources to build up their capital city?
   ○ A. mined precious stones in the mountains
   ○ B. collected tribute from conquered peoples
   ○ C. expanded irrigation to grow bigger crops
   ○ D. printed paper money to buy what it needed

6. The Akkadians used steles to
   ○ A. attack enemy forces.
   ○ B. get water for farming.
   ○ C. record important events.
   ○ D. make objects from metal.

7. For what is Hammurabi best remembered?
   ○ A. a code of laws
   ○ B. a style of battle
   ○ C. a hanging garden
   ○ D. a system of canals

8. What is the best title for this diagram?

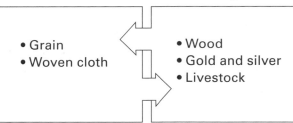

   ○ A. Babylonian Arts
   ○ B. Babylonian Trade
   ○ C. Babylonian Products
   ○ D. Babylonian Inventions

9. How was the legal system of Babylon more advanced than that of other societies at that time?
   - ○ A. It put an end to slavery.
   - ○ B. It used mild punishments.
   - ○ C. It gave women some rights.
   - ○ D. It treated all classes the same.

10. Read the list below.
    - Siege technique
    - Battering rams
    - Movable towers

    The Assyrians use the things on the list mainly to
    - ○ A. collect taxes.
    - ○ B. train soldiers.
    - ○ C. destroy crops.
    - ○ D. conquer cities.

11. Which city was the capital of the Assyrian Empire?
    - ○ A. Ur
    - ○ B. Agade
    - ○ C. Babylon
    - ○ D. Nineveh

12. What was the purpose of Assyrian aqueducts?
    - ○ A. to bring water to the city
    - ○ B. to raise crops in the dry soil
    - ○ C. to let boats pass between rivers
    - ○ D. to protect the palace from attack

13. Who conquered the land of the Israelites and took many Israelites to Babylon as captives?
    - ○ A. Sargon
    - ○ B. Marduk
    - ○ C. Hammurabi
    - ○ D. Nebuchadrezzar

14. Why did Nebuchadrezzar build two walls, some towers, and a moat around his capital?
    - ○ A. to make farmers stay outside
    - ○ B. to protect the city from attacks
    - ○ C. to keep his army from revolting
    - ○ D. to isolate his people from outsiders

15. The Hanging Gardens of Babylon were a wonder of the ancient world. Where were they planted?
    - ○ A. high on the royal palace
    - ○ B. along the irrigation canals
    - ○ C. in the Tigris River marshes
    - ○ D. in front of the imperial prison

16. A problem that all four Mesopotamian empires had was difficulty in
    - ○ A. choosing strong leaders.
    - ○ B. trading with other empires.
    - ○ C. controlling such a large area.
    - ○ D. keeping track of their history.

N a m e _____ D a t e _____

Applying Social Studies Skills

Use the timeline and your knowledge of history to complete the sentences. Write the word or phrase on the line provided.

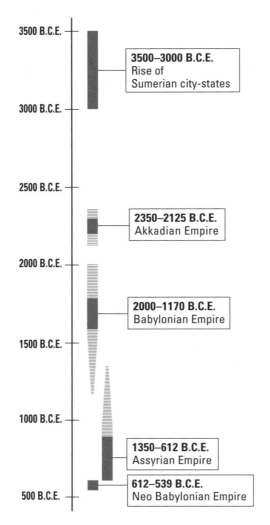

17. After having been part of a larger empire, the city-states of Mesopotamia may have once again had a period of independence, during approximately the

    years _____ to _____.

18. A group called the Hittites ruled much of Mesopotamia off and on between 1600 and 1100 B.C.E. Add this group to the timeline. The periods of Hittite

    rule fell between the height of the _____ and

    _____ Empires as shown on the timeline.

19. One battle in a specific year on the timeline marked the end of one empire

    and the beginning of another. The loser of that battle was the _____

    Empire, and the winner was the _____ Empire.

Exploring the Essential Question

What were the most important achievements of the Mesopotamian empires?

Follow the directions to complete the item below.

20. Below are drawings of four trophies, one for each Mesopotamian empire. At the base of each trophy is a plaque. Fill in the plaque with an important achievement of each empire. Your writing on each plaque should

   • be written in one or more complete sentences.

   • include the main idea and important details of the achievement.

   • show your knowledge of that Mesopotamian empire.

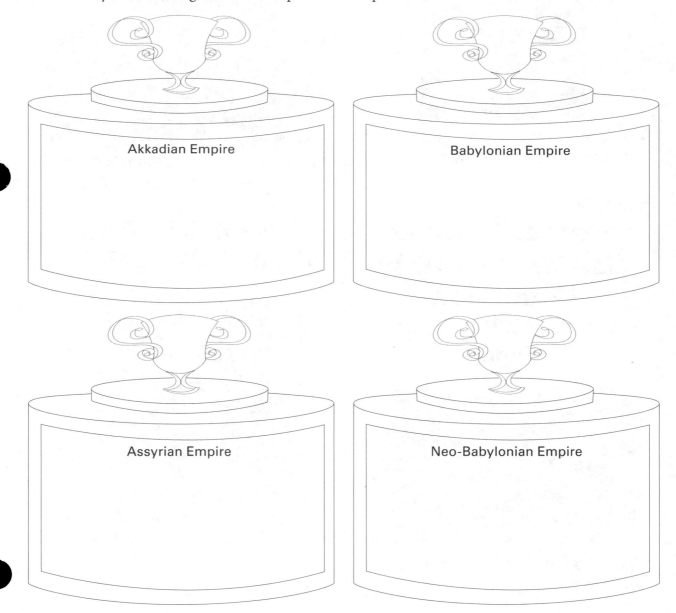

Akkadian Empire

Babylonian Empire

Assyrian Empire

Neo-Babylonian Empire

Unit 1 Timeline Challenge Cards

Homo Erectus, Upright Man
About 1.8 million–200,000 B.C.E.

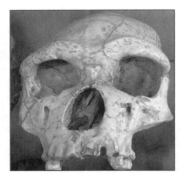

Homo erectus hominids in the Paleolithic Age discover how to use fire.

Homo Sapiens Neanderthalensis, Neanderthal Man
About 230,000–30,000 B.C.E.

Homo sapiens neanderthalensis hominids make tools and live in groups.

Homo Sapiens Sapiens, Doubly Wise Man
About 150,000 B.C.E.–Today

Homo sapiens sapiens create complex tools and art.

Neolithic Age
About 8000–3000 B.C.E.

People learn how to domesticate animals and grow crops for food.

Unit 1 Timeline Challenge Cards

First Cities
About 4000 B.C.E.

Ancient Mesopotamians establish the city of Ur along the Euphrates River.

Sumerians Create City-States
About 3500–3000 B.C.E.

Sumerians use irrigation to provide a stable food supply, enabling villages to grow into powerful city-states.

Cuneiform
About 2400 B.C.E.

Sumerians develop a written language, called cuneiform, to record information about trade.

Akkadian Empire
About 2300–2100 B.C.E.

Akkadians build the world's first empire in the Fertile Crescent region.

Unit 1 Timeline Challenge Cards

Code of Hammurabi
About 1792–1750 B.C.E.

King Hammurabi creates a code of laws to unify and preserve order in the Babylonian Empire.

Assyrian Empire
About 900–612 B.C.E.

Under Assyrian rule, the citizens of Mesopotamia obey their kings and gods.

Neo-Babylonian Empire
About 605–539 B.C.E.

The Neo-Babylonians make advances in the fields of mathematics and astronomy.

Name_____ Date_____

Chapter 7 Assessment

Mastering the Content

Fill in the circle next to the best answer.

1. Because one physical feature was so vital to ancient settlers of Egypt and Kush, **most** of their settlements were
   ○ A. on hills.
   ○ B. in a desert.
   ○ C. near a river.
   ○ D. around trees.

2. Which of these was part of the topography of ancient Egypt?
   ○ A. a river valley
   ○ B. a mountain range
   ○ C. a hot, dry climate
   ○ D. a long growing season

3. Which of these words **best** describes the environment of the Nile Delta?
   ○ A. sea
   ○ B. marsh
   ○ C. desert
   ○ D. mountain

4. How did the desert help the people of Egypt and Kush?
   ○ A. It had fertile land for crops.
   ○ B. It made trade and travel easy.
   ○ C. It was grassy for grazing sheep.
   ○ D. It gave protection from invaders.

5. One of the ways settlers used the Mediterranean Sea was for
   ○ A. catching fish.
   ○ B. watering cattle.
   ○ D. irrigating their crops.
   ○ C. getting drinking water.

6. How did the yearly flooding of the Nile River affect the people of Egypt and Kush?
   ○ A. It isolated the settlements.
   ○ B. It left silt that improved the soil.
   ○ C. It spread diseases that destroyed whole empires.
   ○ D. It attracted hunters and gatherers looking for wildlife.

7. Useful vegetation along the Nile River included
   ○ A. ducks and geese.
   ○ B. barges and boats.
   ○ C. reeds and papyrus.
   ○ D. canals and ditches.

8. In which area on the map below did the Kushites settle?
   ○ A. area A   ○ C. area C
   ○ B. area B   ○ D. area D

Ancient Kush

9. The wet, fertile plains in ancient Canaan bordered the

○ A. Negev Desert.
○ B. Sea of Galilee.
○ C. Mediterranean Sea.
○ D. Lebanon Mountains.

10. Unlike the Mediterranean Sea and the Red Sea, the Sea of Galilee was

○ A. a source of fresh water.
○ B. too stormy for boats.
○ C. often used by traders.
○ D. surrounded by deserts.

11. What was "dead" about the Dead Sea?

○ A. It was too salty for any form of life.
○ B. It was the scene of many historic battles.
○ C. It was thought to be dangerous for fishing boats.
○ D. It lay still, even when winds blew in the hills nearby.

12. How was the Jordan River different from the Nile River?

○ A. It was full of fish.
○ B. It had a weak current.
○ C. It attracted water birds.
○ D. It did not flood regularly.

13. Why were some people in parts of Canaan herders rather than farmers?

○ A. The river was too salty.
○ B. The ground was too cold.
○ C. The land was hilly and dry.
○ D. The sun was hot and strong.

14. The part of Canaan with the **most** vegetation was

○ A. in the Syrian Desert.
○ B. beside the Dead Sea.
○ C. near the Jordan River.
○ D. in the Lebanon Mountains.

15. Which **best** describes herders in Canaan?

○ A. They planted grain crops.
○ B. They lived a nomadic life.
○ C. They built houses of mud bricks.
○ D. They had a stable food supply.

Applying Social Studies Skills

Use the maps and your knowledge of history to complete the sentences. Write the word or phrase in the space provided.

16. One way physical feature A affected people's lives was

17. One way physical feature B affected people's lives was

18. One way physical feature C affected people's lives was

19. One way physical feature D affected people's lives was

Ancient Egypt and Kush

Ancient Canaan

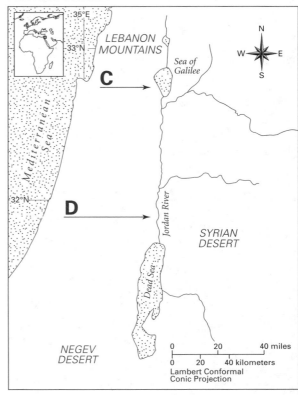

Exploring the Essential Question

How did geography affect early settlement in Egypt, Kush, and Canaan?

Follow the directions to complete the item below.

20. Suppose that you are a real estate developer in ancient Egypt, Kush, or Canaan. Select one location in that region. Write an advertisement to try to persuade people to settle in that location. Your advertisement should include these elements:

- a slogan for your new settlement
- the location of your new settlement
- its geographic features
- at least two reasons people should want to move there
- your response to at least one argument people might have against moving there

How Was the Great Pyramid Built?

For centuries, people have wondered how the ancient Egyptians were able to build the Great Pyramid. Remember, the Great Pyramid is over 450 feet tall, and it is constructed of more than 2 million huge blocks, many of which weigh 3 tons or more. And yet most scientists agree that it was likely built in just 20 years.

There have been several hypotheses put forth to explain how the Great Pyramid was built.

Which hypothesis do you think best explains how the Great Pyramid was built? Be prepared to explain why you made this choice.

Hypothesis #1: Ancient Egyptians cut the huge stone blocks from the earth and dragged the blocks to the site of the pyramid. At the site, the blocks were pulled up a long, sloping ramp and then pushed into position on the pyramid.

Hypothesis #2: Egyptians used local materials to create a cementlike substance, which workers carried up the pyramid. The cement was poured into a mold and mixed with water to form the huge blocks. These molds were placed directly on the pyramid so that when the mixture dried and the mold was removed, the block sat perfectly in place.

Hypothesis #3: Extraterrestrials either built the Great Pyramid or gave technical knowledge to the ancient Egyptians for building it.

The White Chapel: What Does It Tell Us?

The White Chapel was built for Senusret I's first jubilee festival, which was a celebration of the pharaoh's 30th year as ruler. On both sides, ramps and stairs led up to the small rectangular building. Senusret I himself may have sat inside the chapel during part of the festival.

Six hundred years later, another pharaoh tore down this beautiful monument. He used the pieces to fill in one of the pylons, or sloped walls, of a monument he was building. Modern-day archaeologists would have never known about the White Chapel if not for an incredible stroke of luck.

In 1924, Egyptian archaeologists decided to repair the monument in which the pieces of the White Chapel had been buried. While working at the site, archaeologists discovered the blocks of the White Chapel. Even though the blocks had been buried for thousands of years, the intricate carvings on them were generally in excellent condition. Using the broken sections of carvings like puzzle pieces, archaeologists were able to slowly reconstruct the White Chapel.

With your partners, see if you can re-create the painstaking work done by these archaeologists. Try to put back together the broken pieces of one of the "carvings" from the White Chapel. After you have reassembled the carving, examine it and come up with a hypothesis about what it might represent. Remembering why the White Chapel was built in the first place may give you a clue.

Carving from the White Chapel

Hatshepsut's Temple: What Does It Tell Us?

As you have learned, one of Hatshepsut's greatest accomplishments was the trade expedition she sent to the African kingdom of Punt. But what did the expedition bring back to Egypt? Here, in the temple at Dayr al-Bahri, Hatshepsut left visual clues to help us answer that question.

Carefully examine the "carving" on the temple wall that shows the expedition of traders returning to Egypt with goods from Punt. With your partners, make a list of as many different items as you can identify in the carving. Afterward, discuss how the ancient Egyptians might have used these new and exotic things.

Carving from Hatshepsut's Temple

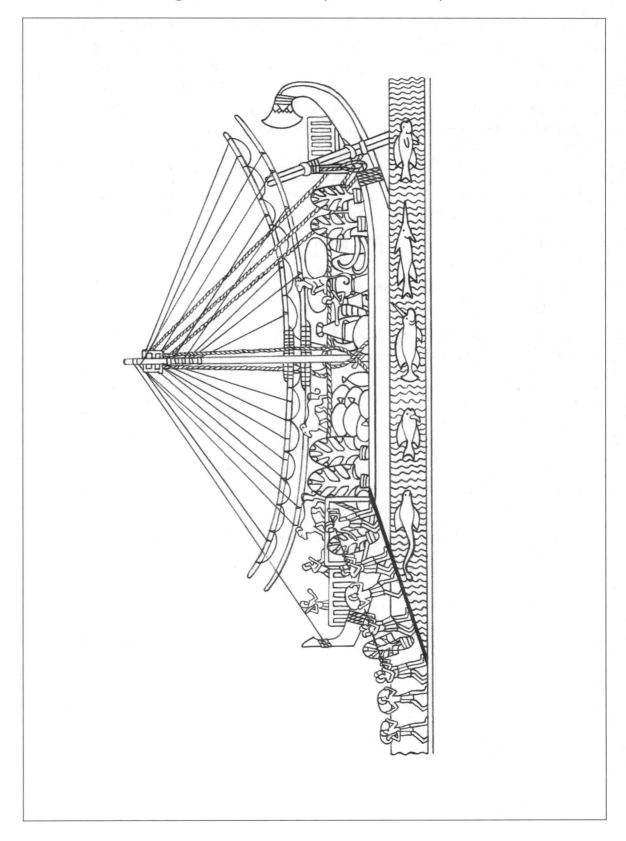

What Happened to the Great Temple of Ramses II?

The Great Temple of Ramses II at Abu Simbel was one of the most incredible architectural achievements of the New Kingdom. Probably the most outstanding features of the temple are the four enormous statues of Ramses, some of which are more than six stories tall. This monument survived for over 3,000 years.

Then, in the 1940s, the Egyptian government decided to build a new dam on the Nile River to generate electricity. Once the dam was built, water would back up behind the dam and bury the temple under hundreds of feet of water. The Egyptian government considered several different options for dealing with this problem.

- **Option A:** Abandon the project and do without the electricity that would have been provided to the Egyptian people.

- **Option B:** Find a new location for the dam, one that would not threaten to flood the Great Temple.

- **Option C:** Continue with the project, even if it meant flooding the Great Temple.

- **Option D:** Cut the entire temple away from the cliff side and move it to a higher location that would not be in the flood zone created by the dam.

Which option would you have recommended to the Egyptian government and why?

Writing a Letter About Your Tour of Ancient Egypt

On a separate sheet of paper, write a letter to a friend or relative about your felucca tour of ancient Egyptian monuments. Use your Reading Notes to help you complete the letter. Be sure to use correct grammar and spelling. Your letter must include these features:

- A proper greeting.
- A short paragraph that describes where you traveled, what you did, and the type of transportation you used.
- Two paragraphs, each describing a different site on the tour. Each paragraph should explain at least one essential and interesting thing you learned about that monument, and at least one relevant detail about the pharaoh who had it built.
- A proper closing.
- At least two "photographs" from your tour. These can be original drawings or copies of photographs from books or from the Internet. Make sure that they relate to what you wrote about in your letter. Write a caption for each image and tell where you found it.
- The use of three or more of the following terms in your letter: *pharaohs, Khufu, Senusret I, Hatshepsut, Ramses II.*

Also, make sure that

- ideas in your letter are expressed clearly so the reader will understand them.
- each paragraph states a main idea and includes supporting details.
- your paragraphs use transitions—such as *At the next site, or After visiting the Great Pyramid*—to ensure a logical flow from one to the next.

Chapter 8 Assessment

Mastering the Content

Fill in the circle next to the best answer.

1. Why is King Tut one of the **most** well-known pharaohs?
   - ○ A. Tut lived and ruled for more than 70 years.
   - ○ B. Amazing artifacts were found in Tut's tomb.
   - ○ C. Tut was the first woman to claim power over Egypt.
   - ○ D. Trade expeditions helped Tut learn about faraway lands.

2. Why did the ancient Egyptians make mummies?
   - ○ A. to decorate palaces of the pharaohs
   - ○ B. to preserve dead bodies of the pharaohs
   - ○ C. to transport goods up and down the Nile
   - ○ D. to educate and protect the royal children

3. What was a **major** purpose for building the pyramids?
   - ○ A. temples for religious worship
   - ○ B. storehouses for reserves of grain
   - ○ C. homes for the pharaohs' servants
   - ○ D. tombs for pharaohs when they died

4. What is one characteristic for which Egypt's Middle Kingdom is especially famous?
   - ○ A. reunification
   - ○ B. great pharaohs
   - ○ C. widespread wars
   - ○ D. military conquests

5. Which period is often called the Golden Age, a time when Egypt had reached the height of its power?
   - ○ A. the Old Kingdom
   - ○ B. the Middle Kingdom
   - ○ C. the New Kingdom
   - ○ D. after the New Kingdom

6. What was one method Khufu used to ensure that his power would be accepted?
   - ○ A. He declared that he was a god.
   - ○ B. He had many children.
   - ○ C. He made strong treaties.
   - ○ D. He killed his rivals.

7. It was built from more than 2 million stone blocks. It had tunnels inside. What was it?
   - ○ A. the Sphinx
   - ○ B. the White Chapel
   - ○ C. the temple at Abu Simbel
   - ○ D. the Great Pyramid at Giza

8. Senusret I controlled a source of natural resources that were used in beautiful works of art. What was that source?
   - ○ A. forests of giant cedar trees
   - ○ B. hot, bubbling mineral springs
   - ○ C. mines for gold, copper, and gems
   - ○ D. flocks of birds with scarlet feathers

9. Why did archaeologists reconstruct the White Chapel?

○ A. It offered tourists shade while they waited for a guide.

○ B. It gave the scientists a place to study what they dug up.

○ C. It was an experiment to learn old construction methods.

○ D. It was built by Senusret I but had been taken apart by a later ruler

10. Hatshepsut was the **first** pharaoh who was

○ A. a god.

○ B. a child.

○ C. a priest.

○ D. a woman.

11. Look at this picture. Under which of these pharaohs did this activity **most** likely take place?

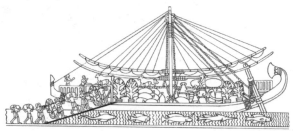

○ A. Khufu

○ B. Senusret I

○ C. Ramses II

○ D. Hatshepsut

12. Which phrase **best** describes Hatshepsut's monument at Dayr al-Bahri?

○ A. a pyramid constructed in the open desert

○ B. a mud-brick structure found on an island

○ C. a shrine dug out of rock below ground level

○ D. a great temple built into a cliff above the river

13. Look at the timeline. In which time period did Egypt have a pharaoh who was especially known for promoting trade?

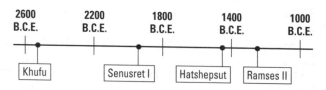

○ A. between 2600 and 2500 B.C.E.

○ B. between 2000 and 1900 B.C.E.

○ C. between 1500 and 1400 B.C.E.

○ D. between 1300 and 1200 B.C.E.

14. Answer the riddle below.

I ruled Egypt for more than 60 years.
I was a famous military leader.
I had hundreds of statues of me built—all over Egypt!
Who was I?

○ A. Khufu

○ B. Senusret I

○ C. Ramses II

○ D. Hatshepsut

15. Who signed the world's first peace treaty?

○ A. Egypt and the Hittites

○ B. Egypt and the Persians

○ C. Egypt and the Assyrians

○ D. Egypt and the Babylonians

16. Compared with any other pharaoh in history, Ramses II produced more

○ A. books of scholarship.

○ B. temples and monuments.

○ C. maps based on expeditions.

○ D. inventions to use in warfare.

Applying Social Studies Skills

Use the chart, the map, and your knowledge of history to answer the questions.
Write the word(s) or phrase(s) in the space provided.

Name	Order of Rule (dynasty = ruling family)	International Affairs	Site of a Major Monument
Khufu	Second pharaoh in 4th dynasty	Name on monuments, over a wide area	Giza
Senusret I	Second pharaoh in 12th dynasty	Military expeditions south along Nile; diplomatic contact with towns in Syria and Canaan	Karnak
Hatshepsut	Fifth pharaoh in 18th dynasty	Trading expeditions to Punt, Sinai, and Lebanon	Dayr al-Bahri
Ramses II	Third pharaoh in 19th dynasty	Exchange of letters with Hittites on cuneiform tablets	Abu Simbel

17. Historians and archaeologists have used written records to learn about individual pharaohs. Using information from the chart, what two forms of these written records can you find?

18. What geographical change, over time, do the sites of the major monuments show?

19. What are three ways the pharaohs interacted with neighboring peoples?

Monument Sites

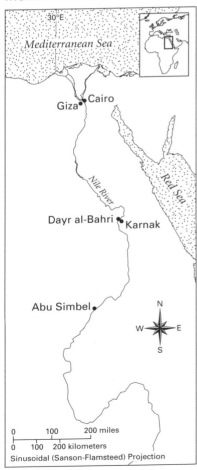

54 Chapter 8

Exploring the Essential Question

What did the pharaohs of ancient Egypt accomplish, and how did they do it?

Follow the directions to complete the item below.

20. Suppose that you are a travel writer for a newspaper or magazine. You are visiting the main temple at Abu Simbel and see four 66-foot statues of Ramses II at the entrance. This image shows one of the four statues. Write a short article of two paragraphs, describing the statue shown in this image. Make sure your article

- engages the interest of the reader.
- states the topic clearly.
- follows a clear organizational pattern.
- develops the topic with supporting details.
- uses precise verbs, nouns, and adjectives to paint a visual image in the mind of the reader.
- ends with a summary related to the purpose for writing.

Preparing an Interactive Dramatization
About Government Officials

Work with your group to create an interactive dramatization about the daily life of ancient Egyptian government officials. Have your teacher initial each step as you complete it.

_____ **Step 1: Assign roles.** Review the roles below. Then choose a role for each member of your group. Make sure each person understands his or her responsibilities. Everyone will participate in the dramatization.

Historian: You will lead the group during Step 2. Make sure the dramatization includes important historical information.

Director: You will lead the group during Step 3. Make sure the dramatization includes all required elements and involves everyone.

Special Effects Designer: You will lead the group during Step 4. Make sure the dramatization is as realistic as possible.

Host: You will lead the group during Step 5. During the dramatization, invite visitors to participate, and answer any questions they may have.

_____ **Step 2: Learn about ancient Egyptian government officials.** The Historian leads the group in examining *Visual 9A: Government Officials* to see what the image reveals about the daily life of ancient Egyptian government officials. Then take turns reading aloud from Section 9.3 and complete the corresponding Reading Notes in your Interactive Student Notebook.

_____ **Step 3: Plan your interactive dramatization.** The Director leads the group in planning a three- to five-minute interactive dramatization about ancient Egyptian government officials, in which all group members plus four members of the audience participate. Your dramatization should bring to life the scene on your visual of a banquet at the home of an important government official.

The dramatization should highlight important information from your completed Reading Notes and include these parts, in order:

1. One of you, acting as the banquet host, greets your visitors, using the ancient Egyptian welcome of *Iiwy em hotep* (EYE-why EM ho-TEP). Invite them to sit with your guests on the appropriate side of the table. Tell the visitors which social class in ancient Egypt you and your guests are from.

2. Proudly "show off" your perfumed hair, jewelry, and fine linen clothing. Tell the visitors what positions you hold in the government and what your responsibilities are. Ask your visitors to describe the responsibilities of their government officials.

3. One of you, acting as a servant, offers food and drink to everyone at the table. Encourage visitors to sample the wide variety of dishes.

4. Say, "Regard one you know like one you don't know, one near you like one far from you," and explain why this is good advice.

5. Describe forms of entertainment that occur at banquets.

6. Ask if your visitors have any questions, and answer them. Thank them for coming, and say good-bye using the ancient Egyptian word *senebti*.

_____ **Step 4: Brainstorm ideas for costumes, props, and special effects.** The Special Effects Designer leads the group in brainstorming ideas for costumes, props, and other special effects that will make the dramatization more realistic. (During your presentation, the transparency will be projected on the screen behind your group.)

_____ **Step 5: Rehearse your dramatization.** The Host leads the group in rehearsing your interactive dramatization. As you rehearse, work on meeting these guidelines:

• Your dramatization is three to five minutes in length.

• All group members actively participate in the dramatization.

• Actors speak their lines loudly, clearly, and at the right time.

• Actors use their costumes and props appropriately.

• The Special Effects Designer knows the cues for any special effects.

• Actors know how and when the visitors will participate in the dramatization.

Preparing an Interactive Dramatization About Priests

Work with your group to create an interactive dramatization about the daily life of ancient Egyptian priests. Have your teacher initial each step as you complete it.

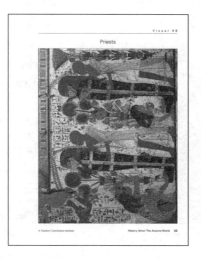

_____ **Step 1: Assign roles.** Review the roles below. Then choose a role for each member of your group. Make sure each person understands his or her responsibilities. Everyone will participate in the dramatization.

Historian: You will lead the group during Step 2. Make sure the dramatization includes important historical information.

Director: You will lead the group during Step 3. Make sure the dramatization includes all required elements and involves everyone.

Special Effects Designer: You will lead the group during Step 4. Make sure the dramatization is as realistic as possible.

Host: You will lead the group during Step 5. During the dramatization, invite visitors to participate, and answer any questions they may have.

_____ **Step 2: Learn about ancient Egyptian priests.** The Historian leads the group in examining *Visual 9B: Priests* to see what the image reveals about the daily life of ancient Egyptian priests. Then take turns reading aloud from Section 9.4 and complete the corresponding Reading Notes in your Interactive Student Notebook.

_____ **Step 3: Plan your interactive dramatization.** The Director leads the group in planning a three- to five-minute interactive dramatization about ancient Egyptian priests, in which all group members plus four members of the audience participate. Your dramatization should bring to life the scene on your visual of priests embalming the body of a dead person to produce a mummy.

The dramatization should highlight important information from your completed Reading Notes and include these parts, in order:

1. Greet your visitors, using the ancient Egyptian welcome of *em hotep nefer*. Introduce yourselves and invite the visitors to join you. Tell them which social class in ancient Egypt you are from.

2. Show some of the items that will be buried with this person's body. Tell your visitors what ancient Egyptians believe happens to people after they die, and why these items are important in the afterlife.

3. Describe the key steps in the embalming process. Be sure to explain why the heart is left in the body. Have your visitors hold the yards of linen used to wrap the mummy.

4. One of you, acting as a woman, point to a nearby temple. Describe the various responsibilities of priests, including the role of women. Ask your visitors what types of jobs women in their society have.

5. Say, "Priests can't eat fish or wear wool, and must bathe at least three times a day," and explain why.

6. Ask if your visitors have any questions, and answer them. Thank them for coming, and say good-bye using the ancient Egyptian word *senebti*.

_____ **Step 4: Brainstorm ideas for costumes, props, and special effects.** The Special Effects Designer leads the group in brainstorming ideas for costumes, props, and other special effects that will make the dramatization more realistic. (During your presentation, the transparency will be projected on the screen behind your group.)

_____ **Step 5: Rehearse your dramatization.** The Host leads the group in rehearsing your interactive dramatization. As you rehearse, work on meeting these guidelines:

• Your dramatization is three to five minutes in length.

• All group members actively participate in the dramatization.

• Actors speak their lines loudly, clearly, and at the right time.

• Actors use their costumes and props appropriately.

• The Special Effects Designer knows the cues for any special effects.

• Actors know how and when the visitors will participate in the dramatization.

Preparing an Interactive Dramatization About Scribes

Work with your group to create an interactive dramatization about the daily life of ancient Egyptian scribes. Have your teacher initial each step as you complete it.

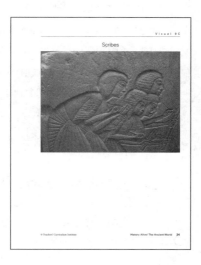

_____ **Step 1: Assign roles.** Review the roles below. Then choose a role for each member of your group. Make sure each person understands his or her responsibilities. Everyone will participate in the dramatization.

Historian: You will lead the group during Step 2. Make sure the dramatization includes important historical information.

Director: You will lead the group during Step 3. Make sure the dramatization includes all required elements and involves everyone.

Special Effects Designer: You will lead the group during Step 4. Make sure the dramatization is as realistic as possible.

Host: You will lead the group during Step 5. During the dramatization, invite visitors to participate, and answer any questions they may have.

_____ **Step 2: Learn about ancient Egyptian scribes.** The Historian leads the group in examining *Visual 9C: Scribes* to see what the image reveals about the daily life of ancient Egyptian scribes. Then take turns reading aloud from Section 9.5 and complete the corresponding Reading Notes in your Interactive Student Notebook.

_____ **Step 3: Plan your interactive dramatization.** The Director leads the group in planning a three- to five-minute interactive dramatization about ancient Egyptian scribes, in which all group members plus four members of the audience participate. Your dramatization should bring to life the scene on your visual of students at a school for scribes.

The dramatization should highlight important information from your completed Reading Notes and include these parts, in order:

1. Greet your visitors, using the ancient Egyptian welcome of *ak em hotep.* Introduce yourselves and invite the visitors to join you inside the school. Tell them which social class in ancient Egypt you are from.

2. Give your visitors a tour of the scribe school classroom. Describe the purpose of scribe schools, who studies there, and for how many years they study. Ask your visitors who studies in their schools and for how many years.

3. Show your visitors the typical tools and materials that scribes use. Have the visitors watch a student use these tools. Let your visitors try using the tools.

4. Say, "A youngster's ear is on his back; he only listens to the man who beats him," and explain what you mean.

5. Have your visitors examine a tablet with hieroglyphs. Explain why scribes are important, and how their status affected their daily life.

6. Ask if your visitors have any questions, and answer them. Thank them for coming, and say good-bye using the ancient Egyptian word *senebti.*

_____ **Step 4: Brainstorm ideas for costumes, props, and special effects.** The Special Effects Designer leads the group in brainstorming ideas for costumes, props, and other special effects that will make the dramatization more realistic. (During your presentation, the transparency will be projected on the screen behind your group.)

_____ **Step 5: Rehearse your dramatization.** The Host leads the group in rehearsing your interactive dramatization. As you rehearse, work on meeting these guidelines:

• Your dramatization is three to five minutes in length.

• All group members actively participate in the dramatization.

• Actors speak their lines loudly, clearly, and at the right time.

• Actors use their costumes and props appropriately.

• The Special Effects Designer knows the cues for any special effects.

• Actors know how and when the visitors will participate in the dramatization.

Preparing an Interactive Dramatization About Artisans

Work with your group to create an interactive dramatization about the daily life of ancient Egyptian artisans. Have your teacher initial each step as you complete it.

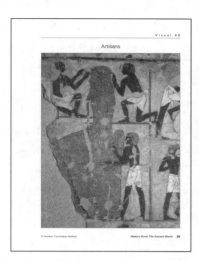

_____ **Step 1: Assign roles.** Review the roles below. Then choose a role for each member of your group. Make sure each person understands his or her responsibilities. Everyone will participate in the dramatization.

Historian: You will lead the group during Step 2. Make sure the dramatization includes important historical information.

Director: You will lead the group during Step 3. Make sure the dramatization includes all required elements and involves everyone.

Special Effects Designer: You will lead the group during Step 4. Make sure the dramatization is as realistic as possible.

Host: You will lead the group during Step 5. During the dramatization, invite visitors to participate, and answer any questions they may have.

_____ **Step 2: Learn about ancient Egyptian artisans.** The Historian leads the group in examining *Visual 9D: Artisans* to see what the image reveals about the daily life of ancient Egyptian artisans. Then take turns reading aloud from Section 9.6 and complete the corresponding Reading Notes in your Interactive Student Notebook.

_____ **Step 3: Plan your interactive dramatization.** The Director leads the group in planning a three- to five-minute interactive dramatization about ancient Egyptian artisans, in which all group members plus four members of the audience participate. Your dramatization should bring to life the scene on your visual of stone carvers working on a sculpture.

The dramatization should highlight important information from your completed Reading Notes and include these parts, in order:

1. Greet your visitors, using the ancient Egyptian greeting of *yii em hotep.* Introduce yourselves and invite the visitors to join you inside the workshop. Tell them which social class in ancient Egypt you are from.

2. Give your visitors a tour of the workshop. Describe the types of work that artisans do, including what the artisans at this site are creating.

3. Have visitors examine the tools you are using and try some of the work you are doing. Make sure they understand why the stone carvers' work is so difficult.

4. Encourage visitors to listen in on a debate between two artisans about whether artisans get credit for the work they do. Ask your visitors to share their opinions.

5. Show visitors an object created by another type of artisan. Tell them about the type of homes artisans generally live in.

6. Ask if your visitors have any questions, and answer them. Thank them for coming, and say good-bye using the ancient Egyptian word *senebti*.

_____ **Step 4: Brainstorm ideas for costumes, props, and special effects.** The Special Effects Designer leads the group in brainstorming ideas for costumes, props, and other special effects that will make the dramatization more realistic. (During your presentation, the transparency will be projected on the screen behind your group.)

_____ **Step 5: Rehearse your dramatization.** The Host leads the group in rehearsing your interactive dramatization. As you rehearse, work on meeting these guidelines:

- Your dramatization is three to five minutes in length.
- All group members actively participate in the dramatization.
- Actors speak their lines loudly, clearly, and at the right time.
- Actors use their costumes and props appropriately.
- The Special Effects Designer knows the cues for any special effects.
- Actors know how and when the visitors will participate in the dramatization.

Preparing an Interactive Dramatization About Peasants

Work with your group to create an interactive dramatization about the daily life of ancient Egyptian peasants. Have your teacher initial each step as you complete it.

_____ **Step 1: Assign roles.** Review the roles below. Then choose a role for each member of your group. Make sure each person understands his or her responsibilities. Everyone will participate in the dramatization.

Historian: You will lead the group during Step 2. Make sure the dramatization includes important historical information.

Director: You will lead the group during Step 3. Make sure the dramatization includes all required elements and involves everyone.

Special Effects Designer: You will lead the group during Step 4. Make sure the dramatization is as realistic as possible.

Host: You will lead the group during Step 5. During the dramatization, invite visitors to participate, and answer any questions they may have.

_____ **Step 2: Learn about ancient Egyptian peasants.** The Historian leads the group in examining *Visual 9E: Peasants* to see what the image reveals about the daily life of ancient Egyptian peasants. Then take turns reading aloud from Section 9.7 and complete the corresponding Reading Notes in your Interactive Student Notebook.

_____ **Step 3: Plan your interactive dramatization.** The Director leads the group in planning a three- to five-minute interactive dramatization about ancient Egyptian peasants, in which all group members plus four members of the audience participate. Your dramatization should bring to life the scene on your visual of peasants working in the fields during harvest time.

The dramatization should highlight important information from your completed Reading Notes and include these parts, in order:

1. Greet your visitors, using the ancient Egyptian greeting of *yeh*. Introduce yourselves and invite the visitors to join you in the fields. Tell them which social class in ancient Egypt you are from.

2. One of you, acting as a woman, point to the Nile River. Describe how the peasants' work changes according to the season. Include in your description the difference in roles between men and women.

3. Show your visitors what you are doing, and explain how you sing songs to help pass the time. Play CD Track 15 and have your visitors work and chant along with you.

4. Say, "Harvest time can bring both reward and punishment," and explain what you mean.

5. Offer your visitors some of the food you brought with you. Tell them about the typical diet for peasants, and what you do for fun.

6. Ask if your visitors have any questions, and answer them. Thank them for coming, and say good-bye using the ancient Egyptian word *senebti*.

_____ **Step 4: Brainstorm ideas for costumes, props, and special effects.** The Special Effects Designer leads the group in brainstorming ideas for costumes, props, and other special effects that will make the dramatization more realistic. (During your presentation, the transparency will be projected on the screen behind your group.)

_____ **Step 5: Rehearse your dramatization.** The Host leads the group in rehearsing your interactive dramatization. As you rehearse, work on meeting these guidelines:

• Your dramatization is three to five minutes in length.

• All group members actively participate in the dramatization.

• Actors speak their lines loudly, clearly, and at the right time.

• Actors use their costumes and props appropriately.

• The Special Effects Designer knows the cues for any special effects.

• Actors know how and when the visitors will participate in the dramatization.

Chapter 9 Assessment

Mastering the Content

Fill in the circle next to the best answer.

1. Why are the social classes of ancient Egypt described by the shape at the left, rather than the shape at the right?

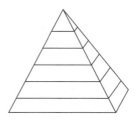 

- ○ A. The triangle represented the three seasons of the Nile.
- ○ B. Most people were in the bottom classes, and the fewest people were at the top.
- ○ C. Scientists like to use a pyramid to keep the layers apart.
- ○ D. Many structures of that design were built in the desert.

2. Who built the giant temples of the pharaohs?
- ○ A. scribes who kept poor records
- ○ B. government officials out of favor
- ○ C. peasant farmers during the flood season
- ○ D. priests hoping to get jobs at the temples

3. Which of these activities was permitted **only** to men?
- ○ A. owning land
- ○ B. running a business
- ○ C. working as a scribe
- ○ D. asking for a divorce

4. How did **most** government officials get their jobs?
- ○ A. They attended school to learn how to govern.
- ○ B. Popular elections showed the vote of the people.
- ○ C. Priests relied on signs from the gods to choose them.
- ○ D. They inherited the position from a family member.

5. What was an important duty of the vizier?
- ○ A. to collect taxes
- ○ B. to lead the army
- ○ C. to decide court cases
- ○ D. to help make alliances

6. Which sentence **best** describes the role of women in religion?
- ○ A. They were worshiped as gods.
- ○ B. They could become priestesses.
- ○ C. They ran all religious ceremonies.
- ○ D. They were not allowed in temples.

7. Which of these was in the sanctuary of a temple?
- ○ A. a statue of a god
- ○ B. a pool for washing
- ○ C. a public meeting area
- ○ D. a bench for women only

8. Why did Egyptians bury some bread and beer with their dead?
- ○ A. to show earthly love
- ○ B. to avoid the risk of poison
- ○ C. to feed them in the afterlife
- ○ D. to perform a sacrifice to the gods

9. What was one of the few ways that a boy from a peasant family could rise to a higher social class?
    ○ A. store a lot of grain
    ○ B. attend scribe school
    ○ C. help build a pyramid
    ○ D. take care of a temple

10. Why did it take many years to become a scribe?
    ○ A. Papyrus was very difficult to write on.
    ○ B. There were hundreds of hieroglyphs to learn.
    ○ C. Students had to save money to buy a position.
    ○ D. Teachers were so harsh that students ran away.

11. Skilled scribes wrote on papyrus, which was made from
    ○ A. a plant.
    ○ B. soft clay.
    ○ C. cotton rags.
    ○ D. animal skins.

12. Of these four groups, which one had the **lowest** social status?
    ○ A. priests
    ○ B. scribes
    ○ C. artisans
    ○ D. government officials

13. How does the work of ancient Egyptian artisans help us learn today about life in ancient Egypt?
    ○ A. They left behind their tools made out of reeds.
    ○ B. They carved and painted scenes of everyday life.
    ○ C. They passed on their skills to sons and daughters.
    ○ D. They wrote histories of events on rolls of papyrus.

14. In the life of a peasant, which season came next after the flooding season?
    ○ A. the festival season
    ○ B. the harvest season
    ○ C. the planting season
    ○ D. the building season

15. Most peasants lived in
    ○ A. rafts in the river.
    ○ B. camel-skin tents.
    ○ C. caves in the cliffs.
    ○ D. mud-brick houses.

16. In what form did many farmers pay their taxes?
    ○ A. grain
    ○ B. paper notes
    ○ C. copper coins
    ○ D. music at banquets

Applying Social Studies Skills

Use the image and your knowledge of history to answer the questions. Write the word or phrase in the space provided.

This painting of stone carvers at work was found on the wall of an ancient tomb. Stone carvers were some of the most skilled workers in the artisan class.

17. What are the stone carvers making? Be specific.

18. From the image, what can you tell about the stone carvers' working methods?

19. Write one question that finding this image might help historians to answer.

Exploring the Essential Question

How did social class affect daily life in ancient Egypt?

Follow the directions to complete the item below.

20. Read the following paragraph.

The Egyptians held the Opet Festival each year, when the Nile River flooded its banks. A statue of the god Amon-Re, decorated with jewelry, was placed on a barque, or ceremonial boat. The barque was brought out of the temple and carried through town on poles. Almost everyone came out to watch.

Write a short story or fictional journal entry related to the Opet Festival. Your narrative should include these elements:

- A setting during the Opet Festival. You may also set your narrative just before or after the Opet Festival if the plot has a clear connection with the festival.

- A reference to all five social classes (government officials, priests, scribes, artisans, and peasants) in a way that shows differences between the classes.

- At least two major characters who belong to different social classes.

- Sensory details and concrete language that develop plot and character.

- Dialogue, suspense, or both.

Bringing to Life the Payment of Tribute to Kush

You will work with your group to bring to life a character in the scene showing Egyptians paying tribute to King Piye of Kush. One member of your group will be randomly selected to play the part of your assigned character. Your character will be interviewed and should be prepared to answer the questions that appear below.

Step 1: Circle the character your group has been assigned. Read the information about that character's perspective.

King Piye: You are pleased to be receiving tribute from representatives of Egypt. These gifts show that they recognize you as the leader of Egypt. You are happy because you have been able to bring peace and stability to Egypt.

Assistant to King Piye: You are privileged to be guarding the gifts from the Egyptians. You are amazed and proud at what you see. You remember stories from your grandfather about how Egypt once dominated Kush for hundreds of years.

Egyptian Prince: You are respectfully bringing gifts to King Piye to show that you recognize him as the leader of Egypt. You are relieved that he has established himself as pharoah. Before he took control, there was much fighting and instability in Egypt.

Egyptian Prince: You are respectfully bringing gifts to King Piye to show that you recognize him as the leader of Egypt. But you are secretly very frustrated. You had hoped to defeat the other Egyptian leaders and become the pharaoh yourself.

Step 2: From your character's perspective, discuss answers to the questions. Make sure everyone can answer the questions so that each group member is prepared to be an actor.

- Who are you and what are you doing?
- How do you feel about what King Piye has done in Egypt? Why?
- In what ways do you think Kush's location has influenced events that are happening here?

Step 3: Discuss how the actor can make the character as realistic as possible. For example, the actor might use certain body postures and movements, facial expressions, and simple props.

Bringing to Life the War Between Kush and Rome

You will work with your group to bring to life a character in the scene showing a Kushite attack on a Roman fort. One member of your group will be randomly selected to play the part of your assigned character. Your character will be interviewed and should be prepared to answer the questions that appear below.

Step 1: Circle the character your group has been assigned. Read the information about that character's perspective.

Kandake Amanirenas: You have courageously led an attack on a Roman fort built on your border with Egypt. You are confident in your army's ability to defend and protect Kush. You are determined to defeat these Romans.

Prince Akinidad: You were excited to assist your mother, the kandake, as she led an attack on a Roman fort built on your border with Egypt. You admire your mother's leadership ability and the courage of Kush's soldiers.

Kush Soldier: You are proud to be a soldier in the Kushite army, participating in the attack on a Roman fort. You are pleased to see how successful this attack has been. But you are also concerned about how the Romans will respond to this defeat.

Roman Army Officer: You are disappointed that you have had to retreat with your soldiers to a safe place. You are surprised that Kush has dared to attack a Roman fort. You are wondering whether it would be better to attack Kush or to make peace.

Step 2: From your character's perspective, discuss answers to the questions. Make sure everyone can answer the questions so that each group member is prepared to be an actor.

- Who are you and what are you doing?
- How do you feel about the Romans in Egypt? Why?
- In what ways do you think Kush's location has influenced events that are happening here?

Step 3: Discuss how the actor can make the character as realistic as possible. For example, the actor might use certain body postures and movements, facial expressions, and simple props.

Chapter 10 Assessment

Mastering the Content

Fill in the circle next to the best answer.

1. An important way historians learn about ancient Kush is through
   - ○ A. Syrian trade agreements.
   - ○ B. Sumerian cuneiform tablets.
   - ○ C. Egyptian tomb wall paintings.
   - ○ D. Nubian books printed on paper.

2. Kush was also called Nubia because of its
   - ○ A. iron deposits.
   - ○ B. deep oil wells.
   - ○ C. rich gold mines.
   - ○ D. brilliant gemstones.

3. What physical feature **most** contributed to both of the following in ancient Kush?
   - Fertile soil   • Foreign trade
   - ○ A. Red Sea
   - ○ B. Nile River
   - ○ C. Nubian Desert
   - ○ D. Mediterranean Sea

4. Which words go best on the lower arrow in the image below?
   - ○ A. silk, bronze, furs
   - ○ B. salt, pepper, spices
   - ○ C. glass, pottery, spears
   - ○ D. ivory, leather, timber

grain
linen

5. Which of these events led to Kushites adopting Egyptian ways of life?
   - ○ A. Kush allied with the Assyrians.
   - ○ B. Scribes traveled to Kush to teach.
   - ○ C. Both armies burned a Roman fort.
   - ○ D. Egyptian pharaohs conquered Kush.

6. During which period on the timeline below did Kush have to pay tribute to Egypt?

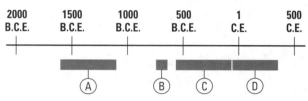

   - ○ A. period A: 1600 to 1100 B.C.E.
   - ○ B. period B: 720 to 630 B.C.E.
   - ○ C. period C: 590 to 24 B.C.E.
   - ○ D. period D: 21 B.C.E. to 350 C.E.

7. How did Kush regain its independence from Egypt?
   - ○ A. The Nile River overflowed.
   - ○ B. The New Kingdom collapsed.
   - ○ C. Nobles voted against the kings.
   - ○ D. A marriage alliance was formed.

8. Which of these is the **best** example of a dynasty?
   - ○ A. the emperor over Sumerian cities
   - ○ B. the land the Assyrians conquered
   - ○ C. military leaders who seized Rome
   - ○ D. the 15th line of Egyptian rulers

9. For what achievement is King Piye of Kush remembered?
○ A. conquering Egypt
○ B. introducing iron tools
○ C. building dams on the Nile
○ D. trading with India and China

10. What technology enabled Assyria to defeat Kush?
○ A. fire
○ B. charcoal
○ C. iron weapons
○ D. wooden wheels

11. What advantage did Meroë have over Napata as a capital of Kush?

Ancient Kingdom of Kush

○ A. It was on a larger oasis.
○ B. It was nearer the desert.
○ C. It was farther from Egypt.
○ D. It had a better water source.

12. Meroë became especially well known for the production of
○ A. iron.
○ C. boats.
○ D. textiles.
○ B. papyrus.

13. Worship of a lion-god in Kush reflected which influence on Kushite culture?
○ A. Arab
○ B. Greek
○ C. Indian
○ D. African

14. How do records left by the Kushites after their separation from Egypt differ from earlier records of Kush?
○ A. They use Egyptian hieroglyphics more poetically.
○ B. They are written in a native language called Meroitic.
○ C. They use pictures because Kush lacked a written language.
○ D. They are made with cuneiform adapted from that of Sumer.

15. How did the kandake Queen Amanirenas help protect Kush?
○ A. She made a treaty with Assyria.
○ B. She led attacks on Roman forts.
○ C. She stopped the Hittite advance.
○ D. She appointed women to top jobs.

Name _____ Date _____

Applying Social Studies Skills

Use the maps and your knowledge of history to answer the questions.
Write the word or phrase in the space provided.

Ancient Kingdom of Kush

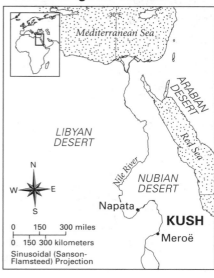

Kush Region Today

16. In what present day country was ancient Kush primarily located?

17. In 350 C.E., Kush fell to invaders from Ethiopia. During the invasion, from what direction would the Kushites have seen danger approaching?

18. On what body of water was the closest seaport to Napata aand Meroë most likely located?

19. To send trade goods from Kush to what is now Saudi Arabia, the Kushites would likely have sent the goods first by _____ and then loaded them onto

_____. (form of transportation)

Exploring the Essential Question

In what ways did location influence the history of Kush?

Follow the directions to complete the item below.

20. Suppose that you are a speaker on a TV panel of experts on the history and geography of ancient Kush. Speakers have been asked to keep their comments brief and specific. You have been given several questions in advance so that you can prepare your comments.

    Answer each question below in two or more sentences. Your comments should make sense to those TV viewers who are not familiar with Kush. Use your knowledge of Kush and the maps on the previous page for reference.

a. How did the location of Kush affect the growth of its trade?

b. How did the location of Kush affect its political and military relations with Egypt?

c. How did the location of Kush affect its culture?

d. How did the location of Kush affect its use of resources?

Designing a Page for an Ancient Scroll

Write and illustrate a page for an ancient scroll commemorating the important achievements of key figures in the history of the Israelites, as described in the Hebrew Bible. Orient your scroll page horizontally. Be sure to leave at least an inch of blank space along the left- and right-hand sides. For your assigned figure(s), include the following items on your scroll page:

- His name, written in both English and Hebrew.

- A title that defines his role in the development of Judaism (for example, "Father of the Jews").

- A visual that illustrates one of his important actions for the Jewish people (for example, Solomon building the First Temple in Jerusalem).

- A one-sentence caption that explains what is shown in the visual.

- A paragraph explaining your figure's contributions to the development of Judaism. Include a quotation from the Hebrew Bible in the paragraph.

- A small visual of one artifact, relating to some aspect of your figure's life (for example, David's slingshot), in each of the four corners of the page.

Chapter 11 Assessment

Mastering the Content

Fill in the circle next to the best answer.

1. When people read from the Torah, they are reading from
   - ○ A. the Prophets and the Writings.
   - ○ B. the first five books of the Hebrew Bible.
   - ○ C. an ancient Egyptian book about the Hebrew people.
   - ○ D. a collection of prayers and poems used by the early Jews.

2. How does the Torah say that Abraham **first** came to the land of Canaan?
   - ○ A. He guided the Israelites out of Egypt.
   - ○ B. He moved with his family from Mesopotamia.
   - ○ C. He passed through the area as a wandering shepherd.
   - ○ D. He led an army that won the land from the Philistines.

3. To complete the diagram, which phrase **best** belongs in the empty box?

Famine in Canaan	▷	

   - ○ A. Israelites move to Egypt
   - ○ B. Israelites start herding goats
   - ○ C. Israelites wander in the desert
   - ○ D. Israelites break into warring tribes

4. How did ancient Judaism differ from other religions at that time?
   - ○ A. more elegant temples
   - ○ B. rules for how to act
   - ○ C. famous leader-heroes
   - ○ D. belief in one God

5. According to the Torah, the faith that would become Judaism began with a covenant, or
   - ○ A. holy dream.
   - ○ B. written contract.
   - ○ C. sacred agreement.
   - ○ D. religious gathering.

6. According to Jewish teaching, what did God promise by changing Abram's name to Abraham?
   - ○ A. to save Abraham's son
   - ○ B. to guide Abraham to Canaan
   - ○ C. to help Abraham build a temple
   - ○ D. to protect Abraham's descendants

7. What place did the Jewish people believe was the promised land?
   - ○ A. Ur
   - ○ B. Egypt
   - ○ C. Canaan
   - ○ D. Babylon

8. Find Isaac on the family tree below.

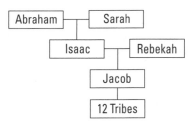

   According to the family tree, Isaac was Sarah's
   - ○ A. son.
   - ○ B. brother.
   - ○ C. husband.
   - ○ D. grandson.

9. Suppose that you were to arrange the following events in order. Which event happened **second**?
   ○ A. Abraham moved to Canaan.
   ○ B. Moses climbed Mount Sinai.
   ○ C. The Israelites moved to Egypt.
   ○ D. David was king of the Jewish people.

10. The word *exodus* means "departure." In the history of the Israelites, the Exodus was the departure from
    ○ A. Ur.
    ○ B. Egypt.
    ○ C. Canaan.
    ○ D. Babylon.

11. According to the Torah, what did Moses bring to his people from Mount Sinai?
    ○ A. food to eat in the desert
    ○ B. the Ten Commandments
    ○ C. most of the Hebrew Bible
    ○ D. directions for building a temple

12. Which of these conclusions does the map support about the Jewish people's trip from Egypt to Canaan?
    ○ A. It was largely by boat.
    ○ B. It followed a direct route.
    ○ C. It cost many people their lives.
    ○ D. It took many years to complete.

Possible Route of the Exodus

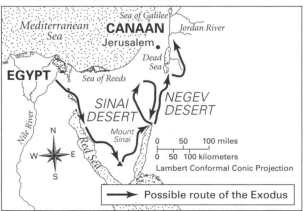

13. Who unified the Israelites into a single nation?
    ○ A. David
    ○ B. Moses
    ○ C. Solomon
    ○ D. Abraham

14. What did David provide for the Jewish people that they did not have before?
    ○ A. a strong army
    ○ B. a famous temple
    ○ C. a set of commandments
    ○ D. a strong central government

15. Why was Jerusalem considered a holy city?
    ○ A. David built his first palace there.
    ○ B. Religious ceremonies were held there.
    ○ C. The Ark of the Covenant was kept there.
    ○ D. The Israelites believed God told them to live there.

16. For which achievement is Solomon **most** famous?
    ○ A. uniting a nation
    ○ B. winning a battle
    ○ C. starting a school
    ○ D. building a temple

Applying Social Studies Skills

Use the information below and your knowledge of history to answer the
questions. Write the word or phrase in the space provided.

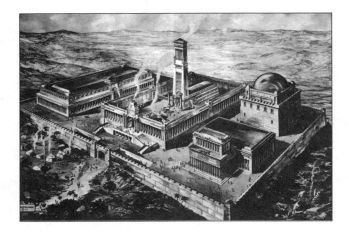

Construction of First Temple in Jerusalem

- Stone shaped at quarry
- Cedar and cypress wood, cut in Lebanon
  and shipped by sea
- Materials prepared by forced labor
- Interior lined with cypress and cedar;
  cedar roof
- Carvings of cherubim (angels), palm trees,
  gourds, and open flowers
- Parts of inside sections overlaid with gold

17. What two mineral resources were used in building the Temple?

18. The construction of the temple required international trade with_____,
    most likely because _____.

19. According to the picture, what did the Israelites build with materials from the quarry?

© Teachers' Curriculum Institute

Name_____ Date_____

Exploring the Essential Question
Follow the directions to complete the item below.

How did Judaism originate and develop?

20. Solomon's construction of the First Temple in Jerusalem was important in the development of Judaism and the ancient Jewish nation of Israel.

    Suppose that three people involved in the construction of the temple are each sending a picture postcard to a friend. One person is a relative of the king who ordered the temple built. Another is a laborer forced to help produce the raw materials. The third is a skilled woodcarver. Each person comments on the construction project from his or her point of view. Write the three postcards, using the information on the previous page as a resource.

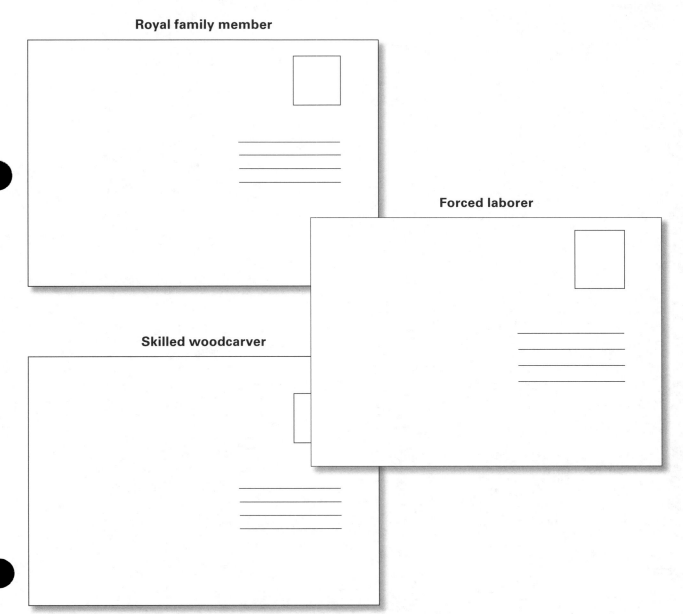

Royal family member

Forced laborer

Skilled woodcarver

Classroom Truths and Movements

Classroom Truth: The one true teacher in this classroom is

Ms./Mr. _____.

(name of classroom teacher)

Movement: Stand straight and at attention, turn to where the "true teacher" is standing, and salute him or her.

Classroom Truth: Respect and follow the classroom truths.

Movement: Put your hand over your heart, close your eyes, and lower your head.

Classroom Truth: Help other students if they are having trouble.

Movement: Reach out your right arm and pretend you are patting someone standing next to you on the shoulder.

Classroom Truth: Complete all assignments creatively and thoughtfully.

Movement: Scratch the top of your head as though you are thinking hard, and then thrust your index finger high into the air to show that you have just come up with a great idea.

Tokens

1	2
3	4
5	6
7	8

The "Preserve and Pass Along" Activity

Objective

In this activity, you will learn four simple "classroom truths" and the corresponding body movements that represent these truths. At the end of the activity, four students will be chosen at random to state the truths and demonstrate the movements. If all four students can do so, they will represent the whole class as having successfully completed the activity.

Guidelines

Teaching Areas

- Teaching will only take place in the four corners of the room.
- Only one "teacher" and one "student" will be allowed in each corner of the room at a time.
- Teachers and students must face away from the center of the room and speak only in whispers.

Time Limits

- Each teacher will have two minutes to teach a student the four classroom truths and movements.
- If a teacher in one corner is unsure about any of the classroom truths or movements, he or she may consult with the teacher at the table in the center of the classroom. However, no extra time will be given for this consultation.

Silence

- When sitting at your desks, you must be silent and complete your Reading Notes for Chapter 12.
- If you are not silent, the classroom teacher may impose a penalty by reducing the two-minute time limit for *all* four corners or by removing you from the activity.

Chapter 12 Assessment

Mastering the Content

Fill in the circle next to the best answer.

1. What weakened the land of the Israelites after the death of Solomon?
   - ○ A. It suffered from a serious famine.
   - ○ B. It fell to attacks by the Philistines.
   - ○ C. It split into two smaller kingdoms.
   - ○ D. It formed unwise foreign alliances.

2. Why did many Jews move to Babylon?
   - ○ A. They were fleeing from attack by the Assyrians.
   - ○ B. They were taken there as captives by Nebuchadrezzar.
   - ○ C. They were hoping to spread the idea that there is one God.
   - ○ D. They were looking for a land with a more stable food supply.

3. Why did the Jewish Diaspora threaten the survival of Judaism?
   - ○ A. Jews became scattered over a wide area.
   - ○ B. Jews paid heavy taxes to pay for a new temple.
   - ○ C. Jews began to learn from rabbis instead of priests.
   - ○ D. Jews depended on oral tradition to remember their history.

4. Which common feature of **most** ancient religions did the Jews reject (refuse, say no to)?
   - ○ A. ritual
   - ○ B. morality
   - ○ C. tradition
   - ○ D. polytheism

5. According to Judaism, standards of right and wrong come from
   - ○ A. God.
   - ○ B. Abraham.
   - ○ C. priests.
   - ○ D. prophets.

6. What is the **best** title for the chart below?

Religious Practices	Morals
• Set aside a holy day each week • (others)	• Do not murder • Do not steal • (others)

   - ○ A. Hammurabi's Code
   - ○ B. Holidays and Holy Days
   - ○ C. Teachings of the Talmud
   - ○ D. The Ten Commandments

7. Which of these phrases **best** describes the Talmud?
   - ○ A. another name for the Torah
   - ○ B. record of conquests of the Jewish people
   - ○ C. ancient Jewish writings about the Hebrew Bible
   - ○ D. list of names of the priests of the Temple of Jerusalem

8. The festival of Passover celebrates the
   - ○ A. Jewish Diaspora.
   - ○ B. Exodus from Egypt.
   - ○ C. rededication of the Temple.
   - ○ D. end of the Babylonian Exile.

9. Which of these is the **best** example of a question of ethics?

   ○ A. What shall I eat for dinner?
   ○ B. When should I brush my teeth?
   ○ C. Should I help a child who is lost?
   ○ D. Which color shall I paint my room?

10. Which major belief of Judaism does the photograph show?

   ○ A. the importance of study
   ○ B. equality and social justice
   ○ C. the celebration of holy days
   ○ D. presence of God in daily life

11. What change of events led to the building of the Second Temple?

   ○ A. Nebuchadrezzar realized the need to reconstruct Judah.
   ○ B. Solomon brought the Ark of the Covenant from its tent.
   ○ C. The Jews drove Antiochus and the Greeks from Jerusalem.
   ○ D. The Persians conquered Babylon and let the Jews go home.

12. Why do Jews consider the Western Wall in Jerusalem a sacred place?

   ○ A. It was built by King Solomon.
   ○ B. It was part of the Second Temple.
   ○ C. It was where many Jews died in rebellion against Rome.
   ○ D. It was constructed with the stones that held the Ten Commandments.

13. What was the result of Yohanan ben Zaccai's meeting with the Roman general?

   ○ A. the building of a temple
   ○ B. the founding of a school
   ○ C. the betrayal of the rabbis
   ○ D. the destruction of Jerusalem

14. How was the city of Yavneh important to the survival of Judaism?

   ○ A. as the site of a temple
   ○ B. as the political capital
   ○ C. as a center for learning
   ○ D. as a source of rebellion

15. Why did Jews in the Diaspora have to develop new forms of worship, such as a synagogue service?

   ○ A. They spoke several languages.
   ○ B. They mingled with other cultures.
   ○ C. They came under the rule of rabbis.
   ○ D. They could no longer use the Temple rituals.

16. Jewish forms of worship and ways of life were taught in many different countries by

   ○ A. rabbis.
   ○ B. priests.
   ○ C. prophets.
   ○ D. professors.

Applying Social Studies Skills

Use the timeline and your knowledge of history to answer the questions.
Write the word or phrase in the space provided.

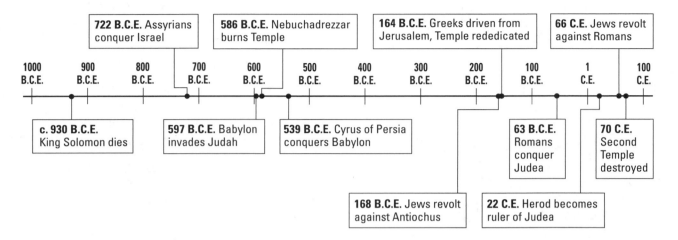

17. What was the name of the part of Solomon's former territory that was self-governing in 600 B.C.E.?

18. Where did most Jews live in the year 550 B.C.E.?

19. Who ruled the city of Jerusalem at the time that Herod ordered major construction on the Temple?

Exploring the Essential Question

What are the central teachings of Judaism, and why did they survive to modern day?

Follow the directions to complete the item below.

20. Explain an important reason why one major teaching of Judaism survived to modern times. Before you start to write, think about these points:

- which teaching you will write about
- why it was in danger of not surviving
- why you think it survived

After you have chosen your main points, write on the scrolls below. The first few words of each scroll have been filled in for you. When you are finished, the three scrolls taken together should tell one clear and well-reasoned story.

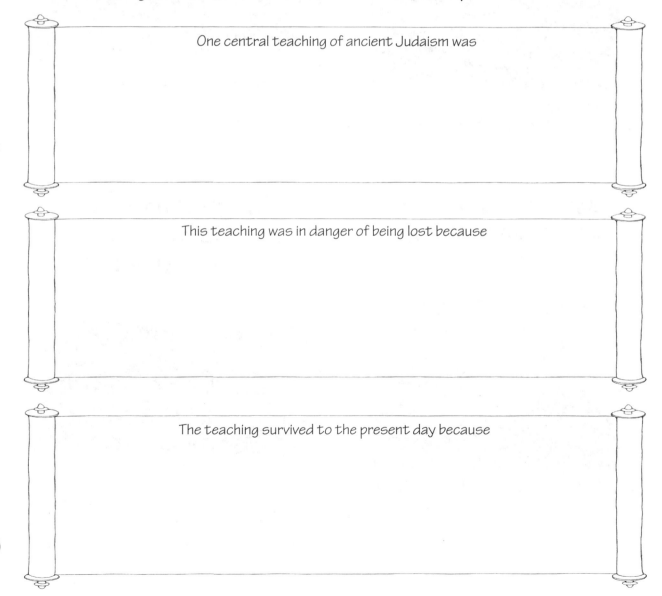

One central teaching of ancient Judaism was

This teaching was in danger of being lost because

The teaching survived to the present day because

Unit 2 Timeline Challenge Cards

Rule of Kushite Pharaohs
About 730–655 B.C.E.

Kushite pharaohs rule a united Egypt and Kush after the surrender of northern Egypt to Kush.

Babylonian Exile
586–539 B.C.E.

The Babylonians destroy Jerusalem and take many Jews into captivity. The Persians conquer the Babylonians and release the Jews, many to return home.

Kush Attack on Roman Forts
24 B.C.E.

Kandake Amanirenas and her son defend Kush by leading an attack that destroys several Roman forts on Kush's borders.

Final Jewish Diaspora Begins
135 C.E.

The final Jewish Diaspora begins with the Roman army's defeat of another Jewish revolt.

Physical Features Cards

Brahmaputra River	Deccan Plateau
Eastern and Western Ghats	Ganges River
Himalaya Mountains	Hindu Kush
Indus River	Thar Desert

Brahmaputra River	Deccan Plateau
Eastern and Western Ghats	Ganges River
Himalaya Mountains	Hindu Kush
Indus River	Thar Desert

Critical Thinking Questions

Most Likely

Least Likely

For each Critical Thinking Question, arrange the physical features cards on the spectrum below.

Critical Thinking Question A:
Which physical feature is likely to produce a dependable food supply?

Critical Thinking Question B:
Which physical feature is likely to support quality trade?

Critical Thinking Question C:
Which physical feature is likely to be the site of India's earliest settlement?

Physical Features of India

Brahmaputra River

Deccan Plateau

Eastern and Western Ghats

Ganges River

Himalaya
Mountains

Hindu Kush

Indus River

Thar Desert

Name _____ Date _____

Chapter 13 Assessment

Mastering the Content

Fill in the circle next to the best answer.
You may use the map for reference.

Physical Features of India

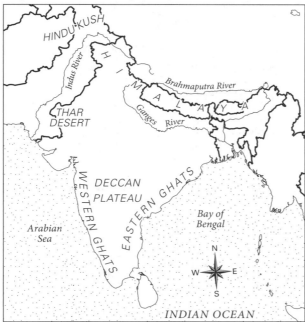

1. Because of its large size and its position in relation to large masses of land and water, India is called

   ○ A. a plateau.
   ○ B. an isthmus.
   ○ C. an ecosystem.
   ○ D. a subcontinent.

2. As the Brahmaputra River flows from the mountains into the valley, it becomes

   ○ A. slower and deeper.
   ○ B. clearer and cleaner.
   ○ C. rockier and rougher.
   ○ D. narrower and colder.

3. During the summer in India, the monsoon brings

   ○ A. heavy rain.
   ○ B. dust storms.
   ○ C. unbearable heat.
   ○ D. pleasant mornings.

4. Farmers in the Deccan Plateau use the iron-rich black soil principally to raise

   ○ A. tea.
   ○ B. sheep.
   ○ C. cotton.
   ○ D. oranges.

5. Compared with the Eastern and Western Ghats, the Deccan Plateau has

   ○ A. denser forests.
   ○ B. a drier climate.
   ○ C. a longer coastline.
   ○ D. steeper mountains.

6. On the map, find the northern tip of the Bay of Bengal. Why is the nearby soil so fertile?

   ○ A. Many kinds of fish live in the bay.
   ○ B. Flooding rivers deposit rich minerals.
   ○ C. Pure water flows from the mountains.
   ○ D. People have farmed there for centuries.

7. Which phrase **best** describes the Eastern and Western Ghats?

○ A. fertile plains
○ B. sandy beaches
○ C. mountain ranges
○ D. marshy wetlands

8. Which of the following parts of India has the **most** fertile farmland?

○ A. the Hindu Kush
○ B. the Deccan Plateau
○ C. the Himalaya Mountains
○ D. the plains along the Ganges

9. Much of the water in the Indus, Ganges, and Brahmaputra rivers comes from

○ A. natural springs in the desert.
○ B. melting ice in the mountains.
○ C. rain-fed streams in the plateau.
○ D. large lakes in the northern plain.

10. How has the location of the Himalaya Mountains benefited India?

○ A. roads for trade routes
○ B. consistent water supply
○ C. protection from enemies
○ D. prevention of earthquakes

11. Travelers went through the Khyber Pass to cross the

○ A. Hindu Kush.
○ B. Eastern Ghats.
○ C. Deccan Plateau.
○ D. Himalaya Mountains.

12. The lower Indus River (the part nearer the sea) flows through what is now the country of

○ A. Iran.
○ B. Tibet.
○ C. Nepal.
○ D. Pakistan.

13. A traveler in the Thar Desert would be likely to see many

○ A. elephants.
○ B. sand dunes.
○ C. small farms.
○ D. walled cities.

14. Where were the earliest known settlements in India?

○ A. on the plateau
○ B. near the desert
○ C. beside the rivers
○ D. in the mountains

15. How are the Indus and Ganges rivers similar to the Nile River in Egypt?

○ A. They begin in the same general area.
○ B. They carry silt that enriches the soil.
○ C. They flow in the same general direction.
○ D. They have big floods that prevented early settlement.

Applying Social Studies Skills

Use the graph and your knowledge of history to answer the questions. Write the word or phrase in the space provided.

Average Rainfall per Year in Selected Cities of India

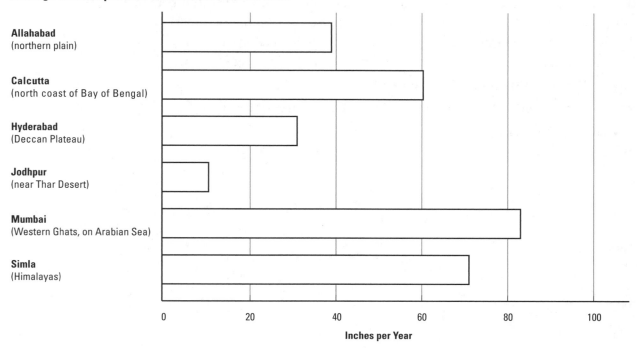

16. Which of these cities gets the least amount of rainfall—Simla, Mumbai, or Calcutta?

17. What is the location of the city on the graph with the largest amount of rain?

18. Because of the quantity of rainfall, farming would likely be especially difficult around which city?

19. Suppose that a specific crop grows best with a certain amount of rainfall. The area near Hyderabad in the Deccan Plateau gets too little rain for that crop, and the area near Calcutta on the north coast of the Bay of Bengal gets too much. Where would that crop most likely grow best?

Exploring the Essential Question

How did geography affect early settlement in India?

Follow the directions to complete the item below.

20. Suppose that you have bought land in ancient India and you want to persuade people to settle there. Make a poster to advertise your land. Use precise words and supporting details that help readers "see" the area as a place where they might want to live. Your poster should include the following elements:

   • a slogan to attract people to settle there

   • a description of the geography and physical features of the area

   • at least two reasons why this would be a good place to settle

Excavating the Ruins of Mohenjodaro

Follow these steps when visiting each research station located at the ruins of Mohenjodaro.

Step 1: Locate the artifact. Each research station contains a placard that represents the artifact. To locate the placard, you will have to perform a task similar to that of professional archaeologists.

- Station A: Move the pile of "bricks."
- Station B: Climb over the "walls" (desks) and dig through "dirt."
- Station C: Assemble the broken artifact.
- Station D: Move the square objects.
- Station E: Dig through "dirt."
- Station F: Look through "windows."
- Station G: Assemble the broken artifact.
- Station H: Move the pile of "bricks."

Step 2: Excavate the artifact. Once you have found the placard, "excavate" the artifact by turning the placard over to reveal the image.

Step 3: Analyze the artifact. With your partner, examine the image that appears on the placard. Then, in the appropriate section of your Reading Notes, complete the drawing.

Step 4: Interpret the artifact. With your partner, discuss possible answers to the question on the placard and record your ideas in your Reading Notes for that station. After you complete the excavation, you will read the corresponding section in your book and record the archaeologists' ideas.

Step 5: Return the station to the condition in which you found it.

Excavation Materials

Female Statue Puzzle for Station C

Seals for Station D

Window for Station F

Game Piece Puzzle for Station G

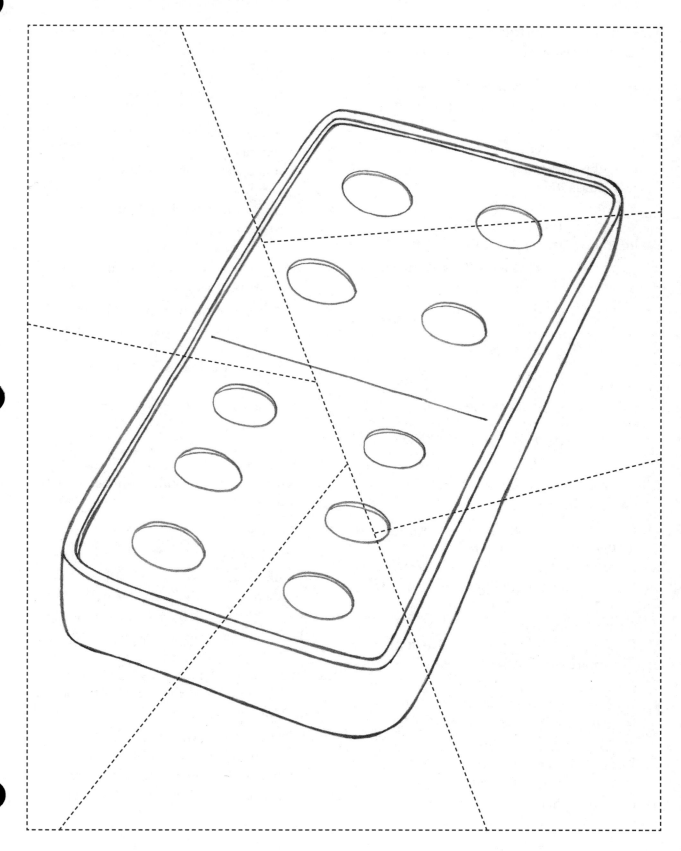

Chapter 14 Assessment

Mastering the Content

Fill in the circle next to the best answer.

1. Harappan civilization, which included ancient Mohenjodaro, developed in the
   ○ A. Western Ghats.
   ○ B. Deccan Plateau.
   ○ C. Indus River valley.
   ○ D. Ganges River valley.

2. Which letter on the map shows the location of Mohenjodaro?
   ○ A. M
   ○ B. N
   ○ C. O
   ○ D. P

The Indus River Valley

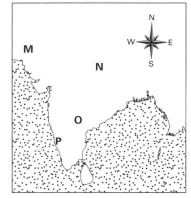

3. In which of these years was Mohenjodaro an active settlement?
   ○ A. 8000 B.C.E., while people were discovering how to farm
   ○ B. 2550 B.C.E., while the Great Pyramid was being built in Egypt
   ○ C. 1000 B.C.E., while King David was ruling over Israel
   ○ D. 600 B.C.E., while the Neo-Babylonian Empire ruled Mesopotamia

4. How did modern scholars learn that Mohenjodaro had ever existed?
   ○ A. Astronauts saw it from space.
   ○ B. Historians read ancient scrolls.
   ○ C. Archaeologists found its ruins.
   ○ D. Geographers studied old maps.

5. Part of Mohenjodaro was raised and surrounded by a wall. What does this suggest about the city?
   ○ A. It had traders who stayed near the roads.
   ○ B. It had religious leaders who lived separately.
   ○ C. It had rich people who owned the best homes.
   ○ D. It had enemies who might attack the residents.

6. Which fact shows that Mohenjodaro was carefully planned?
   ○ A. Wheeled carts were pulled by animals.
   ○ B. The workshops were made of mud bricks.
   ○ C. Some of the houses were larger than others.
   ○ D. Nine streets divided the lower city into blocks.

7. What does the list below show about the civilization that included Mohenjodaro?
   • Invaders
   • Floods
   • Earthquakes
   ○ A. likely causes for its beginning
   ○ B. theories for why it disappeared
   ○ C. problems with being near a river
   ○ D. reasons it was led by strong rulers

8. The discovery of a scale, stone weights, and a marked rod suggests that the people of Mohenjodaro
   ○ A. had uniform ways to measure.
   ○ B. knew how to make tools of iron.
   ○ C. traded with people from far away.
   ○ D. started a new kind of mathematics.

9. Archaeologists found a structure that was 39 feet long and 8 feet deep, with a well nearby and a drain along one side. How was it likely used?
   ○ A. for bathing
   ○ B. for cooking
   ○ C. for making wine
   ○ D. for grinding grain

10. What evidence shows us how men in Mohenjodaro might have dressed?
    ○ A. pictographs
    ○ B. an ancient statue
    ○ C. a report by a visitor
    ○ D. remains of an old robe

11. What do these seals tell historians about Mohenjodaro?

    ○ A. the types of jobs people did
    ○ B. the types of animals people saw
    ○ C. the types of jewelry people wore
    ○ D. the types of gods people worshipped

12. Which feature of Mohenjodaro was quite different from other settlements of that time?
    ○ A. high wall
    ○ B. dirt roads
    ○ C. brick homes
    ○ D. sewer system

13. Where did **most** of the people of Mohenjodaro live?
    ○ A. in the citadel
    ○ B. in the tall tower
    ○ C. in the lower city
    ○ D. in the courtyards

14. Homes in Mohenjodaro had from one to a dozen rooms. What does this suggest about the city?
    ○ A. Some houses had indoor bathrooms.
    ○ B. Some apartments held several families.
    ○ C. Some people were wealthier than others.
    ○ D. Some families had grandparents living with them.

15. A war game played in ancient India is thought to be an early form of
    ○ A. chess.
    ○ B. hockey.
    ○ C. dominoes.
    ○ D. basketball.

16 Which of these questions about Mohenjodaro would be hardest to answer on the basis of artifacts?
    ○ A. What foods did people eat?
    ○ B. What songs did people sing?
    ○ C. What games did people play?
    ○ D. What clothes did people wear?

Applying Social Studies Skills

Use the information in the table below and your knowledge of social studies to complete the sentences. Write the word or phrase in the space provided.

Archaeologists at Mohenjodaro	
Rakhaldas Banerji (Indian)	led first dig at Mohenjodaro in 1922
Sir John Marshall (British)	led extensive excavations in Harappa and Mohenjodaro in the 1920s and 1930s
Ahmad Hasa Dani (Indian/Pakistani) and Sir Mortimer Wheeler (British)	did further excavations in 1945
George F. Dales (U.S.)	undertook last major excavation in 1964–65
Later excavations—denied permission because of weather damage to the site	

17. Excavations (digging by archaeologists) at Mohenjodaro took place between

    _____ and _____.

18. The ancient city of Mohenjodaro was buried under centuries of dirt before archaeologists began to excavate its secrets. While their digging provided important new information, it also threatened the ruins because

19. In his lifetime, Professor Dales probably knew more than Banerji or Marshall had known about ancient Mohenjodaro because

Exploring the Essential Question

What can artifacts tell us about daily life in Mohenjodaro?

Follow the directions to complete the item below.

20. Suppose that you are a magazine editor who will print an article about the ancient city of Mohenjodaro. You plan to use these two pictures of artifacts to illustrate the article. Write a caption for each picture. Your captions should

    - include information about what the picture shows.
    - tell what the artifact suggests about daily life in Mohenjodaro.
    - be written in two to three complete sentences.

Caption:

Caption:

Chapter 15 Assessment

Mastering the Content
Fill in the circle next to the best answer.

1. The Vedic religion is named for the Vedas, which are
   ○ A. a collection of sacred texts.
   ○ B. a group of people from Europe.
   ○ C. the three most important deities.
   ○ D. the temples where rituals were performed.

2. Who were the Aryans?
   ○ A. the highest caste in Indian society
   ○ B. the original tribes of southern India
   ○ C. a nomadic people who moved into India
   ○ D. a group of scribes who recorded Indian teachings

3. Which of these is the **best** reason for someone in India to study Sanskrit?
   ○ A. to read the ancient texts
   ○ B. to understand road signs
   ○ C. to run for political office
   ○ D. to talk to ordinary people

4. What change marked the transition from early Vedic religion to Brahmanism?
   ○ A. As the land became crowded, many people moved to the cities.
   ○ B. As scholars learned Sanskrit, the oral traditions were written down.
   ○ C. As rituals grew more complex, a special class arose to perform them.
   ○ D. As different groups moved into India, their gods became part of the religion.

5. In the caste system, how were people in India placed into a certain social class?
   ○ A. by skill
   ○ B. by birth
   ○ C. by wealth
   ○ D. by education

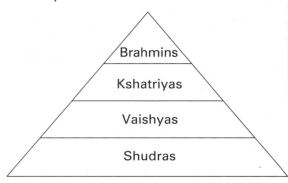

6. Which job was a Shudra **most** likely to do?
   ○ A. herd sheep
   ○ B. plow a field
   ○ C. interpret religious law
   ○ D. hold a government post

7. A person who spoke these words **most** likely belonged to which caste?
   "I have been learning about battle. My father is showing me how to use different kinds of weapons so I will be a good warrior."
   ○ A. Shudras
   ○ B. Vaishyas
   ○ C. Brahmins
   ○ D. Kshatriyas

8. Why did Untouchables live in separate communities?
   ○ A. They wanted to stay pure.
   ○ B. They shared all their goods.
   ○ C. They had to eat a special diet.
   ○ D. They were considered unclean.

9. To Hindus, the soul, or atman, is a part of
   ○ A. Shiva.
   ○ B. the sun.
   ○ C. Brahman.
   ○ D. the ocean.

10. Which of these sentences is true of **most** Hindu temples?
   ○ A. They contain elaborate sculptures.
   ○ B. They face west toward the setting sun.
   ○ C. They are placed as far from cities as possible.
   ○ D. They are small so as not to distract worshipers.

11. In some Hindu traditions, Brahma is the creator and Vishnu is the preserver. What does Shiva do?
   ○ A. teach
   ○ B. perfect
   ○ C. enlarge
   ○ D. destroy

12. The festival of Divali, which begins the Hindu New Year, celebrates
   ○ A. the changing of the seasons.
   ○ B. the victory of good over evil.
   ○ C. the food from a good harvest.
   ○ D. the long life of the wise elders.

13. The ancient social class system was called varna. What did early Hindus mean by varna dharma?
   ○ A. Each caste had its own duties.
   ○ B. Caste determined social status.
   ○ C. People married within their caste.
   ○ D. Religious texts defined the castes.

14. Which animal became a symbol for the Hindu belief in reverence for life?
   ○ A. the lion
   ○ B. the cow
   ○ C. the camel
   ○ D. the elephant

15. How was the Hindu belief about karma related to the caste system?
   ○ A. People's caste determines which deities they worship.
   ○ B. People in the lowest castes will come back as animals.
   ○ C. People in different castes work different kinds of jobs.
   ○ D. People are in a caste because of how they lived in past lives.

16. Which image **best** represents samsara, the Hindu view of birth, life, and death?

○ A. 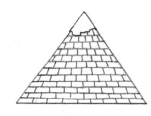   ○ B.

○ C. 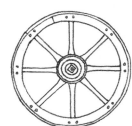   ○ D.

Applying Social Studies Skills
Use the story and your knowledge of history to complete the sentences.
Write the word or phrase in the space provided.

A Story from the *Ramayana*

When a king retired in ancient India, his oldest son was in line to become the next king. Rama was the oldest son of a king, but his stepmother wanted her son—Rama's younger brother Bharata—to be king instead. She persuaded the king to send Rama into the forest for 14 years.

"Of course I will go. A son should always obey his parents," Rama said.

Rama's wife, Sita, decided to go with him into the forest. "A wife's place is with her husband," Sita explained.

When Bharata learned what had happened, he went to the forest to find his brother. "Rama, you should be king, not me. Please come home," Bharata said.

"You are a good brother and a good man," Rama said. "Some people struggle their whole lives to become willing to give up riches and power. You are willing to give them up right now. But I cannot disobey my father's command."

"All right, I will rule in your place until you come back, but everyone will know that you are the real king," Bharata said. He ruled for 14 years. Then Rama and Sita came back, and Rama took over the throne that his brother had kept for him.

---

17. The Hindu ideal that Rama says is a lifelong struggle for some people is to

18. The Hindu belief that this story **best** illustrates is the belief in

19. This story is often told to Hindu children to teach them to

Name_____   Date_____

Exploring the Essential Question

What are the origins and beliefs of Hinduism?

Follow the directions to complete the item below.

20. Complete the graphic organizer below by writing in each of the four sections. Your writing should follow these guidelines:

- Answer the question in each section of the graphic organizer.
- Base your answers on the story from the *Ramayana,* on the previous page.
- Use examples or details from the story to support your answers.
- Include information from what you have learned about Hinduism.
- Use complete sentences.

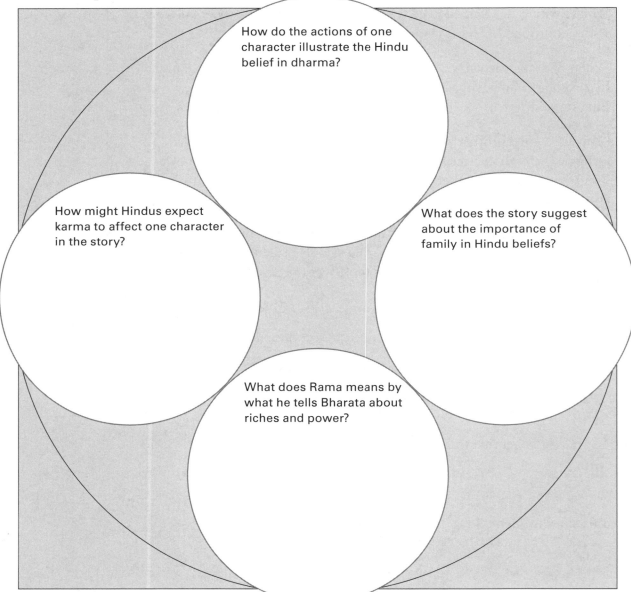

How do the actions of one character illustrate the Hindu belief in dharma?

How might Hindus expect karma to affect one character in the story?

What does the story suggest about the importance of family in Hindu beliefs?

What does Rama means by what he tells Bharata about riches and power?

Bringing to Life Siddhartha as a Baby

You will work with your partner to bring to life a character in the scene of Siddhartha as a baby. Your teacher may select one member of your pair to play the part of your assigned character. Follow these steps to prepare your part in the act-it-out:

Step 1: Circle the character your pair has been assigned. When you bring this character to life, you should try for historical accuracy by expressing the same tone and feeling represented in the image.

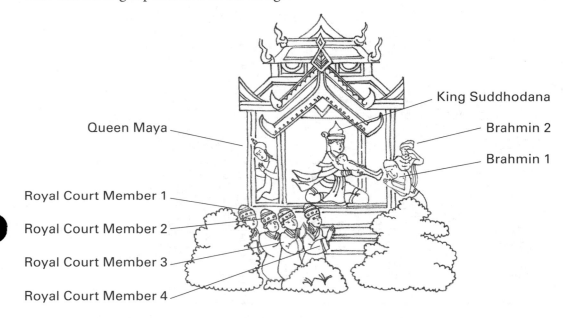

Queen Maya

King Suddhodana

Brahmin 2

Brahmin 1

Royal Court Member 1

Royal Court Member 2

Royal Court Member 3

Royal Court Member 4

Step 2: Plan what your character will say. Each actor will play a character in the form of a "talking statue." If you are selected, your teacher will press a "button" on your shoulder to bring your statue to life. Your statue will then make a statement.

Write your statue's statement. Use your character's perspective to complete the sentences below.

I am _____. I predict Prince Siddhartha will become a

_____ because _____.

Step 3: Discuss how your character will move. As a "talking statue," you will start in a frozen position. When your statue comes to life to make your statement, you will use simple and appropriate movements for your character. You will finish by refreezing in the original frozen position.

Start in "frozen" position ⟶ Movements ⟶ End in "frozen" position

Discuss with your partner what your statue's frozen position and movements will be for the act-it-out. *Use a blank piece of paper to sketch your ideas.*

Bringing to Life Siddhartha's Discovery of Suffering

You will work with your partner to bring to life a character in the scene of Siddhartha's discovery of suffering. Your teacher may select one member of your pair to play the part of your assigned character. Follow these steps to prepare your part in the act-it-out:

Step 1: Circle the character your pair has been assigned. When you bring this character to life, you should try for historical accuracy by expressing the same tone and feeling represented in the image.

Step 2: Plan what your character will say. Each actor will play a character in the form of a "talking statue." If you are selected, your teacher will press a "button" on your shoulder to bring your statue to life. Your statue will then make a statement.

Write your statue's statement. Use your character's perspective to complete the sentences below.

I am _____. *I think that life outside the palace is*

_____ *because* _____.

Step 3: Discuss how your character will move. As a "talking statue," you will start in a frozen position. When your statue comes to life to make your statement, you will use simple and appropriate movements for your character. You will finish by refreezing in the original frozen position.

Start in "frozen" position   ⟶   Movements   ⟶   End in "frozen" position

Discuss with your partner what your statue's frozen position and movements will be for the act-it-out. *Use a blank piece of paper to sketch your ideas.*

Chapter 16 Assessment

Mastering the Content

Fill in the circle next to the best answer.

1. The name "Buddha" meant one who was
    ○ A. sorrowful.
    ○ B. awakened.
    ○ C. everlasting.
    ○ D. all-powerful.

2. Which of these events took place at about the same time as the Buddha lived?
    ○ A. A cave wall was painted in southern France about 15,000 B.C.E.
    ○ B. Hammurabi began writing his code in Babylon in 1792 B.C.E.
    ○ C. The Persians conquered Babylon and let Jews return home in 539 B.C.E.
    ○ D. The Romans destroyed the Second Temple in Jerusalem in 70 C.E.

3. Which of these beliefs did Hinduism and Buddhism have in common?
    ○ A. many gods
    ○ B. caste system
    ○ C. ritual bathing
    ○ D. many lifetimes

4. Which goal did Buddhism teach people to move toward?
    ○ A. converting everybody
    ○ B. reaching enlightenment
    ○ C. making elaborate sacrifices
    ○ D. completing a big pilgrimage

5. Who was Siddhartha Gautama?
    ○ A. the prince who became the Buddha
    ○ B. the priest who taught about the Buddha
    ○ C. the enemy who was defeated by the Buddha
    ○ D. the leader who organized the Buddha's followers

6. According to Buddhist tradition, what happened to the Buddha's mother before he was born?
    ○ A. She gave up all her wealth.
    ○ B. She received a visit from an angel.
    ○ C. She dreamed about a white elephant.
    ○ D. She married against her parents' wishes.

7. Why had the Buddha **not** learned about suffering as a child?
    ○ A. His father protected him.
    ○ B. He was not interested in others.
    ○ C. He understood that pain is not real.
    ○ D. The gods granted him special favors.

8. Which of these events happened **first** in the Buddha's life?
    ○ A. He left the palace.
    ○ B. He became an ascetic.
    ○ C. He gained enlightenment.
    ○ D. He and his wife had a son.

9. What troubled the Buddha on his first few trips out into the world?

○ A. inequality of wealth
○ B. aging, sickness, and death
○ C. prejudice against lower castes
○ D. cruelty, evil, and lack of caring

10. If you decided to live as an ascetic, what would you do?

○ A. abandon your religion
○ B. become ruler of a kingdom
○ C. give up most of what you own
○ D. become a parent of a large family

11. Why did the Buddha become thin from lack of food?

○ A. Nobody would give him alms.
○ B. He fasted for spiritual reasons.
○ C. He was locked away in a tower.
○ D. Famine spread over the country.

12. Why did the Buddha decide to follow a "middle way"?

○ A. Neither riches nor being an ascetic led to nirvana.
○ B. Neither struggle nor acceptance summed up all of life.
○ C. Neither life on Earth nor life after death seemed most important.
○ D. Neither the Four Truths nor the Eight-fold Path worked without the other.

13. What did the Buddha discover under the Bodhi tree?

○ A. basic truths for living
○ B. a chest filled with jewels
○ C. the entrance to a deep cave
○ D. a wise man who guided him

14. Why did the Buddha decide **not** to escape into enlightenment right away?

○ A. He preferred to follow a middle way.
○ B. He forgot his dream when he woke up.
○ C. He wanted to teach people the path he had found.
○ D. He did not want to leave his wife and child behind.

15. Which of the following is one of the Four Noble Truths?

○ A. Study leads to wisdom.
○ B. Joy is achieved by praying.
○ C. Only death can end cravings.
○ D. Suffering is caused by desires.

16. The Eightfold Path of Buddhism is **most** similar to which of these Hindu beliefs?

○ A. castes
○ B. karma
○ C. deities
○ D. dharma

Applying Social Studies Skills

Use the passage and your knowledge of history to answer the questions.
Write the word or phrase in the space provided.

> Friends, just as the footprints of all legged animals are encompassed by the footprint of the elephant, and the elephant's footprint is reckoned the foremost among them in terms of size; in the same way, all skillful qualities are gathered under the four noble truths. Under which four? Under the noble truth of stress, under the noble truth of the origination of stress, under the noble truth of the cessation of stress, and under the noble truth of the path of practice leading to the cessation of stress.
>
> —*Sariputta, a disciple of the Buddha*

17. Instead of using the word *suffering,* as in the Four Noble Truths, what word does this translation use?

18. Sariputta says that all skillful qualities fit within the Four Noble Truths in the same way that the footprints of smaller animals fit within the footprint of what animal?

19. What does Sariputta likely mean by "all skillful qualities"?

Exploring the Essential Question

What are the main beliefs and teachings of Buddhism?

Follow the directions to complete the item below.

20. In each box on the path below, write one sentence to illustrate that principle. Two of the boxes have been completed as examples.

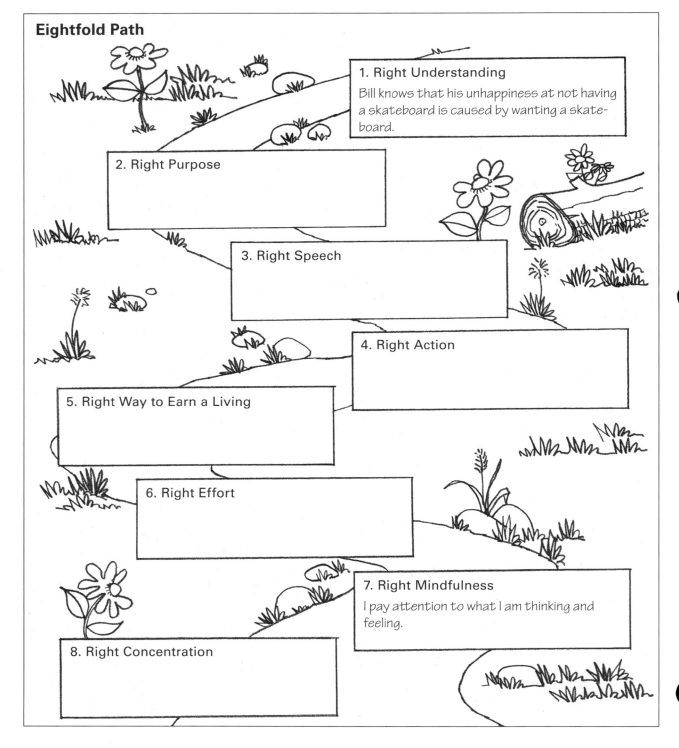

Eightfold Path

1. Right Understanding
Bill knows that his unhappiness at not having a skateboard is caused by wanting a skateboard.

2. Right Purpose

3. Right Speech

4. Right Action

5. Right Way to Earn a Living

6. Right Effort

7. Right Mindfulness
I pay attention to what I am thinking and feeling.

8. Right Concentration

Creating Billboards for Ashoka's Edicts

With your partner, follow these steps to create billboards for Ashoka's edicts:

Step 1: Read your assigned edict. On the handout, underline or highlight key words. Make sure you know the meanings of these words.

Step 2: Interpret your assigned edict. Discuss what you think the edict means and which of Ashoka's four goals it best emphasizes. On the back of the handout, write one or two sentences that summarize the edict's main idea and goal.

Step 3: Brainstorm and draft your billboard. Your classmates will use your billboard to understand what the edict means and to identify which of Ashoka's four goals is emphasized. Do *not* name the goal on your billboard. On the back of the handout or on a separate piece of paper, sketch your billboard, using catchy phrases and visuals that represent the edict's main idea and goal. Review your draft with your teacher to receive feedback.

Step 4: Create your billboard. Use the paper that your teacher gives you to carefully create your billboard. Incorporate your teacher's feedback. Use color and other creative touches to make the billboard visually appealing.

Sample Edict

To do good is difficult. One who does good first does something hard to do. I have done many good deeds, and, if my sons, grandsons, and their descendants up to the end of the world act in like manner, they too will do much good. But whoever amongst them neglects this, they will do evil. Truly, it is easy to do evil.

Ashoka's Edicts

Edict A

On the roads . . . trees have been planted for the enjoyment of animals and men. I have had ponds dug and shelters erected along the roads. Everywhere I have had wells dug.

Edict B

It is good to be obedient to one's mother and father, friends, and relatives. It is good not only to spend little, but to own the minimum of property.

© Teachers' Curriculum Institute

Edict C

My officers have been appointed for the welfare [safety] and happiness of the . . . people. I have given them . . . authority in judgment and punishment. But it is desirable that there should be uniformity [sameness] in judicial [trial] procedure and punishment.

Edict D
This world and the other [world after death] are hard to gain without great love of righteousness [correct behavior], great self-examination, great obedience, and great effort.

Edict E

If the unconquered peoples on my border ask what is my will, they should understand this: I desire that they should trust me and should have only happiness in their dealings with me.

Edict F

This . . . has been engraved so that the officials of the city should always see to it that no one is ever imprisoned or tortured without good cause. To ensure this, officers who are not fierce or harsh shall be sent out every five years on a tour of inspection.

Edict G
There is no gift comparable to
the gift of dharma [righteousness,
or correct behavior], which is
good behavior toward slaves
and servants; obedience to
parents; generosity toward friends,
acquaintances, and relatives; . . .
and abstention [staying away]
from killing living beings.

Edict H

Everywhere, I, Ashoka, King Priyadarsi, Beloved of the Gods, have arranged for two kinds of medical treatment: medical treatment for people and medical treatment for animals.

Edict I

Men who are sentenced to death are to be given three days' respite [waiting period before being put to death]. During this period, relatives may plead for the prisoners' lives, or the accused may make donations or undertake a fast [period of not eating] for a better rebirth in the next life.

Interpreting Ashoka's Edicts

With your partner, carefully examine *Edicts A–I* and the billboards posted near them. Circle the goal that you think is best emphasized in each edict, and explain your choice.

Edict	Goal	Why We Chose This Goal
Edict A: "On the roads, . . . trees have been planted for the enjoyment of animals and men. I have had ponds dug and shelters erected along the roads. Everywhere I have had wells dug."	Buddhist Values General Welfare Justice Security	
Edict B: "It is good to be obedient to one's mother and father, friends, and relatives. It is good not only to spend little, but to own the minimum of property."	Buddhist Values General Welfare Justice Security	
Edict C: "My officers have been appointed for the welfare [safety] and happiness of the . . . people. I have given them . . . authority in judgment and punishment. But it is desirable that there should be uniformity [sameness] in judicial [trial] procedure and punishment."	Buddhist Values General Welfare Justice Security	
Edict D: "This world and the other [world after death] are hard to gain without great love of righteousness [correct behavior], great self-examination, great obedience, and great effort."	Buddhist Values General Welfare Justice Security	

Edict	Goal	Why We Chose This Goal
Edict E: "If the unconquered peoples on my border ask what is my will, they should understand this: I desire that they should trust me and should have only happiness in their dealings with me."	Buddhist Values General Welfare Justice Security	
Edict F: "This . . . has been engraved so that the officials of the city should always see to it that no one is ever imprisoned or tortured without good cause. To ensure this, officers who are not fierce or harsh shall be sent out every five years on a tour of inspection."	Buddhist Values General Welfare Justice Security	
Edict G: "There is no gift comparable to the gift of dharma [righteousness, or correct behavior], which is good behavior toward slaves and servants; obedience to parents; generosity toward friends, acquaintances, and relatives; . . . and abstention [staying away] from killing living beings."	Buddhist Values General Welfare Justice Security	
Edict H: "Everywhere, I, Ashoka, King Priyadarsi, Beloved of the Gods, have arranged for two kinds of medical treatment: medical treatment for people and medical treatment for animals."	Buddhist Values General Welfare Justice Security	
Edict I: "Men who are sentenced to death are to be given three days' respite [waiting period before being put to death]. During this period, relatives may plead for the prisoners' lives, or the accused may make donations or undertake a fast [period of not eating] for a better rebirth in the next life."	Buddhist Values General Welfare Justice Security	

Chapter 17 Assessment

Mastering the Content

Fill in the circle next to the best answer.

1. What was the **main** achievement of the Maurya family?
   ○ A. to unify India
   ○ B. to impose Buddhism
   ○ C. to build famous temples
   ○ D. to improve the lives of peasants

2. How did Chandragupta Maurya begin building his empire?
   ○ A. He sent ships to far-off islands.
   ○ B. He conquered neighboring kingdoms.
   ○ C. He sponsored settlements by colonists.
   ○ D. He persuaded other rulers to unite with him.

3. Which of these would you **not** consider an achievement under Chandragupta's rule?
   ○ A. He created a strong central government.
   ○ B. He used torture and spies to make people obey.
   ○ C. He made sure farmers had water for their crops.
   ○ D. He built a royal road more than one thousand miles long.

4. Why was Chandragupta poor in his later years?
   ○ A. He put a stop to foreign trade.
   ○ B. He was overthrown by his son.
   ○ C. He decided to live as an ascetic.
   ○ D. He lost the conquered territories.

The Mauryan Empire

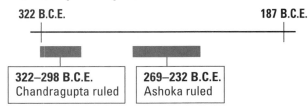

322 B.C.E.   187 B.C.E.

322–298 B.C.E. Chandragupta ruled

269–232 B.C.E. Ashoka ruled

5. Which conclusion about the Mauryan Empire does the timeline **best** support?
   ○ A. It fell apart when Ashoka died.
   ○ B. It expanded for a hundred years.
   ○ C. It had only two kings altogether.
   ○ D. Its first ruler was Chandragupta.

6. King Ashoka was Chandragupta's
   ○ A. father.
   ○ B. enemy.
   ○ C. brother.
   ○ D. grandson.

7. Ashoka expanded the Mauryan Empire until he
   ○ A. moved to China.
   ○ B. gave up violence.
   ○ C. reached the mountains.
   ○ D. surrendered to his cousin.

8. Which experience led to a deep change in Ashoka's values?
   ○ A. marrying a Buddhist
   ○ B. seeing a very bloody battle
   ○ C. hearing Buddha's first sermon
   ○ D. discovering old age and illness

9. Which Buddhist value did these actions by Ashoka reflect?

   • He gave up hunting.

   • He became a vegetarian.

   ○ A. respect for all living things
   ○ B. toleration of other religions
   ○ C. honesty in words and actions
   ○ D. awareness that everything changes

10. How did Chandragupta's rule differ from Ashoka's?

   ○ A. Chandragupta had a larger empire than Ashoka did.
   ○ B. Chandragupta used Buddhism to keep his people happy.
   ○ C. Chandragupta made laws that were fairer than Ashoka's laws.
   ○ D. Chandragupta used force to be sure no one threatened his power.

11. Ashoka often spoke of the people he ruled as his

   ○ A. friends.
   ○ B. children.
   ○ C. students.
   ○ D. brothers.

12. Which of Ashoka's actions best expressed his Buddhist values?

   ○ A. allowing slavery
   ○ B. keeping a strong army
   ○ C. putting criminals to death
   ○ D. treating all of his servants well

13. What did Ashoka do with the territories the Mauryas had conquered?

   ○ A. returned them to their former rulers
   ○ B. used them as a base for new conquests
   ○ C. kept them as peaceful parts of his empire
   ○ D. granted them to wealthy merchants as gifts

14. In what important way did Ashoka spread Buddhist teachings?

   ○ A. He required conquered people to convert.
   ○ B. He had edicts carved into pillars and walls.
   ○ C. He had peasants taught how to read and write.
   ○ D. He made speeches in many places around the empire.

15. One of Ashoka's edicts announced that people would only be jailed for a good reason. Which of his goals did this promote most?

   ○ A. Justice
   ○ B. Security
   ○ C. General Welfare
   ○ D. Buddhist Values

Applying Social Studies Skills

Use the map and your knowledge of history to answer the questions.
Write the word or phrase in the space provided.

The Spread of Buddhism

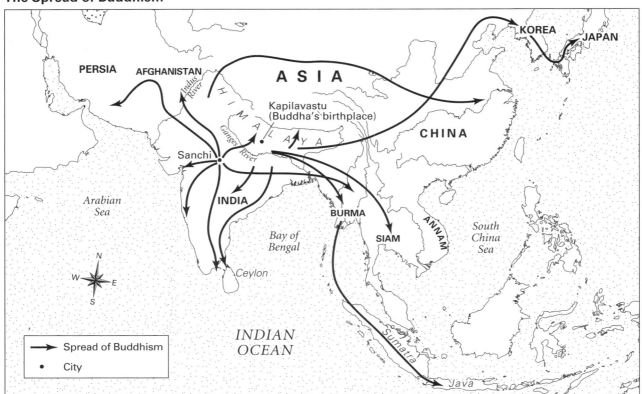

16. Tradition says that King Ashoka sent his son to Ceylon to convert that kingdom to Buddhism. In what body of water is Ceylon?

17. Buddhist ideas also spread across water to reach what two places?

18. What two places on the mainland of Southeast Asia later converted to Buddhism?

19. What was the biggest natural barrier to the spread of ideas from India into Central Asia?

© Teachers' Curriculum Institute

Name_____ Date_____

Exploring the Essential Question

How did Ashoka unify the Mauryan Empire and spread Buddhist values?

Follow the directions to complete the item below.

20. Suppose that you are a teacher grading King Ashoka on his achievements. For each topic below, create a report card that includes the following:

- A letter grade—A, B, C, D, or F—that represents how you would evaluate Ashoka's achievements in that area.
- A teacher comment that explains why you are giving Ashoka that grade. Express your comment in one or more complete sentences.

Report Card on Unifying the Empire	**Grade:**
Teacher Comment:	

Report Card on Spreading Buddhism	**Grade:**
Teacher Comment:	

Report Card on Promoting the Good of the People	**Grade:**
Teacher Comment:	

Travel Sites

Station A: Bakshali

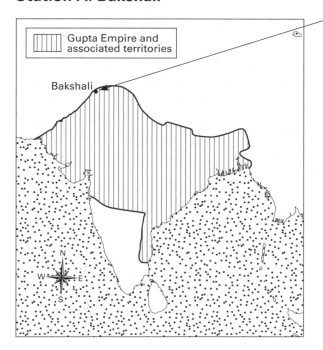

Gupta Empire and associated territories

Bakshali

N W E S

You are in Bakshali, located in the northwest corner of the Gupta Empire. You see the peaks of the surrounding mountain ranges. You feel the hot, dry air as you stand on the rocky land. You hear two Gupta officials discussing how they will collect one-fourth of the local peasants' harvest as taxes.

Teachers, place sticky note here.

Mathematics
Read Section 18.8.

Lift the flap to check your answer.

1. Map Your Location. Read the above description of Bakshali. Then, on the map of the Gupta Empire in your Interactive Student Notebook, record three details about this site.

2. Identify the Achievement. In the above description of Bakshali, find the clue that describes a Gupta achievement. Match the clue to one of the achievements described in Sections 18.3 to 18.9 of your book. Then lift the flap to check your answer.

3. Discover the Achievement. Read the section of Chapter 18 for this achievement and complete the corresponding Reading Notes. Then, on the map of the Gupta Empire in your Interactive Student Notebook, draw your symbol for this achievement, either on or near Bakshali.

Travel Sites

Station B: Meharauli

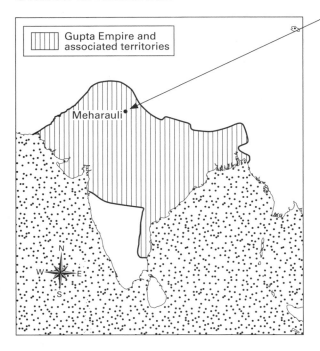

You are in Meharauli, located in northern India between the empire's most fertile plain and the Thar Desert. Standing before you, you see an enormous pillar made of solid iron. You feel the dry, brown earth of the flat landscape beneath your feet. You hear Gupta artisans complaining about the hot and humid weather.

Teachers, place sticky note here.

Metalwork
Read Section 18.7.

Lift the flap to check your answer.

1. Map Your Location. Read the above description of Meharauli. Then, on the map of the Gupta Empire in your Interactive Student Notebook, record three details about this site.

2. Identify the Achievement. In the above description of Meharauli, find the clue that describes a Gupta achievement. Match the clue to one of the achievements described in Sections 18.3 to 18.9 of your book. Then lift the flap to check your answer.

3. Discover the Achievement. Read the section of Chapter 18 for this achievement and complete the corresponding Reading Notes. Then, on the map of the Gupta Empire in your Interactive Student Notebook, draw your symbol for this achievement, either on or near Meharauli.

Travel Sites

Station C: Sarnath

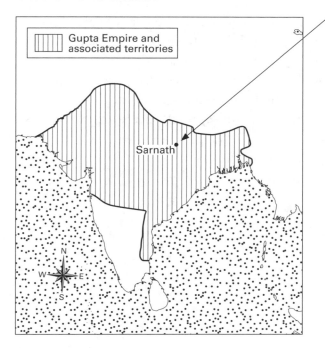

You are in Sarnath, located in northeast India near the Ganges River. You see crops growing on the flat and green land. You feel the cool night breeze from the distant Himalayas, bringing relief from the day's heat. You hear the sounds of Gupta artists busily working with chisels on the city's many famous works of art.

Teachers, place sticky note here.

Sculpture
Read Section 18.6.

Lift the flap to check your answer.

1. Map Your Location. Read the above description of Sarnath. Then, on the map of the Gupta Empire in your Interactive Student Notebook, record three details about this site.

2. Identify the Achievement. In the above description of Sarnath, find the clue that describes a Gupta achievement. Match the clue to one of the achievements described in Sections 18.3 to 18.9 of your book. Then lift the flap to check your answer.

3. Discover the Achievement. Read the section of Chapter 18 for this achievement and complete the corresponding Reading Notes. Then, on the map of the Gupta Empire in your Interactive Student Notebook, draw your symbol for this achievement, either on or near Sarnath.

Travel Sites

Station D: Pataliputra

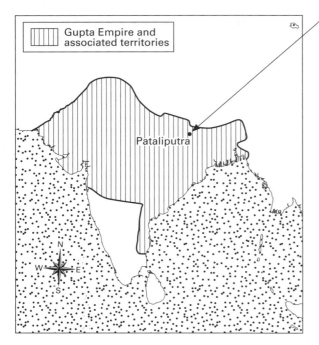

Gupta Empire and associated territories

Pataliputra

N
W E
S

You are on a road located just outside Pataliputra, the capital of the Gupta Empire. You see that the road is made of hard-packed dirt and is raised a little higher than the surrounding land. You feel the hot and humid air around you. You hear the local farmers talking about their abundant crops.

Teachers, place sticky note here.

Roads
Read Section 18.9.

Lift the flap to check your answer.

1. **Map Your Location.** Read the above description of Pataliputra. Then, on the map of the Gupta Empire in your Interactive Student Notebook, record three details about this site.

2. **Identify the Achievement.** In the above description of Pataliputra, find the clue that describes a Gupta achievement. Match the clue to one of the achievements described in Sections 18.3 to 18.9 of your book. Then lift the flap to check your answer.

3. **Discover the Achievement.** Read the section of Chapter 18 for this achievement and complete the corresponding Reading Notes. Then, on the map of the Gupta Empire in your Interactive Student Notebook, draw your symbol for this achievement, either on or near Pataliputra.

Travel Sites

Station E: Nalanda

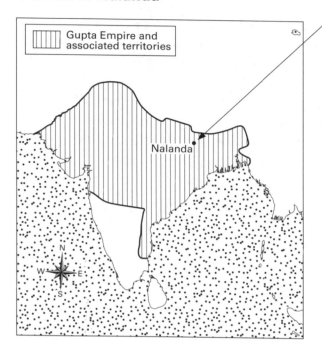

Gupta Empire and associated territories

Nalanda

N W E S

You are in Nalanda, located in northeast India. You see that the flat landscape is lush and green from the season's drenching rains. You feel the intense heat, but you spot relief nearby as dark thunderclouds loom on the horizon. You hear the lively debates of some of the Gupta's brightest individuals, who have come to Nalanda to study.

Teachers, place sticky note here.

Universities
Read Section 18.3.

Lift the flap to check your answer.

1. **Map Your Location.** Read the above description of Nalanda. Then, on the map of the Gupta Empire in your Interactive Student Notebook, record three details about this site.

2. **Identify the Achievement.** In the above description of Nalanda, find the clue that describes a Gupta achievement. Match the clue to one of the achievements described in Sections 18.3 to 18.9 of your book. Then lift the flap to check your answer.

3. **Discover the Achievement.** Read the section of Chapter 18 for this achievement and complete the corresponding Reading Notes. Then, on the map of the Gupta Empire in your Interactive Student Notebook, draw your symbol for this achievement, either on or near Nalanda.

Travel Sites

Station F: Ajanta

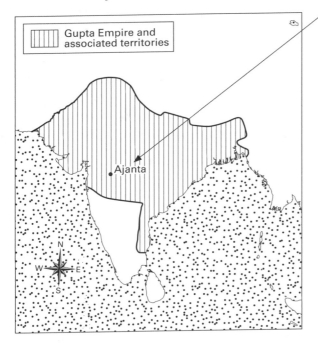

Gupta Empire and associated territories

Ajanta

You enter the Ajanta caves, located on the Deccan Plateau in central India. You feel the coolness of the cave, after the intense heat and humidity outside. You see beautiful murals showing scenes of the lives of Gupta nobles. As you leave the cave, you hear very little sound coming from the flat, dry land that surrounds you.

Teachers, place sticky note here.

Painting
Read Section 18.5.

Lift the flap to check your answer.

1. **Map Your Location.** Read the above description of Ajanta. Then, on the map of the Gupta Empire in your Interactive Student Notebook, record three details about this site.

2. **Identify the Achievement.** In the above description of Ajanta, find the clue that describes a Gupta achievement. Match the clue to one of the achievements described in Sections 18.3 to 18.9 of your book. Then lift the flap to check your answer.

3. **Discover the Achievement.** Read the section of Chapter 18 for this achievement and complete the corresponding Reading Notes. Then, on the map of the Gupta Empire in your Interactive Student Notebook, draw your symbol for this achievement, either on or near Ajanta.

Travel Sites

Station G: Ujjain

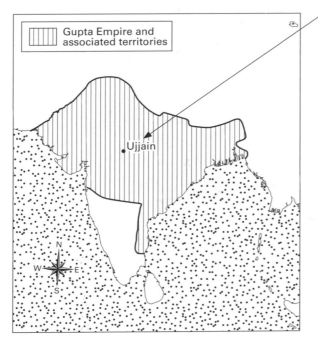

Gupta Empire and associated territories

Ujjain

You are in Ujjain, a city located in central India. You see a large audience gathering to watch the performance of a play. You feel the warm air of this hilly and rocky land. You hear the local people wishing for the rains of the summer monsoons that will bring life to the dry and brown earth.

Teachers, place sticky note here.

Literature
Read Section 18.4.

Lift the flap to check your answer.

1. Map Your Location. Read the above description of Ujjain. Then, on the map of the Gupta Empire in your Interactive Student Notebook, record three details about this site.

2. Identify the Achievement. In the above description of Ujjain, find the clue that describes a Gupta achievement. Match the clue to one of the achievements described in Sections 18.3 to 18.9 of your book. Then lift the flap to check your answer.

3. Discover the Achievement. Read the section of Chapter 18 for this achievement and complete the corresponding Reading Notes. Then, on the map of the Gupta Empire in your Interactive Student Notebook, draw your symbol for this achievement, either on or near Ujjain.

Creating a Palm-Leaf Book

During your tour of the Gupta Empire, you learned about seven impressive "golden age" achievements. Describe your travels and discoveries by writing and illustrating a palm-leaf book. Your book should clearly explain why the period during the Gupta Empire is known as a "golden age." Include the following elements in your book:

- A cover with a title and an illustration.

- An introduction page with a paragraph introducing the Gupta Empire and the focus of your palm-leaf book.

- Three main pages, each on one achievement. Select the achievements you think best demonstrate why historians consider the period during the Gupta Empire a "golden age." Each page should include a paragraph that describes the place you visited and the information you learned about the achievement. Use descriptive words and specific details that will help create a visual image in the mind of the reader.

- A conclusion page that summarizes your main points and emphasizes why these achievements define the period during the Gupta Empire as a "golden age."

- Simple visuals for your introduction page and your three main pages, illustrating the achievements or geographic setting.

- Any other creative and decorative touches that make the book more realistic and interesting.

© Teachers' Curriculum Institute

Palm-Leaf Book Page

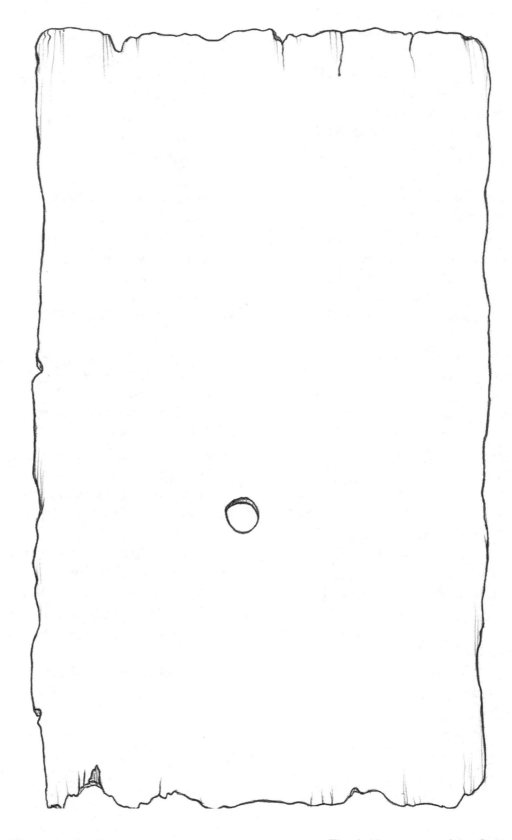

Chapter 18 Assessment

Mastering the Content

Fill in the circle next to the best answer.

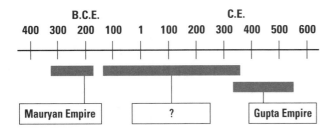

1. What happened on the Indian subcontinent in the time period between the Mauryan and Gupta empires?
   - ○ A. It went through a golden age.
   - ○ B. It experienced a great famine.
   - ○ C. It was filled with small kingdoms.
   - ○ D. It was conquered by the Sumerians.

2. How did the first Gupta ruler form alliances with other rulers?
   - ○ A. by giving them land
   - ○ B. by arranging marriages
   - ○ C. by killing them in battle
   - ○ D. by sending wise advisers

3. How was the Gupta Empire different from the Mauryan Empire?
   - ○ A. It got rid of the caste system.
   - ○ B. It was governed with harsh laws.
   - ○ C. It was made up of five kingdoms.
   - ○ D. It gave local areas a lot of independence.

4. Which factors in the Gupta Empire **most** helped the growth of learning?
   - ○ A. peace and stability
   - ○ B. poverty and hunger
   - ○ C. power and conquest
   - ○ D. change and rebellion

5. Which of these finds by an archaeologist would be evidence of a golden age?
   - ○ A. walled cities
   - ○ B. fine sculptures
   - ○ C. metal weapons
   - ○ D. animal skeletons

6. The images of Gupta kings on coins show that the empire had people who were skilled in
   - ○ A. writing literature.
   - ○ B. planning buildings.
   - ○ C. conducting warfare.
   - ○ D. working with metal.

7. How did individuals in the Gupta Empire learn the skills listed below?
   - Question patients
   - Make cures from bark and roots
   - Stitch up wounds
   - ○ A. by making a palm-leaf book
   - ○ B. by praying to the deity of doctors
   - ○ C. by studying medicine at a university
   - ○ D. by journeying abroad with a merchant

8. What change took place in Hinduism during the Gupta Empire?
   - ○ A. Many of its laws were improved.
   - ○ B. Many of its legends were written down.
   - ○ C. Many of its complex rituals were abandoned.
   - ○ D. Many of its most sacred temples were destroyed.

9. Which is the **best** title for the list below?

   • *Puranas*

   • *Mahabharata*

   • *Bhagavad Gita*

   ○ A. Gupta Paintings
   ○ B. Hindu Sculptures
   ○ C. Buddhist Folklore
   ○ D. Sanskrit Literature

10. The famous ancient paintings in a Buddhist monastery at Ajanta were painted on the

   ○ A. walls of caves.
   ○ B. robes of monks.
   ○ C. covers of a book.
   ○ D. ceilings of a temple.

11. In the Gupta Empire, what was an important use for all the following materials?

   • Stone

   • Wood

   • Bronze

   • Terra-cotta clay

   ○ A. weapons
   ○ B. sculptures
   ○ C. cooking pots
   ○ D. wheeled carts

12. Which sense correctly describes the level of technology in the Gupta Empire?

   ○ A. They did not yet know how to work copper.
   ○ B. They used copper but did not yet know how to make bronze.
   ○ C. They made bronze but did not yet know how to work iron.
   ○ D. They had skill in working with iron.

13. Which feature of modern arithmetic came from ancient India by way of the Arabs?

   ○ A. zero
   ○ B. addition
   ○ C. counting
   ○ D. subtraction

14. Which of the following groups of people made it possible to construct complex buildings like this one?

   ○ A. slaves
   ○ B. monks
   ○ C. astrologers
   ○ D. mathematicians

15. Which achievement of the Gupta Empire **most** encouraged long-distance trade?

   ○ A. astronomy
   ○ B. large schools
   ○ C. well-built roads
   ○ D. large monasteries

16. Why were wells constructed along trade routes?

   ○ A. so deities would be pleased
   ○ B. so roads would not get muddy
   ○ C. so travelers could cook and drink
   ○ D. so merchants could pay for water

Applying Social Studies Skills

Use the images and your knowledge of history to answer the questions. Write your answers in the space provided.

Gupta sculpture of the river deity Ganga

Gupta sculpture of the Buddha

17. What details in the sculpture of Ganga suggest a river?

18. Which religious tradition does the sculpture of Ganga represent?

    How can you tell?

19. How does the sculpture of Buddha illustrate a Buddhist ideal or value?

Exploring the Essential Question

Why is the period during the Gupta Empire known as a "golden age"?

Follow the directions to complete the item below.

20. Suppose that you are organizing a group tour of highlights of India during the Gupta Empire. In the space below, either design a poster _____ or write text for a booklet _____ to advertise the tour. Follow these guidelines:

   - Check (✓) one of the lines above to select either a poster or a booklet.

   - Tell why the reader might want to sign up for your tour. Be persuasive.

   - Identify three sites that will be included on the tour. Explain why they are interesting and important.

The Gupta Empire

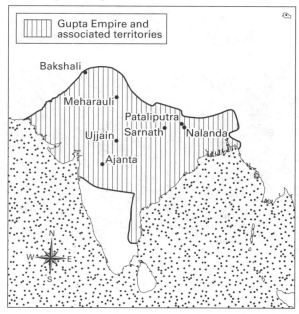

Unit 3 Timeline Challenge Cards

Settlement in India
About 6500–5000 B.C.E.

Indian farmers establish early settlements along the Indus and the Ganges rivers.

Harappan Civilization
About 2700–1900 B.C.E.

Harappan civilization flourishes in walled cities with advanced sewer systems.

Vedas
About 1500–1200 B.C.E.

The Vedas are the earliest Indian texts, from which Hinduism traces its roots.

Ramayana Composed
About 300 B.C.E.

The *Ramayana* and other epic texts are famous stories that become part of Hindu tradition.

Unit 3 Timeline Challenge Cards

First Unification of India
About 322 B.C.E.

Chandragupta Maurya, shown here, unites India. His grandson, Ashoka, expands the Mauryan Empire to include nearly all of the Indian subcontinent.

Prince Siddhartha Gautama Born
About 563 B.C.E.

Queen Maya gives birth to Siddhartha, who, tradition says, can already walk and talk.

Buddhism Founded
About 528 B.C.E.

According to tradition, Siddhartha Gautama reaches enlightenment, establishing the Buddhist religion.

Reign of Ashoka
269–232 B.C.E.

King Ashoka posts edicts in public places to unify his empire and spread Buddhist values.

Unit 3 Timeline Challenge Cards

Fall of Mauryan Empire
About 187 B.C.E.

The Mauryan Empire falls, and India breaks apart into separate kingdoms.

Rise of Gupta Empire
About 320 C.E.

The Gupta family unites northern India and organizes the empire into provinces.

India's Golden Age
About 320–550 C.E.

A golden age of peace and prosperity advances the arts and sciences in ancient India.

Aryabhatiya Published
About 499 C.E.

Aryabhata publishes his mathematic and scientific discoveries in the *Aryabhatiya*.

Relief Map of China

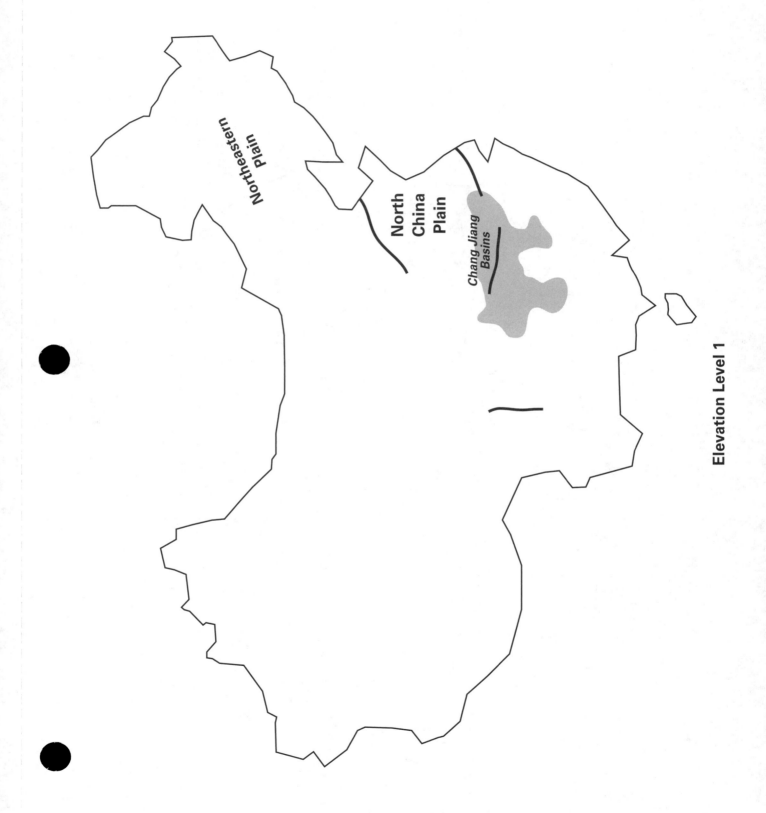

Northeastern Plain

North China Plain

Chang Jiang Basins

Elevation Level 1

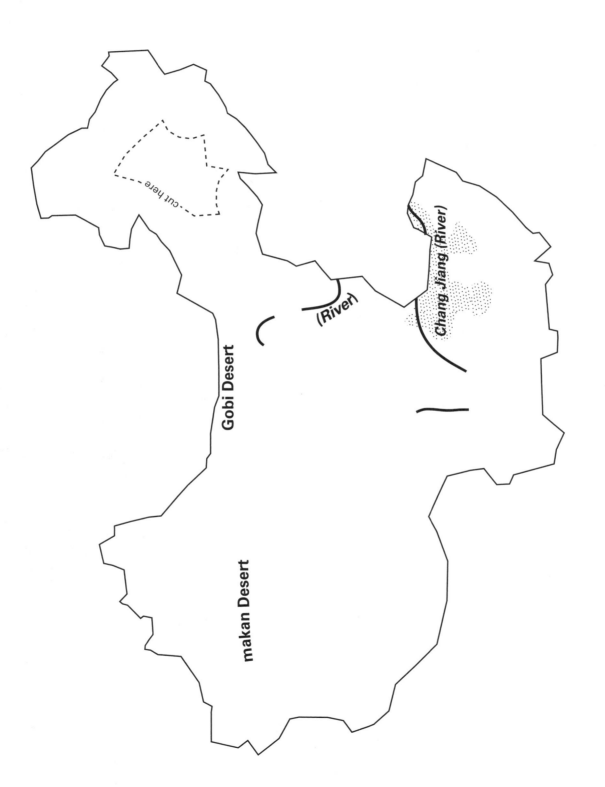

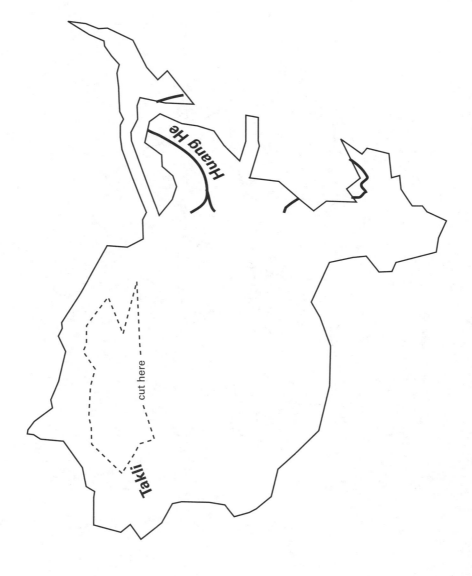

Elevation Level 3

Tibet-Qinghai
Plateau

Elevation Level 4

Geographic Data Sheets

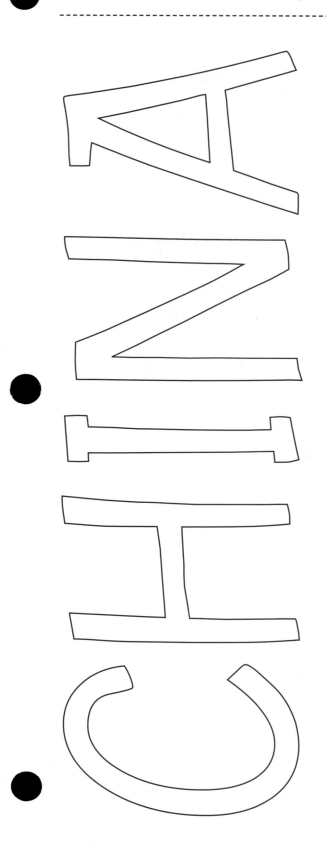

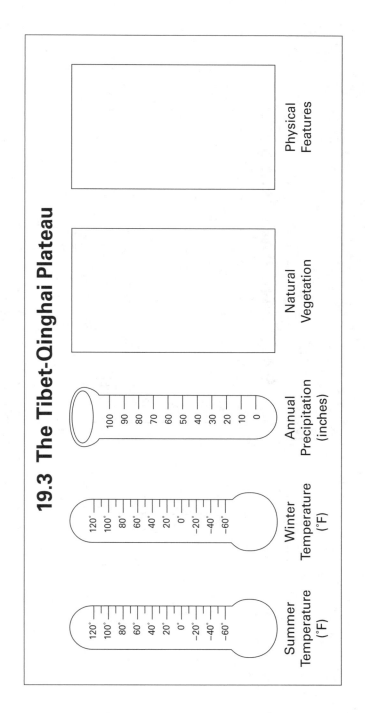

19.3 The Tibet-Qinghai Plateau

Summer Temperature (°F)	Winter Temperature (°F)	Annual Precipitation (inches)	Natural Vegetation	Physical Features

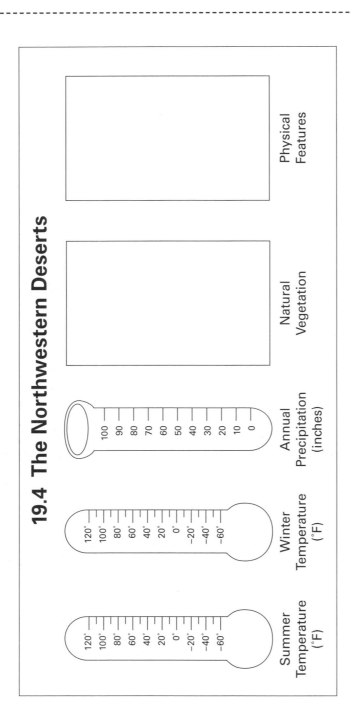

19.4 The Northwestern Deserts

Summer Temperature (°F)

Winter Temperature (°F)

Annual Precipitation (inches)

Natural Vegetation

Physical Features

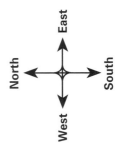

North East South West

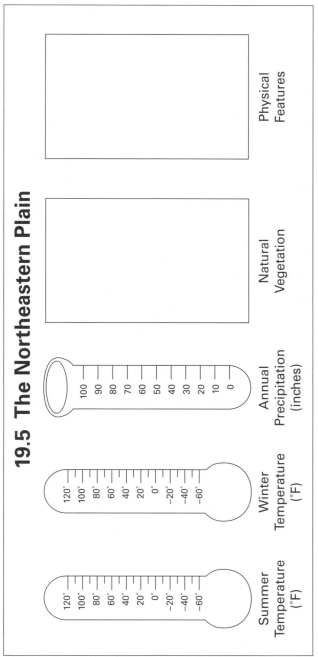

19.5 The Northeastern Plain

Physical Features

Natural Vegetation

Annual Precipitation (inches)

100 90 80 70 60 50 40 30 20 10 0

Winter Temperature (°F)

120° 100° 80° 60° 40° 20° 0° −20° −40° −60°

Summer Temperature (°F)

120° 100° 80° 60° 40° 20° 0° −20° −40° −60°

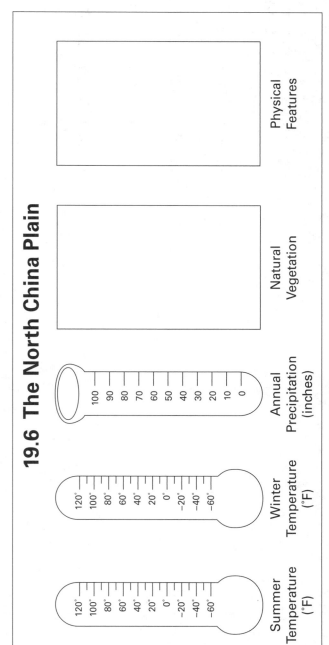

19.6 The North China Plain

Physical Features

Natural Vegetation

Annual Precipitation (inches)

100 90 80 70 60 50 40 30 20 10 0

Winter Temperature (°F)

120° 100° 80° 60° 40° 20° 0° −20° −40° −60°

Summer Temperature (°F)

120° 100° 80° 60° 40° 20° 0° −20° −40° −60°

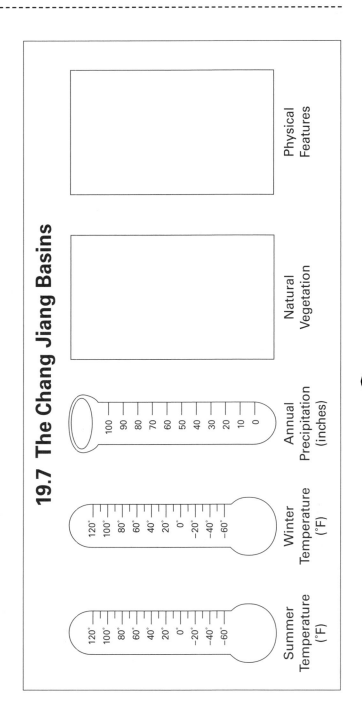

Elevations

Level 1: 0–1,150 feet

Level 2: 4,150–8,200 feet

Level 3: 4,500–8,200 feet

Level 4: 8,200–18,000 feet

19.7 The Chang Jiang Basins

Summer Temperature (°F)

Winter Temperature (°F)

Annual Precipitation (inches)

Natural Vegetation

Physical Features

Steps for Creating a Geographic Poster of China

Work with your group to create a poster about China's geography. The poster will include a relief map of China and information about the country's five important regions. Have your teacher initial each step as you complete it.

_____ **Step 1: Assign roles.** Review the roles below. Choose a role for each member of your group. Make sure everyone understands his or her responsibilities.

Cartographer You will lead the group during Step 2 to create a relief map of China.

Data Specialist You will lead the group during Step 3 to complete geographic data sheets for each region of China.

Production Supervisor You will lead the group during Step 4 to assemble the completed data sheets into a poster.

Educational Coordinator You will lead the group during Step 5 as group members share information about China's regions and complete their Reading Notes.

_____ **Step 2: Create the relief map of China.** The Cartographer (mapmaker) will distribute one page of *Student Handout 19A: Relief Map of China* to each group member. Group members will follow these steps:

- Color Elevation Level 1 green, Elevation Level 2 yellow, Elevation Level 3 brown, and Elevation Level 4 purple.

- Carefully cut out each Elevation Level.

- Place Elevation Level 2 on top of Elevation Level 1. Make sure the borders and the rivers are properly lined up, and then glue it down. Repeat this process for Elevation Levels 3 and 4, making sure the words and borders are properly positioned.

_____ **Step 3: Complete geographic data sheets for each region of China.** The Data Specialist will distribute one page of *Student Handout 19B: Geographic Data Sheets* to each group member. Group members will follow these steps:

- Read the section of *History Alive! The Ancient World* that corresponds to the region on your page. Then complete the Reading Notes for your region. (**Note:** One of the sheets covers two regions—Sections 19.5 and 19.6.)

- Create the geographic data sheet for your region. Color the thermometers and the precipitation gauge to show the climate. Draw and label illustrations of your region's vegetation and physical features.

The Data Specialist should review each page as it is completed, and assist other group members as needed.

____ **Step 4: Assemble the poster.** The Production Supervisor will lead the group in constructing the geographic poster. Group members will follow these steps:

- Color the word *China.* Color code the elevation key to match the colors on the relief map.

- Position the four geographic data sheets so the arrows on each page point to the center. Tape them together to create a poster or glue them to a piece of poster board.

- Neatly glue your relief map over the arrows in the center of the poster. Make sure the words on the map are right side up.

- Your poster should look like this:

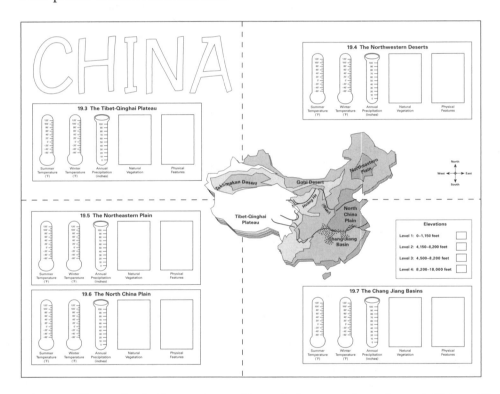

____ **Step 5: Share the information collected about each region of China.** The Educational Coordinator will direct each group member to share what he or she discovered about his or her assigned region. Each group member will follow these steps when sharing his or her information.

- Have all students turn to the page of the section in *History Alive! The Ancient World* you were assigned.

- Use the relief map of China to describe the elevation of your region.

- Use the geographic data sheet and the image in the book to describe the climate, natural vegetation, and important physical features of your region.

- Have all group members complete their Reading Notes for your section.

Chapter 19 Assessment

Mastering the Content

Fill in the circle next to the best answer.

1. Of all the countries in the world, China has the
   - ○ A. largest area.
   - ○ B. most people.
   - ○ C. longest river.
   - ○ D. worst weather.

2. Why did fewer people settle in Outer China than in Inner China?
   - ○ A. The land was in larger estates.
   - ○ B. The climate was more extreme.
   - ○ C. The roads were more dangerous.
   - ○ D. The invasions drove farmers away.

3. In Inner China, which natural events improved the soil?
   - ○ A. floods
   - ○ B. hurricanes
   - ○ C. sandstorms
   - ○ D. earthquakes

4. Why is the Tibet-Qinghai Plateau called the "Roof of the World"?
   - ○ A. It is very high above sea level.
   - ○ B. It has mountains on every side.
   - ○ C. It covers a very large land area.
   - ○ D. It is the source of several rivers.

5. Why did ancient people on the Tibet-Qinghai Plateau herd yaks rather than grow crops?
   - ○ A. Yaks found food in thick forests.
   - ○ B. The region was too wet for crops.
   - ○ C. The region was too cold for crops.
   - ○ D. Yaks could be sold in the markets.

6. What made the Taklimakan Desert one of the most dangerous deserts in the world?
   - ○ A. bandits and nomadic tribes
   - ○ B. wild animals near the rivers
   - ○ C. sandstorms and shifting dunes
   - ○ D. flash floods after thunderstorms

7. How is the Gobi Desert different from the Taklimakan Desert?
   - ○ A. The air grows hot in the daytime.
   - ○ B. Winter is very similar to summer.
   - ○ C. Very little rain falls during a year.
   - ○ D. Pebbles cover much of the surface.

8. How did the natural vegetation of the Northeastern Plain affect the lives of ancient settlers there?
   - ○ A. Fruit trees attracted settlement around oases.
   - ○ B. Varieties of plant life encouraged raising crops.
   - ○ C. Dense woods supported hunting and gathering.
   - ○ D. Prairie grass provided food for horses and sheep.

9. Several groups of invaders from the Northeastern Plain traveled to Inner China

○ A. across the Gobi Desert.
○ B. by boat across the ocean.
○ C. on frozen rivers in winter.
○ D. along a narrow coastal plain.

10. Why is the North China Plain sometimes called the "Land of the Yellow Earth"?

○ A. Millet is an important grain on farms in the region.
○ B. Limestone silt from the Gobi Desert covers the soil.
○ C. Gold has been discovered in the surrounding mountains.
○ D. One of the world's muddiest rivers runs through the region.

11. How did the Huang He **most** influence settlement near its banks?

○ A. By flooding dangerously, it kept people at a distance.
○ B. By carrying boats of raiders, it drove households away.
○ C. By fertilizing the soil, it attracted communities of farmers.
○ D. By swarming with fish, it led to the growth of fishing villages.

12. What do the Turfan Depression and the Chang Jiang Basins have in common?

○ A. They both have a large amount of rainfall.
○ B. They are both used mostly for grazing animals.
○ C. They both experience extremes in temperature.
○ D. They are both lower than many other parts of China.

13. Because rice requires warm, wet weather, where did the ancient Chinese grow rice?

○ A. the North China Plain
○ B. the Chang Jiang Basins
○ C. the Northeastern Plateau
○ D. the Tibet-Qinghai Plateau

14. In ancient times, what limited settlement in the Chang Jiang Basins compared with that in the North China Plain?

○ A. Herds had to be moved from place to place.
○ B. Crops did not grow well in the harsh climate.
○ C. Lack of natural barriers brought attacks from the south.
○ D. Rainforest vegetation may have limited the space for farming.

15. What protected Inner China from invasion from the northwest?

○ A. wide rivers
○ B. grassy plains
○ C. barren deserts
○ D. high mountains

16. Later in Chinese history, which of these geographical features made governing China as a unified state **most** difficult?

○ A. its large size
○ B. its long rivers
○ C. its broad plains
○ D. its different crops

Name_____   Date_____

Applying Social Studies Skills

Use the map and your knowledge of history to answer the questions below.
Write the word or phrase in the space provided.

Inner and Outer China, About 1700 B.C.E.– 220 C.E.

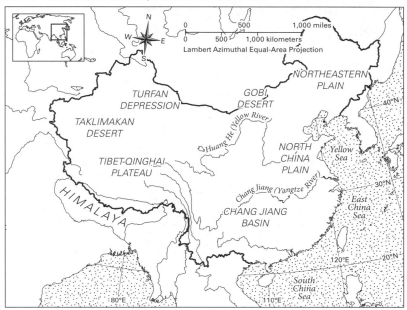

17. The major rivers of ancient China flowed down from what region?

18. What three natural barriers, shown on the map, helped protect Inner China
    from invasion?

19. What is one factor that may have made east-west travel easier than
    north-south travel within Inner China in ancient times?

Exploring the Essential Question

How did geography affect life in ancient China?

Follow the directions to complete the item below.

20. Suppose that you live in ancient China. You want to persuade your family to move to a different region. Fill in the form below to prepare your arguments.

Part I: The Region Where You Live Now

   a. Name of region _____

   b. Description of region (climate, land, vegetation)

     _____

     _____

   c. How the features of the region affect your family's life, including how you make your living

     _____

     _____

Part II: The Region You Want to Move To

   a. Name of region _____

   b. Description of region (climate, land, vegetation)

     _____

     _____

   c. How the features of the region would affect your family's life, including how you would make your living

     _____

     _____

Part III: The Reasons Why You Think Your Family Should Move

     _____

     _____

     _____

Decoders

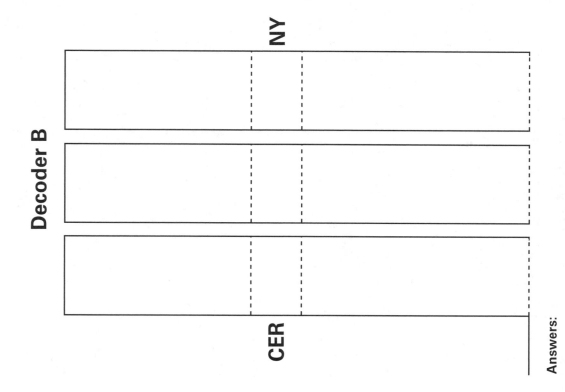

Decoder B

NY

CER

Answers:

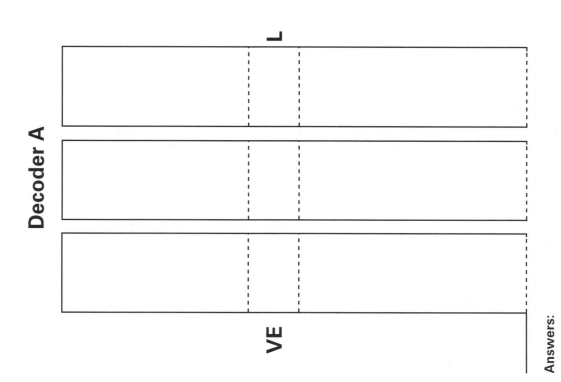

Decoder A

L

VE

Answers:

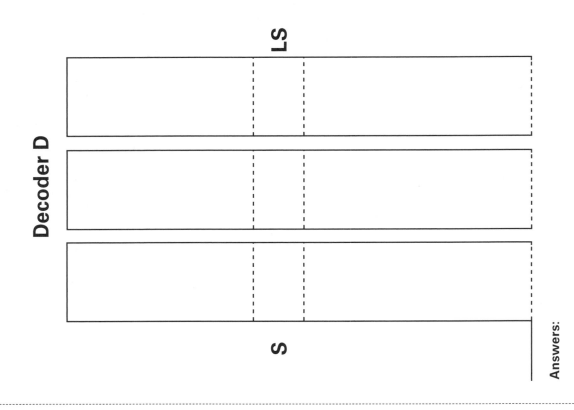

Decoder D

LS

S

Answers:

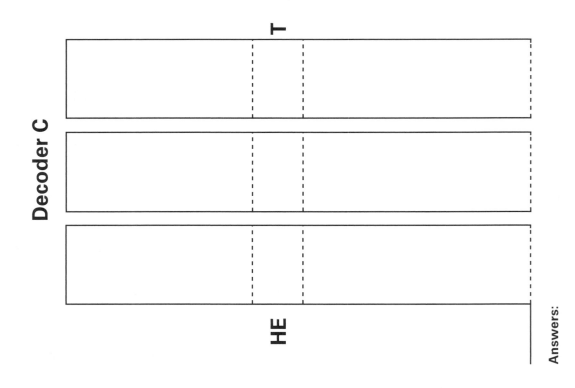

Decoder C

T

HE

Answers:

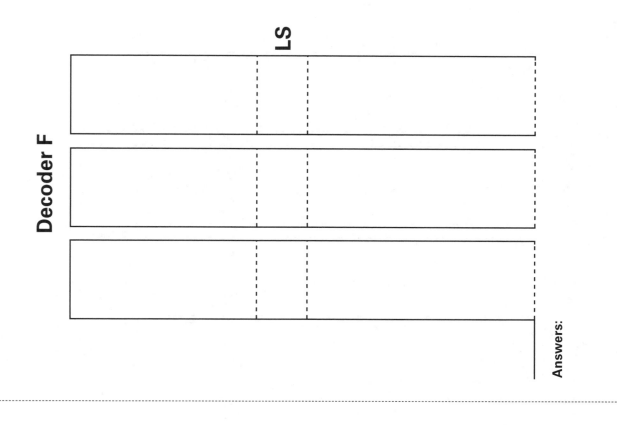

Decoder F

LS

Answers:

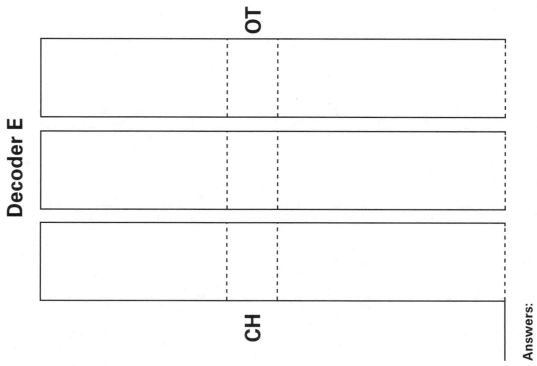

Decoder E

OT

CH

Answers:

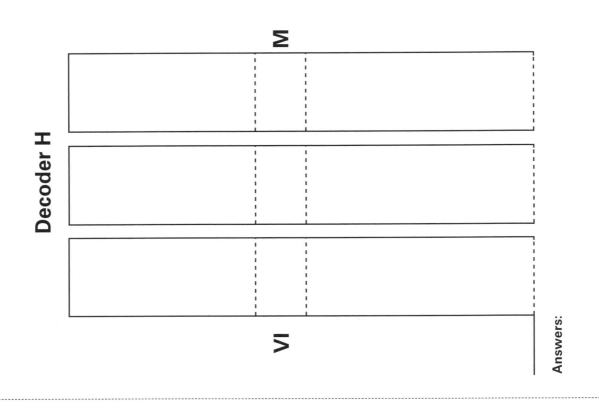

Decoder H

M

VI

Answers:

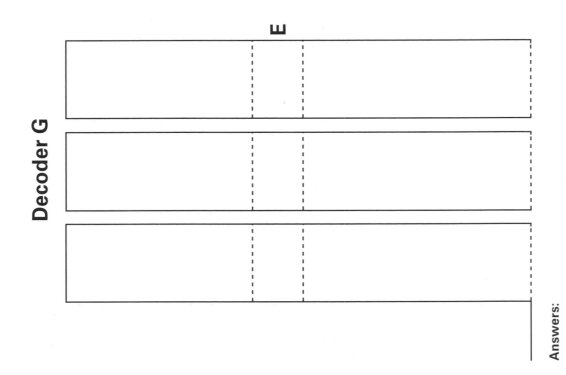

Decoder G

E

Answers:

Answer Bars for Decoders

Answers for Decoder B

Bar 3 for Decoder B

| Y 5 | C 4 | P 7 | 0 2 | | A | B | C | D | **3** |

Bar 2 for Decoder B

| J 0. | M 0. | R 0. | K 0. | | A | B | C | D | **2** |

Bar 1 for Decoder B

| E 2 | W 2 | T 2 | V 2 | | A | B | C | D | **1** |

Answers for Decoder A

Bar 3 for Decoder A

| F 8 | N 4 | P 3 | E 7 | | A | B | C | D | **3** |

Bar 2 for Decoder A

| M 0. | B 0. | S 0. | L 0. | | A | B | C | D | **2** |

Bar 1 for Decoder A

| Q 2 | Z 2 | R 2 | S 2 | | A | B | C | D | **1** |

Answers for Decoder D

Bar 3 for Decoder D

					A	B	C	D	3
V 6	L 9	T 2	P 3						

Bar 2 for Decoder D

					A	B	C	D	2
E 0.	B 0.	L 0.	I 0.						

Bar 1 for Decoder D

					A	B	C	D	1
H 2	T 2	D 2	A 2						

Answers for Decoder C

Bar 3 for Decoder C

					A	B	C	D	3
E 8	M 6	Q 3	N 4						

Bar 2 for Decoder C

					A	B	C	D	2
P 0.	C 0.	Y 0.	M 0.						

Bar 1 for Decoder C

					A	B	C	D	1
K 2	R 2	J 2	L 2						

Answers for Decoder F

Bar 3 for Decoder F: M 3 | D 5 | O 4 | V 6 | | A | B | C | D | **3**

Bar 2 for Decoder F: Y 0. | O 0. | L 0. | P 0. | | A | B | C | D | **2**

Bar 1 for Decoder F: T 2 | W 2 | I 2 | X 2 | | A | B | C | D | **1**

Answers for Decoder E

Bar 3 for Decoder E: I 3 | M 5 | Q 6 | N 7 | | A | B | C | D | **3**

Bar 2 for Decoder E: P 0. | C 0. | Y 0. | R 0. | | A | B | C | D | **2**

Bar 1 for Decoder E: K 2 | R 2 | J 2 | A 2 | | A | B | C | D | **1**

Answers for Decoder H

Bar 3 for Decoder H: D 3 | I 5 | V 6 | N 7 | A | B | C | D | 3

Bar 2 for Decoder H: W 0. | X 0. | T 0. | R 0. | A | B | C | D | 2

Bar 1 for Decoder H: L 2 | B 2 | J 2 | C 2 | A | B | C | D | 1

Answers for Decoder G

Bar 3 for Decoder G: M 4 | O 7 | T 3 | N 6 | A | B | C | D | 3

Bar 2 for Decoder G: H 0. | O 0. | X 0. | J 0. | A | B | C | D | 2

Bar 1 for Decoder G: F 2 | B 2 | R 2 | A 2 | A | B | C | D | 1

Shang Artifact Log

Follow these steps to excavate artifacts from a Shang tomb:

1. Excavate an artifact and retrieve a matching decoder.

2. Try to predict the correct answer to each placard question. Use the decoder to check your answer choices. Move the answer strip so that the letters of your answers line up at the bottom. If your answer choices are correct, the decoder will display a secret word. If a secret word does not appear, revise your answers until a word is revealed.

3. In the chart below, write the correct answers to the placard questions. Then record both the secret word and the section number shown on the decoder.

4. Read that section of *History Alive! The Ancient World* and complete the corresponding Reading Notes in your Interactive Student Notebook.

5. In the chart, check all the characteristics of the Shang civilization that this artifact reveals. Be prepared to justify your choices.

Artifact	Answers to Placard Questions	Secret Word and Section Number	Government	Social Structure	Religion	Writing	Arts	Technology
			Characteristics of the Shang Dynasty This Artifact Reveals					
A	1. The object was made of . . . 2. The object was used . . . 3. The animal parts seen are. . .							
B	1. The object is . . . 2. The object was owned by . . . 3. The object was used . . .							
C	1. The object was made of . . . 2. The object was used . . . 3. The object was made by . . .							

Artifact	Answers to Placard Questions	Secret Word and Section Number	Characteristics of the Shang Dynasty This Artifact Reveals					
			Government	Social Structure	Religion	Writing	Arts	Technology
D	1. Objects are . . . 2. Objects were obtained by. . . 3. Objects were used. . .							
E	1. Indentations were made by . . . 2. The animal tied to the bar was . . . 3. _____ stood here.							
F	1. Objects were made of . . . 2. Objects were used . . . 3. Objects were used by . . .							
G	1. The object was made of . . . 2. The marks on the object are . . . 3. The marks were important because . . .							
H	1. The skeletons are . . . 2. The missing skeleton part is . . . 3. Skeletons are incomplete because . . .							

Chapter 20 Assessment

Mastering the Content
Fill in the circle next to the best answer.

1. In which area of China, as shown on the
    map, did the Shang dynasty rule?

China

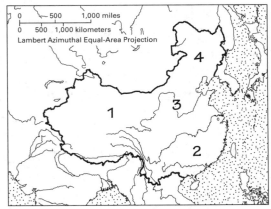

0   500   1,000 miles
0   500 1,000 kilometers
Lambert Azimuthal Equal-Area Projection

○ A. area 1
○ B. area 2
○ C. area 3
○ D. area 4

2. How did scholars learn that the Shang
    dynasty was real and not just a myth?
○ A. They read old books.
○ B. They found artifacts.
○ C. They learned the language.
○ D. They asked Chinese elders.

3. In the Shang civilization, Anyang was the
○ A. chief ruler.
○ B. capital city.
○ C. royal army.
○ D. state religion.

4. What led archaeologists to conclude that
    the Shang believed in life after death?
○ A. finding food and weapons buried with
    kings
○ B. figuring out the characters carved into
    bones
○ C. seeing pots used for ceremonies in the
    temples
○ D. studying the position in which bodies
    were laid out

5. What **most** helped Shang kings stay in
    power?
○ A. use of a powerful army
○ B. belief in magical dragons
○ C. kindness to ordinary people
○ D. marriage into leading families

6. Shang weapons were especially strong
    because skilled artisans made these
    objects from
○ A. iron.
○ B. stone.
○ C. bones.
○ D. bronze.

7. What have scholars concluded from the
    large number of wild animal bones found
    at Shang sites?
○ A. The Shang kept livestock.
○ B. The Shang rode elephants.
○ C. The Shang were active hunters.
○ D. The Shang feared animal attacks.

8. Which of these Shang people had the
    lowest social status?
○ A. merchants
○ B. jade carvers
○ C. stonemasons
○ D. grain farmers

9. The modern Chinese word for "merchant" is *shang ren*, which means "Shang man." What does this suggest about Shang culture?

 ○ A. The Shang traded a great deal.
 ○ B. Most Shang could read and write.
 ○ C. Most Shang bartered for their goods.
 ○ D. The Shang used cowrie shells as money.

10. What often happened to people the Shang captured in wars?

 ○ A. They married into the royal family.
 ○ B. They worked on construction, as slaves.
 ○ C. They were given land to start new farms.
 ○ D. They learned the skills to become artisans.

11. For what purpose would a Shang leader **most** likely use an oracle bone made from a turtle shell?

 ○ A. to serve a ceremonial meal
 ○ B. to make music for his family
 ○ C. to send messages to the nobles
 ○ D. to ask advice from his ancestors

12. If two nobles from distant parts of China met during the Shang dynasty, what would be the **best** way for them to communicate with each other?

 ○ A. by speaking, because they spoke the same language
 ○ B. by trading, because they used the same type of money
 ○ C. by writing, because they wrote with the same characters
 ○ D. by fighting, because they fought with the same weapons

13. What technology did the Shang use to make strong helmets?

 ○ A. soaking wood in salt water
 ○ B. letting pottery harden in a mold
 ○ C. weaving bamboo strips into a mat
 ○ D. shaping a mixture of copper and tin

14. How may the Shang king and his nobles have weakened their economy?

 ○ A. They bought more and more land.
 ○ B. They spent too much on their palaces.
 ○ C. They rarely paid artisans for their work.
 ○ D. They discouraged trade with other regions.

15. How did Zhou, a frontier state, **most** affect the Shang dynasty?

 ○ A. Rebels from Zhou overthrew the king.
 ○ B. Warriors from Zhou led the royal army.
 ○ C. Jade mines in Zhou made the king wealthy.
 ○ D. Travelers through Zhou promoted foreign trade.

Name_____ Date_____

Applying Social Studies Skills

The image below shows a ceremonial cooking vessel (container) from the Shang dynasty. Use the image and your knowledge of history to answer the questions. Write the word or phrase in the space provided.

16. What kind of metal is this artifact made of?

Explain your reasoning:

17. How would the handles and legs make this artifact easier to use for cooking?
    a. Handles:

    b. Legs:

18. What might be the significance or purpose of the face on the artifact?

19. Ceremonial cooking vessels were marks of status in Shang society. What suggests that the owner of this one may have been high in status?

Exploring the Essential Question

What do Shang artifacts reveal about this civilization?

Follow the directions to complete the item below.

20. Chinese writing consists of pictographs (pictures that symbolize objects) and logographs (pictures that symbolize words).

    a. Invent two pictographs. Each one should

      • symbolize an object that is important in the Shang dynasty.

      • have a caption that explains what it symbolizes.

    b. Invent two logographs. Each one should

      • symbolize a descriptive word, such as *good*.

      • have a caption that explains what it symbolizes.

Pictograph	Pictograph
Logograph	**Logograph**

Experiencing Confucianism

Step 1: Create a new seating arrangement in your classroom.

- Divide into four groups. Then move the desks into the seating arrangement shown in the diagram.

- Elders, sit calmly on your desks to show that you are respected "models of virtue."

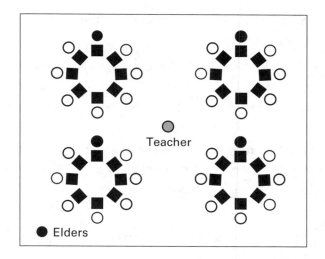

Step 2: Review the standards for appropriate behavior.

- Elders, remind members of your group that they must be attentive and respectful throughout the activity on Confucianism.

- Elders, teach members of your group how to stand, bow, and say the following greeting in unison: *"We are honored to learn from such a wise and noble teacher."*

Step 3: Learn about Confucianism.

- Elders, choose students to read Section 21.3 aloud, until the entire section has been read.

- Elders, make sure all students have correctly answered the questions for Section 21.3 in the Reading Notes of their Interactive Student Notebooks. Also, make sure all members of the group can answer the questions from memory.

Step 4: Demonstrate an understanding of Confucianism.

- All students, respond to questions from your teacher by standing and speaking in a clear voice.

- When accepting rewards for answering questions correctly, be sure to thank your elder for skillfully teaching your group about Confucianism.

Experiencing Daoism

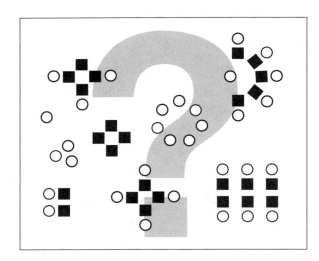

Step 1: Create a new seating arrangement in your classroom.

- There will be no formal seating arrangement for this activity.
- You may sit on the floor or move your desk to a new location.
- You may sit next to anyone you like, as long as the arrangement encourages a harmonious and peaceful atmosphere.

Step 2: Review the standards for appropriate behavior.

- Speak softly and move quietly.
- Sit still, and move and speak only when necessary.
- Avoid bringing attention to yourself.

Step 3: Learn about Daoism.

- Either alone or with others, read Section 21.4.
- Follow the directions in your Reading Notes for Section 21.4.
- If you have questions about the reading on Daoism, try to answer them yourself, rather than asking for help.

Step 4: Demonstrate an understanding of Daoism.

- If asked, share with the class the way you have decided to demonstrate your answers to the questions in the Reading Notes. Read your answers, show your drawings, present your pantomime, or share whatever other technique you have used to show your understanding of the answers.

Experiencing Legalism

Step 1: Create a new seating arrangement in your classroom.

- Quickly and silently move desks into six rows, as shown in the diagram.
- Your desk must not be within arms' reach of another student's desk.

Step 2: Review the standards for appropriate behavior.

- Speak only when given permission by the teacher.
- Sit with your back straight—no slouching.
- Keep your hands folded and on top of your desk.

Step 3: Learn about Legalism.

- Silently study Section 21.5.
- Complete the questions for Section 21.5 in the Reading Notes. You must be able to answer all questions from memory.

Step 4: Demonstrate an understanding of Legalism.

- Respond to questions from the teacher by standing and by speaking in a clear voice. Never look the teacher in the eyes.
- Politely thank the teacher for any reward. Do not argue about any punishment you are given.

Chapter 21 Assessment

Mastering the Content
Fill in the circle next to the best answer.

1. In the later years of the Zhou dynasty, what condition in China led to new philosophies?
   ○ A. wealth
   ○ B. disorder
   ○ C. feudalism
   ○ D. democracy

2. The Zhou dynasty came after which dynasty?
   ○ A. Qin
   ○ B. Han
   ○ C. Chin
   ○ D. Shang

3. According to belief in the Mandate of Heaven, earthquakes and floods might be signs that
   ○ A. the king did not govern well.
   ○ B. the end of the world was near.
   ○ C. the people did not obey the laws.
   ○ D. the natural world ignored humans.

4. Which group belongs in the shaded area of the diagram?

   Feudalism in Ancient China

   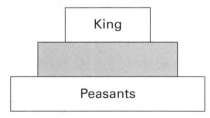

   ○ A. lords
   ○ B. soldiers
   ○ C. farmers
   ○ D. servants

5. What happened during the Warring States period?
   ○ A. Dozens of clan leaders set up military states.
   ○ B. The Zhou army won control of the state by force.
   ○ C. Six or seven large Chinese states fought for power.
   ○ D. China fought to protect the state from invaders from the north.

6. Which of these would Confucius have valued **most** highly?
   ○ A. riches
   ○ B. respect
   ○ C. freedom
   ○ D. creativity

7. Which phrase below **best** completes the following quotation?

   "I am a follower of Confucius. I am the oldest of three children in my family. My younger sister and brother have to obey me. In return, I . . ."
   ○ A. "may do whatever I want."
   ○ B. "can punish them harshly."
   ○ C. "must set a good example."
   ○ D. "have to grant their wishes."

8. Which later practice in China **most** shows the influence of Confucian thought?
   ○ A. new inventions
   ○ B. trade with Europe
   ○ C. land given to peasants
   ○ D. exams for civil servants

9. If you were a laborer, what would Confucius say that you should do?
   - ○ A. plan to rise to a higher status
   - ○ B. behave properly for your role
   - ○ C. try to outwit those around you
   - ○ D. relax and stop working so hard

10. Scholars disagree about the origins of Daoism. What is one point on which scholars agree?
    - ○ A. Daoism had little effect on beliefs in ancient China.
    - ○ B. Daoism's founder, Laozi, lived at the same time as Confucius.
    - ○ C. Daoism's book, the *Dao De Jing,* was written by many writers.
    - ○ D. Daoism provided the best form of government in ancient China.

11. Daoists taught that people could gain happiness by
    - ○ A. reading the ancient texts.
    - ○ B. serving in government jobs.
    - ○ C. living in harmony with nature.
    - ○ D. working hard to become wealthy.

12. In a chart titled "Yin and Yang," pleasure would be paired with
    - ○ A. pain.
    - ○ B. reward.
    - ○ C. afterlife.
    - ○ D. enjoyment.

13. What is one way Daoism influenced China?
    - ○ A. It got scholars to study.
    - ○ B. It led to fights for power.
    - ○ C. It encouraged stricter laws.
    - ○ D. It became a popular religion.

14. What was the Legalist view of human nature?
    - ○ A. People are basically selfish.
    - ○ B. People are naturally curious.
    - ○ C. People are motivated by love.
    - ○ D. People want to do what is right.

15. Hanfeizi, whose teachings were the basis for Legalism, wrote that rulers should emphasize
    - ○ A. honesty and trust.
    - ○ B. scholarship and ideas.
    - ○ C. trade and manufacturing.
    - ○ D. rewards and punishments.

16. What did Hanfeizi say that rulers must do to avoid being overthrown?
    - ○ A. exercise absolute power
    - ○ B. let people do as they want
    - ○ C. earn the Mandate of Heaven
    - ○ D. be popular through good deeds

Applying Social Studies Skills

Use the quotations and your knowledge of history to complete the items below. Write your responses in the space provided.

17. Describe how a government based on the philosophy of Confucianism as expressed in this quotation would **most** likely act.

"To be able under all circumstances to practice five things constitutes perfect virtue; these five things are gravity, generosity of soul, sincerity, earnestness, and kindness."

—*Confucius*

18. Describe how a government based on the philosophy of Daoism as expressed in this quotation would **most** likely act.

"Windows and doors are cut into a wall. It is their emptiness that makes the windows and doors useful."

—*the* Dao De Jing

19. Describe how a government based on the philosophy of Legalism as expressed in this quotation would **most** likely act

"No country is permanently strong. Nor is any country permanently weak. If conformers to law are strong, the country is strong; if conformers to law are weak, the country is weak."

—*Hanfeizi*

Exploring the Essential Question

How did Confucianism, Daoism, and Legalism influence political rule in ancient China?

Follow the directions to complete the item below.

20. Circle one of these three philosophies:

Confucianism   **Daoism**   **Legalism**

Fill in the chart below to describe how that philosophy influenced political rule in ancient China. Use complete sentences.

What was the goal of that philosophy for the country?

How did that philosophy say that the goal could be achieved?

How did political rule in ancient China show the influence of that philosophy?

Protecting the Northern Border Act-It-Out

Your group will be assigned a character in Visual 22C. Bring the character to life by following the steps below. One member of your group will be selected to play the part of the character. A reporter will interview the characters.

Step 1: Circle the character your group has been assigned.

man with a whip

worker carrying a basket attached to poles over the shoulders

worker standing on top of the wall

worker digging up stones

Step 2: Discuss the questions for your character. Make sure everyone in your group can answer them so that each person is prepared to be the actor.

Man with a whip:

- Why were you sent here to work on the wall?
- Why do you need a whip?
- How is this wall being constructed?
- What is the purpose of this wall?
- Do you think the wall will protect people from their enemies to the north? Why or why not?

Worker carrying a basket, standing on the wall, or digging up stones:

- Why were you sent here to work on the wall?
- What job do you perform in this construction project?
- Which job do you think is the hardest?
- What are some of the hardships you face while working here?
- How do you feel about the man with the whip?

Step 3: Discuss how the person who is chosen to perform can make the character come alive. For example, the actor might use certain body postures and movements, facial expressions, and simple props.

Ending Opposition Act-It-Out

Your group will be assigned a character in Visual 22D. Bring the character to life by following the steps below. One member of your group will be selected to play the part of the character. A reporter will interview the characters.

Step 1: Circle the character your group has been assigned.

emperor

emperor's adviser

soldier

Confucian scholar

Step 2: Discuss the questions for your character. Make sure everyone in your group can answer them so that each person is prepared to be the actor.

Emperor and emperor's adviser:

- Why do you dislike the teachings of Confucian scholars?
- Why did you decide to burn the books of Confucian scholars?
- Which books have you decided to save?
- Why did you decide to execute (kill) some Confucian scholars?

Soldier:

- How do you feel about burning the books? Do you think that this will stop people from following Confucian beliefs? Why or why not?
- How do you feel about executing the Confucian scholars? Do you think killing his enemies will make the emperor a stronger or a weaker ruler? Why?
- What would happen to you if you refused to do what the emperor ordered?
- How do you think people will react when they learn about these actions?

Confucian scholar:

- As a Confucian scholar, how do you believe an emperor should rule?
- What are some things the emperor has done that have angered you?
- Why did you choose to die rather than give up your books to the emperor?
- How do you think the Chinese people will react when they learn about the emperor's actions?

Step 3: Discuss how the person who is chosen to perform can make the character come alive. For example, the actor might use certain body postures and movements, facial expressions, and simple props.

Chapter 22 Assessment

Mastering the Content

Fill in the circle next to the best answer.

1. Qin Shihuangdi, the first emperor of China, began life as
   ○ A. an invader from Central Asia.
   ○ B. a prince of one Chinese state.
   ○ C. a member of the Zhou dynasty.
   ○ D. a farmer in the North China Plain.

2. In which year would a visitor to China have found a unified Chinese state under the rule of its first emperor?
   ○ A. 1250 B.C.E.
   ○ B. 540 B.C.E.
   ○ C. 220 B.C.E.
   ○ D. 70 C.E.

3. What was one difference between feudalism and the Emperor of Qin's system of government?
   ○ A. Under feudalism, power was held locally; the Emperor of Qin held all the power.
   ○ B. Under feudalism, lords met with the king; the Emperor of Qin did not have meetings.
   ○ C. Under feudalism, leadership came from a few men; the Emperor of Qin had many leaders.
   ○ D. Under feudalism, peasants chose their lords; the Emperor of Qin chose their lords for them.

4. Which Chinese teaching **most** influenced Qin Shihuangdi's style of rule?
   ○ A. Daoism
   ○ B. Legalism
   ○ C. Buddhism
   ○ D. Confucianism

5. What actions related to the areas listed below did the emperor take to help unify China?
   • Laws
   • Money
   • Weights and measures
   • Writing
   ○ A. He set up schools where they were taught.
   ○ B. He took ideas about them from other countries.
   ○ C. He let officials adjust them to meet local needs.
   ○ D. He standardized practices that had differed in all parts of the county.

6. Which group most likely had the **best** life under the Emperor of Qin's rule?
   ○ A. artists
   ○ B. scholars
   ○ C. peasants
   ○ D. merchants

7. Under Qin rule, what would happen if a rich person and a poor person committed the same crime?
   ○ A. The rich person would pay a larger fine.
   ○ B. The two would have to exchange places.
   ○ C. The two would suffer the same punishment.
   ○ D. Only the poor person would be punished.

8. What was the purpose of building the Great Wall?
   ○ A. to keep invaders out
   ○ B. to provide employment
   ○ C. to reward followers with land
   ○ D. to punish critics of the emperor

9. Why did many people sent to work on the Great Wall **not** return home?

○ A. They became wandering nomads.
○ B. They ran away to other countries.
○ C. They died under harsh conditions.
○ D. They decided to live near the wall.

10. To a large extent, the Great Wall was built by

○ A. forced labor.
○ B. foreign workers.
○ C. skilled stonemasons.
○ D. close friends of the emperor.

11. This scene from an ancient scroll shows something being done to scholars. Why did this happen?

○ A. The soldiers did not know how to read.
○ B. The royal family had to pick a teacher.
○ C. The philosophers wanted to get back to nature.
○ D. The emperor hoped to stop criticism of the government.

12. Why did the Emperor of Qin order all Confucian books brought to the capital?

○ A. so he could destroy them
○ B. so he could learn from them
○ C. so he could start a new library
○ D. so he could have them translated

13. Where did archaeologists find a life-sized army made of terra-cotta, a kind of clay?

○ A. in the Great Wall
○ B. next to the royal palace
○ C. along the southern border
○ D. inside the emperor's tomb

14. What happened after the Qin emperor's death?

○ A. tight military control
○ B. rebellions and civil war
○ C. peaceful easing of policies
○ D. worship of the emperor as a god

15. Why did later Chinese historians have very different opinions of the Emperor of Qin?

○ A. Little is known about him.
○ B. His tomb could not be found.
○ C. He acted both wisely and cruelly.
○ D. His advisers made most decisions.

Applying Social Studies Skills

Use the map and your knowledge of history to answer the questions below. Write the word or phrase in the space provided.

The Qin Empire, About 221 B.C.E.

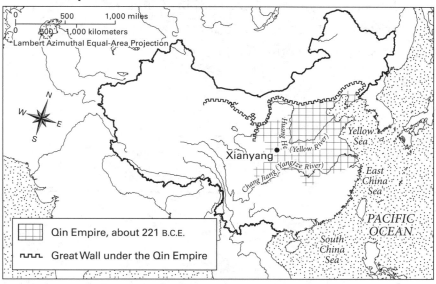

16. What does this symbol on the map show?

17. Boats carrying goods to the Qin capital at Xianyang would have traveled on which waterway?

18. When Qin power expanded from the area around Xianyang during the Warring States period, it did not expand equally in all directions. Qin power expanded **mostly** in which direction?

19. What is the most likely reason that Qin power did **not** expand equally in other directions?

Exploring the Essential Question

Was the Emperor of Qin an effective leader?

Follow the directions to complete the item below.

20. Think of six actions taken by the Emperor of Qin that helped or hurt China.

- Write each action on the appropriate side of the diagram below.
- Then write your answer to the question at the bottom of the page.
- Use complete sentences.

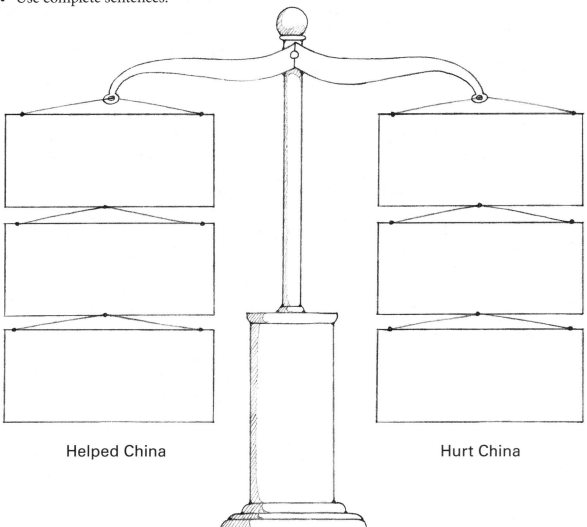

Helped China   Hurt China

Do you think the Emperor of Qin was an effective leader? Why or why not?

Warfare

Follow these steps to learn about warfare during the Han dynasty.

1. Make sure you have the following materials at this station:
   - *Station Materials 23A: Map of the Han Dynasty*

2. Read Section 23.2 and complete Questions 1–3 of the Reading Notes in your Interactive Student Notebook.

3. Use the map of the Han dynasty to label the following physical features on the map in your Interactive Student Notebook:
   - Northeastern Plain
   - North China Plain
   - Chang Jiang Basins
   - Taklimakan Desert
   - Gobi Desert
   - Tibet-Qinghai Plateau
   - Himalayas

4. Add the location of the Han empire to your map and create a key. Title your map, "The Han Empire, About 80 B.C.E."

5. Answer the Activity Question in your Interactive Student Notebook.

6. Return the station to the condition in which you found it. Have your teacher check your work.

Map of the Han Dynasty

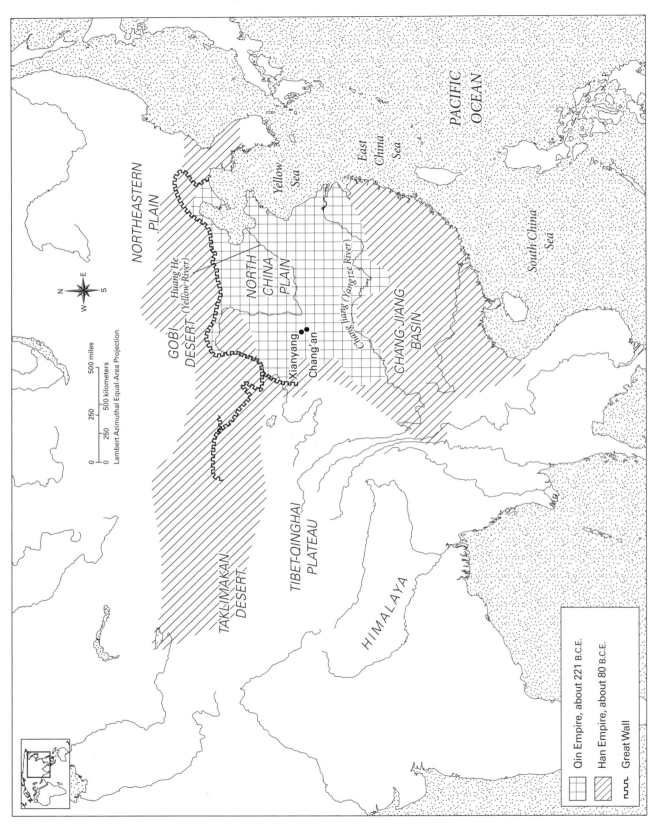

NORTHEASTERN PLAIN

PACIFIC OCEAN

Yellow Sea

East China Sea

South China Sea

Huang He (Yellow River)

NORTH CHINA PLAIN

GOBI DESERT

Xianyang
Chang'an

Chang Jiang (Yangtze River)

CHANG JIANG BASIN

500 miles

500 kilometers

Lambert Azimuthal Equal-Area Projection

250

250

TAKLIMAKAN DESERT

TIBET-QINGHAI PLATEAU

HIMALAYA

Qin Empire, about 221 B.C.E.

Han Empire, about 80 B.C.E.

Great Wall

Government

Follow these steps to learn about government during the Han dynasty.

1. Make sure you have the following materials at this station:
   - exams for civil service positions (placed facedown on table)
   - folder for completed exams

2. Read Section 23.3 and complete Questions 1–4 of the Reading Notes in your Interactive Student Notebook.

3. Study the following passage from the writings of Confucius.

   Highest are those who are born wise. Next are those who become wise by learning. After them come those who have to toil [work] painfully in order to acquire learning. Finally, to the lowest class of the common people belong those who toil painfully without ever managing to learn.

   —Confucius

4. When you think you have learned the information in the passage, turn this paper over. Then take an "exam" for a civil service position by turning over one of the tests on the desk and answering the questions. Put your finished exam in the folder.

5. Answer the Activity Question in your Interactive Student Notebook.

6. Neatly stack the remaining exams facedown at the station. Have your teacher check your work.

Exams for Civil Service Positions

Name _____

According to Confucius, who are the second highest in society?

According to Confucius, who are the third highest in society?

Name _____

According to Confucius, who are the second highest in society?

According to Confucius, who are the third highest in society?

Name _____

According to Confucius, who are the second highest in society?

According to Confucius, who are the third highest in society?

Name _____

According to Confucius, who are the second highest in society?

According to Confucius, who are the third highest in society?

Name _____

According to Confucius, who are the second highest in society?

According to Confucius, who are the third highest in society?

Name _____

According to Confucius, who are the second highest in society?

According to Confucius, who are the third highest in society?

Agriculture

Follow these steps to learn about agriculture during the Han dynasty.

1. Make sure you have the following materials at this station:
    *   12 puzzle pieces (mixed together)

2. Read Section 23.4 and complete Questions 1–3 of the Reading Notes in your Interactive Student Notebook.

3. Arrange the puzzle by identifying the short-term and long-term effects of each Han agricultural invention. Lay out the pieces as shown below, and then complete the puzzle.

Invention	Short-term Effect	Long-term Effect
1. The Han invent the chain pump.	?	?
2. The Han invent the iron plow.	?	?
3. The Han invent the wheelbarrow.	?	?

4. Answer the Activity Question in your Interactive Student Notebook.

5. Have your teacher check your work. Then mix up the puzzle pieces and return the station to the condition in which you found it.

Cause and Effect Puzzle

Invention	Short-term Effect	Long-term Effect
1. The Han invent the chain pump.	Water can more easily be moved from low irrigation ditches to fields.	Droughts can be more easily survived, and enough food can be grown to feed families.
2. The Han invent the iron plow.	Less work is needed to push dirt away from the row being plowed.	Large areas of land can be planted more quickly, allowing farmers more time to build homes.
3. The Han invent the wheelbarrow.	Heavy loads can be carried longer distances, with less effort.	More agricultural products are brought to market and to shared grain storehouses.

Industry

Follow these steps to learn about industry during the Han dynasty.

1. Make sure you have the following materials at this station:
   - 1 glass filled with water
   - 1 empty glass
   - 1 straw

2. Read Section 23.5 and complete Questions 1–3 of the Reading Notes in your Interactive Student Notebook.

3. Perform this experiment to discover how the Chinese got salt from the earth.
   - Place the straw in the glass of water.
   - Cover the end of the straw with your finger.
   - Lift up the straw and transfer some of the water to the empty glass.

4. Answer the Activity Question in your Interactive Student Notebook.

5. Return the station to the condition in which you found it. Have your teacher check your work.

Art

Follow these steps to learn about art during the Han dynasty.

1. Make sure you have the following materials at this station:
   - a set of watercolors and brushes
   - a container of water (for painting)
   - 6" squares of white drawing paper
   - masking tape

2. Read Section 23.6 and complete Questions 1–4 of the Reading Notes in your Interactive Student Notebook.

3. On a sheet of drawing paper, paint the following Chinese character. Be sure you make the strokes in the correct order. Paint quickly, as if you are inspired by the flow of nature. Then tape your character to the wall near this station.

How to Write *Tree* in Chinese

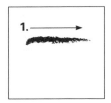 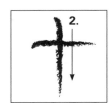  

tree, wood

4. Answer the Activity Question in your Interactive Student Notebook.

5. Return the station to the condition in which you found it. Have your teacher check your work.

Medicine

Follow these steps to learn about medicine during the Han dynasty.

1. Read Section 23.7 and complete Questions 1–4 of the Reading Notes in your Interactive Student Notebook.

2. Another technique in Chinese medicine is acupressure. Read this description about how acupressure points work in Chinese medicine:

    Acupressure is based on the belief that our bodies contain a flow of energy, called qi (chee). Qi travels along pathways in our bodies. If your qi is blocked, you may feel stress or get sick. To release the blocked energy, you can press a specific point along the pathway, called an acupressure point.

3. Are you worried about a test, an important game, or anything else? How do you calm yourself down? What is a technique that Chinese students might use?

3. If you wish, try this exercise based on acupressure points:
    *   Locate the acupressure point at the top of your head. Follow an imaginary line between the upper tips of your ears and the top of your head.
    *   With your middle finger, gently press and hold this point. Then slowly massage it forward and backward.
    *   Take slow, deep breaths. If it helps you concentrate, close your eyes.
    *   Whisper your name as you breathe out.

4. Answer the Activity Question in your Interactive Student Notebook.

5. Return the station to the condition in which you found it. Have your teacher check your work.

Science

Follow these steps to learn about science during the Han dynasty.

1. Read Section 23.8 and complete Questions 1–4 of the Reading Notes in your Interactive Student Notebook.

2. Review the table below. Discuss these questions with your partner:
   - What interesting details do you notice?
   - When and where was the deadliest earthquake in world history?

Deadliest Earthquakes in the World

Rank	Year	Location	Country	Death Toll
1	1556	Shensi	China	830,000
2	1976	Tangshan	China	255,000
3	1138	Aleppo	Syria	230,000
4	2004	Indian Ocean	Indonesia	227,898
5	1920	Haiyuan	China	200,000

Source U.S. Department of the Interior | U.S. Geological Survey URL: http://earthquake.usgs.gov/regional/world/most_destructive.php

3. In your Interactive Student Notebook, complete the bar graph to compare the death toll of the three worst earthquakes in Chinese history. Title your graph, "Deadliest Earthquakes in China."

4. Answer the Activity Question in your Interactive Student Notebook.

5. Return the station to the condition in which you found it. Have your teacher check your work.

Chapter 23 Assessment

Mastering the Content

Fill in the circle next to the best answer.

1. Compared with the Qin dynasty, the Han dynasty
   ○ A. was much smaller.
   ○ B. lasted much longer.
   ○ C. had much worse rulers.
   ○ D. had far fewer inventions.

2. How did the Han emperors gradually change the way China was ruled?
   ○ A. They returned most power to local nobles.
   ○ B. They put more emphasis on family connections.
   ○ C. They moved from Legalism to Confucian ideals.
   ○ D. They punished people who tried to spread Daoist beliefs.

3. What new technology **most** helped the Han in warfare?
   ○ A. invention of the wheel
   ○ B. advances in working iron
   ○ C. steam-powered riverboats
   ○ D. improvements in gunpowder

4. What Han invention did the Chinese use for these military purposes?
   • Send messages from one part of the army to another
   • Frighten the enemy with strange noises at night
   ○ A. kite
   ○ B. scroll
   ○ C. crossbow
   ○ D. fish-scale armor

5. Which shape **best** illustrates the structure of the Han bureaucracy?
   ○ A.    ○ B.

   ○ C.   ○ D.

6. Which of these men would **most** likely be hired for the Han bureaucracy?
   ○ A. one who did well on an exam
   ○ B. one who was born in the capital
   ○ C. one who had an important family
   ○ D. one who inherited a lot of money

7. How did the Han emperors keep civil servants from doing special favors for their friends?
   ○ A. made them file a weekly report
   ○ B. forbid them to make any decisions
   ○ C. executed their friends and relations
   ○ D. placed them away from their home districts

8. The chain pump increased harvests by helping farmers
   ○ A. move heavy goods.
   ○ B. plow the soil for planting.
   ○ C. bring water up to their fields.
   ○ D. store grain so it would not spoil.

9. What change made silk production **more** efficient?

○ A. a kind of tree that was better for silkworms

○ B. an invention that wound fibers onto a large reel

○ C. a road on which trade goods could be carried safely

○ D. a law that all farmers must weave for one month a year

10. What was one effect of the invention of the drill shown in this image?

○ A. better harvests
○ B. more oil for heat
○ C. more wealth from trade
○ D. better earthquake prediction

11. Which tool did ancient Chinese scribes use for writing?

○ A. a reed
○ B. a brush
○ C. a stylus
○ D. a feather

12. What did the Chinese write on before they invented paper?

○ A. silk and bamboo
○ B. hides and leather
○ C. seaweed and straw
○ D. tree bark and leaves

13. Ancient Chinese healers used the technique of acupuncture to

○ A. satisfy the gods.
○ B. achieve immortality.
○ C. teach people to live with pain.
○ D. rebalance the forces of yin and yang.

14. Which of these discoveries did the Chinese make, more than a thousand years before people in Europe did?

○ A. that blood circulates through the body

○ B. that comets can be seen in the night sky

○ C. that wheeled carts can be pulled by oxen

○ D. that metal can be shaped into strong swords

15. The Chinese invented the magnetic compass to show which way was south. What was their **earliest** reason for wanting to know directions?

○ A. to know the best time to plant their crops

○ B. to foretell what would happen in the future

○ C. to navigate ships safely out of sight of land

○ D. to position buildings correctly for good fortune

Applying Social Studies Skills

Use the timeline and your knowledge of history to answer the questions below.
Write the word or phrase in the space provided.

Timeline of the Han Dynasty

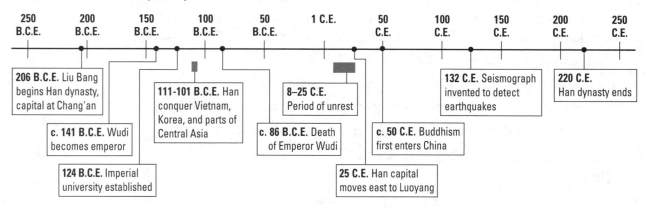

16. List three events from the timeline that relate to thought, learning, and
    science:

    a. (event) _____ (date) _____

    b. (event) _____ (date) _____

    c. (event) _____ (date) _____

17. During the period when the Han dynasty was expanding its empire beyond
    the borders of present-day China, where was the Han capital and who was
    the ruler of the empire?

18. What event does the timeline suggest was **most** likely the cause of the
    relocation of the capital city?

19. Use information from the timeline to write a brief summary of Emperor
    Wudi's rule.

Exploring the Essential Question

In what ways did the Han dynasty improve government and daily life in China?

Follow the directions to complete the item below.

20. Suppose that you work in the Han government. Your job is to hire civil servants to help govern China well. Write a "help wanted" ad to attract qualified people to apply for the job. Make sure your ad does the following:

    • explains what government officials do
    • explains how someone becomes a government official
    • identifies one advantage of working for the government
    • identifies one difficulty that job applicants should be aware of

Help Wanted

Greeting and Product Tokens

Tokens for Traders at Dunhuang

You will start in Dunhuang. This Han city was located in western China. To greet other traders, use the Mandarin Chinese greeting *ni hao* (nee how), which means "hello."

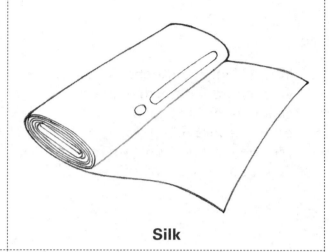

Silk

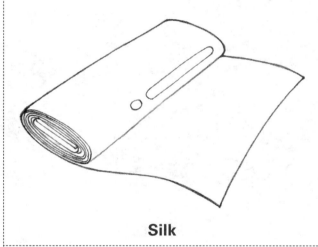

Silk

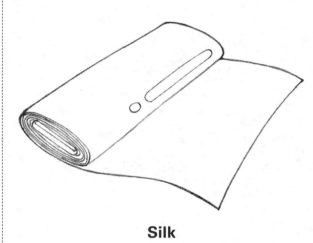

Silk

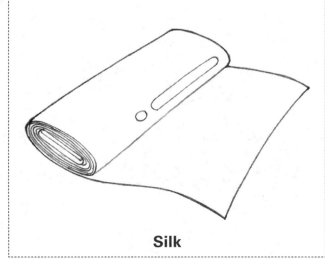

Silk

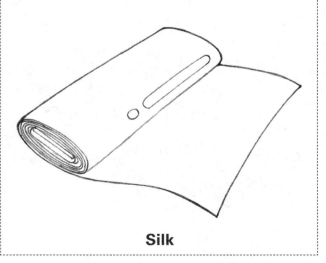

Silk

Tokens for Traders at Kucha

You will start in Kucha. This city was located in northwestern China, near Mongolia. Greet other traders using the Mongolian greeting *sain uu* (sayn oo), which means "hello."

Gold

Gold

Gold

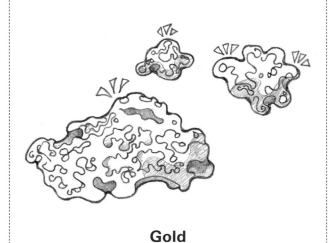

Gold

Gold

Tokens for Traders at Kashgar

You will start in Kashgar. This city was located in southwestern China, near ancient India. Greet other traders using the Hindi greeting *namaste* (NUHM-uh-stay), which means "I bow to you."

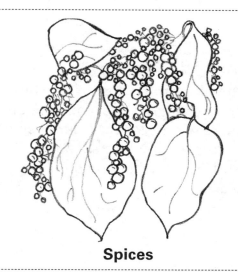

Spices

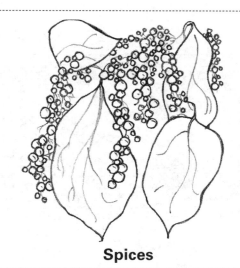

Spices

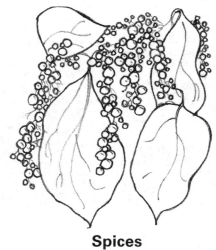

Spices

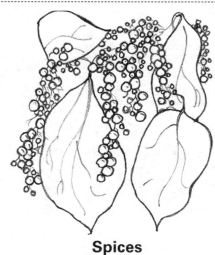

Spices

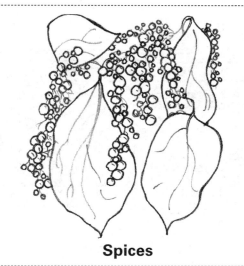

Spices

Tokens for Traders at Ctesiphon

You will start in Ctesiphon. This city was located near the Persian empire. Greet other traders using the Persian greeting *salaam* (suh-LAHM), which means "peace."

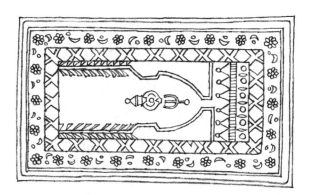

Carpets

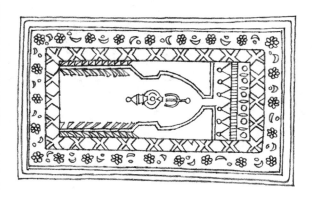

Carpets

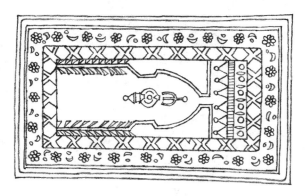

Carpets

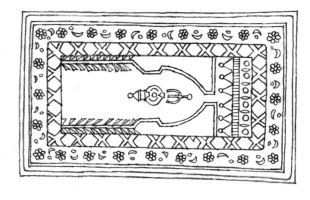

Carpets

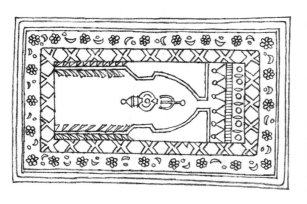

Carpets

Tokens for Traders at Antioch

You will start in Antioch. This city was located in Syria, on the Mediterranean Sea. It was a major trading center for Roman products. Greet other traders using the Latin greeting *salve* (SAL-vee), which means "hail."

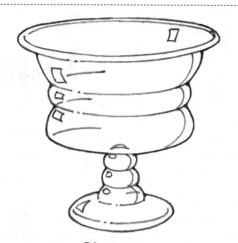

Glassware

Glassware

Glassware

Glassware

Glassware

Trading Centers

Dunhuang

Kucha

Kashgar

Ctesiphon

Antioch

Warning Signs

Danger! Bandits!
Crawl low to the ground.

Danger! Sandstorm!
Cover your eyes and look down.

Danger! Mountains!
Carefully climb over the desks.

Danger! Animals!
Hop over the pictures.

Animals

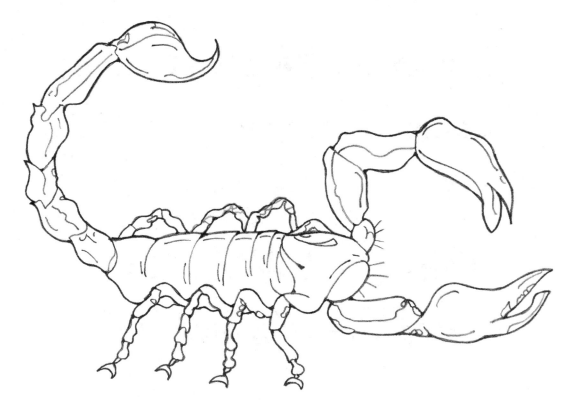

Rules for Trading Along the Silk Road

Your goal is to collect five different products. Follow these rules:

Rule 1: Each person in your group will be assigned a number, starting from 1. You may move only when your number is called.

Rule 2: When your number is called, you may travel in either direction along the masking tape (Silk Road). Go to the nearest "trading center," symbolized by a group of four desks. You may move to only one trading center per turn. As you travel, hold your product tokens on your shoulder to symbolize that you are carrying a heavy load.

Rule 3: You must cross certain obstacles when moving from one trading center to another.

- When moving between Dunhuang and Kucha, you must crawl low to the ground (to avoid bandits).
- When moving between Kucha and Kashgar, you must cover your eyes and look down (to protect yourselves from sandstorms).
- When moving between Kashgar and Ctesiphon, you must climb *carefully* over the desks (mountains) that block your route.
- When moving between Ctesiphon and Antioch, you must hop over the pictures (to avoid dangerous animals along the route).

Rule 4: If you fail to follow any of these rules, you must return to the trading center from which you started this turn, and you miss your opportunity to trade.

Rule 5: When you arrive at each new trading center, greet other traders in your assigned language. Then you may trade one of your products for a product someone else has. Only a new arrival may suggest a possible trade.

Rule 6: When you have traded for five different products, wait for your next turn, and then begin your trip back to your home trading center. You do not have to trade during your return trip. However, you may move only when your number is called, and you may move to only one center at a time. When you arrive at your home center, raise your hand. The teacher will check your products. Then step to the side of the room and patiently wait until the teacher ends the trading session.

Chapter 24 Assessment

Mastering the Content

Fill in the circle next to the best answer.

1. At the time of the Han dynasty, which people particularly threatened China from the north?
   - ○ A. the Huns
   - ○ B. the Romans
   - ○ C. the Persians
   - ○ D. the Japanese

2. Why is Zhang Qian often called the Father of the Silk Road?
   - ○ A. This teacher encouraged the exchange of ideas.
   - ○ B. This explorer brought back word of western cultures.
   - ○ C. This emperor forced peasants to work on construction.
   - ○ D. This military leader made the highway safe for traders.

3. Why did people in China want horses from Central Asia?
   - ○ A. The horses were scarce in China.
   - ○ B. The horses gave the Chinese a way to sell their silk.
   - ○ C. The horses were larger and more powerful than Chinese horses.
   - ○ D. The horses were considered prettier than the ones in China.

4. What made silk valuable in the West?
   - ○ A. The Syrians thought wool was too itchy.
   - ○ B. The Indians found cotton to be too expensive.
   - ○ C. The Romans wanted to buy it to make banners.
   - ○ D. The Chinese were the only ones who knew how to make it.

5. One of the **most** important Roman products that trade along the Silk Road brought to China was
   - ○ A. fur.
   - ○ B. paper.
   - ○ C. livestock.
   - ○ D. glassware.

6. The Silk Road split into a northern route and a southern route. What was one advantage of taking the northern route?
   - ○ A. Oases were closer together.
   - ○ B. Road surfaces were smoother.
   - ○ C. Scenery was more attractive.
   - ○ D. Travelers were safer from bandits.

7. What was the **most** important reason why traders formed long caravans to cross the desert?
   - ○ A. to learn the route
   - ○ B. to lift heavy goods
   - ○ C. to protect each other
   - ○ D. to prevent sandstorms

8. What belongs in the blank space on the diagram?
   - ○ A. wool carpets
   - ○ B. fine dishware
   - ○ C. ground coffee
   - ○ D. polished ivory

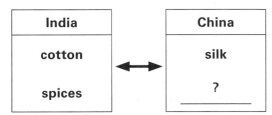

9. Merchants used camels to move goods on the Eastern Silk Road. What animals carried goods on the Western Silk Road?

○ A. dogs
○ B. yaks
○ C. goats
○ D. elephants

10. Which part of the Silk Road exposed travelers to the dangers listed below?

   • Lack of oxygen
   • Narrow passes
   • Steep cliffs
   • Snowstorms

○ A. the Tigris River
○ B. the Gobi Desert
○ C. the Iranian Plateau
○ D. the Pamir Mountains

11. Why did the Western Silk Road end at Mediterranean ports such as Antioch?

○ A. After such a long journey, most traders wanted to stop.
○ B. Most of the goods the Chinese wanted came from that region.
○ C. Goods could be loaded there onto ships to be taken to other lands.
○ D. The Roman Empire did not allow Chinese goods within its borders.

12. What is the likely reason why the Roman emperor told Romans **not** to wear silk?

○ A. He worried that buying silk was taking too much of the empire's gold.
○ B. He believed that cotton was softer and more comfortable than silk.
○ C. He was afraid the silkworms would eat too many leaves off the trees.
○ D. He wanted to save as much silk as possible to make army banners.

13. Which of these facts relating to the Silk Road is an example of cultural diffusion?

○ A. China became wealthy trading silk.
○ B. Travelers faced many dangers on their journey.
○ C. Different animals carried goods on different parts of the route.
○ D. Europeans learned some Chinese manufacturing methods.

14. What do the three items pictured below have in common?

○ A. They all came to the West from China.
○ B. They were all kept secret by Chinese emperors.
○ C. They all began in India and spread along the Silk Road.
○ D. They were all trade goods from Mesopotamia on the Silk Road.

15. How did the Silk Road **most** affect the spread of Buddhism?

○ A. Travelers carried Buddhist beliefs from India to China.
○ B. Chinese philosophers wrote Buddhist texts to sell in Antioch.
○ C. The Buddha encouraged people to seek enlightenment in the desert.
○ D. Dangers on the route supported the Buddhist idea that life is suffering.

16. When some Chinese Buddhists crossed Central Asia to learn more about their religion, what did they bring back?

○ A. robes from Egypt
○ B. leather from Russia
○ C. sacred texts from India
○ D. golden bowls from Rome

Applying Social Studies Skills

Use the map and your knowledge of history to answer the questions. Write the word or phrase in the space provided.

The Silk Road

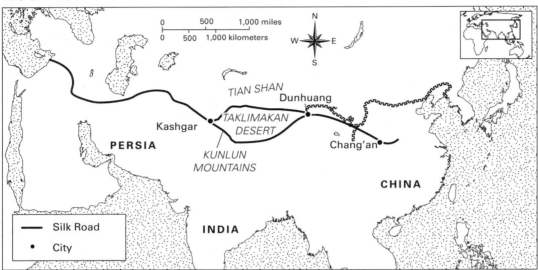

17. A traveler going from Dunhuang to Kashgar on the northern route of the Silk Road might see the physical feature called the _____ to the left (south) and the physical feature called the _____ _____ to the right (north).

18. As shown on the map, the Great Wall offered some protection to travelers between what two cities?

19. According to the map, what is one reason that Kashgar became a major trading center?

Exploring the Essential Question

How did the Silk Road promote an exchange of goods and ideas?

Follow the directions to complete the item below.

20. Today, billboards are large roadside advertising signs. Some billboards describe outlet malls or other places ahead on the road where drivers can shop.

    In the space below, create a billboard that might have been seen on the Silk Road. Include the following on your billboard:

    • Describe the places that are encouraging people to stop.

    • Identify four goods that would likely be traded in the area.

    • Identify where at least two goods come from.

    • Explain why people would want to have these goods.

    • Use correct English.

Unit 4 Timeline Challenge Cards

Shang Dynasty
About 1700–1122 B.C.E.

The Shang, one of China's earliest civilizations, rule the Huang He Valley.

Early Chinese Writing
About 1400 B.C.E.

Early Chinese writing includes about 3,000 characters. Oracle bones have writing in the form of logographs.

Zhou Dynasty
About 1045–256 B.C.E.

The Zhou claim the Mandate of Heaven and rule China under a system of feudalism.

Life of Laozi
About 6th century B.C.E.

According to legend, Laozi teaches about the Dao and yin and yang.

Unit 4 Timeline Challenge Cards

Life of Confucius
551–479 B.C.E.

Confucius teaches that people should act properly and respect relationships.

Life of Hanfeizi
280–233 B.C.E.

Hanfeizi proposes Legalism, a philosophy emphasizing a system of strong central government.

First Unification of China
221–210 B.C.E.

Emperor Qin Shihuangdi unites northern China, standardizes the culture, and builds the Great Wall.

Han Dynasty
About 206 B.C.E.–220 C.E.

The Han develop a bureaucratic system of government and improve life in China.

Unit 4 Timeline Challenge Cards

Expansion of Han Empire
About 80 B.C.E.

Military technology and strategy allow the Han empire to expand into Central Asia and parts of Korea and Vietnam.

First Trade Along Silk Road
138 B.C.E.

Chinese explorer Zhang Qian establishes trade relationships with Central Asian peoples, using a network of routes that become known as the Silk Road.

Spread of Buddhism into China
65 C.E.

Cultural diffusion occurs as Buddhism spreads from India to China.

Chinese Invent Paper
About 105 C.E.

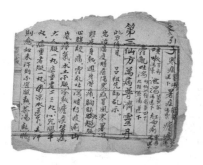

The Chinese invent paper during the Han dynasty, making it easier for people to communicate and create documents and records.

Chapter 25 Assessment

Mastering the Content

Fill in the circle next to the best answer.

1. What makes much of Greece a peninsula?
   ○ A. the lack of large rivers
   ○ B. the water on three sides
   ○ C. the steep mountain slopes
   ○ D. the large number of islands

2. How did the Greek mountains affect communication?
   ○ A. They isolated communities.
   ○ B. They promoted road building.
   ○ C. They led people to write letters.
   ○ D. They made farmers stop speaking.

3. The ancient Greeks did **not** like to travel on land because they
   ○ A. did not want to offend the earth god.
   ○ B. were afraid of people from other villages.
   ○ C. used the land for farming instead of roads.
   ○ D. found traveling through the mountains difficult.

4. What made farming in ancient Greece **especially** difficult?
   ○ A. mud   ○ C. bandits
   ○ B. rocks   ○ D. climate

5. The ancient Greeks worshiped the sea god Poseidon. What does this tell about the Greeks?
   ○ A. They believed in only one god.
   ○ B. They lived in separated villages.
   ○ C. They relied on the sea for travel and trade.
   ○ D. They stayed away from the sea as much as they could.

6. Suppose an adviser told a farmer, *"You could grow more crops by using irrigation."* What would the farmer **most** likely reply?
   ○ A. Our land is too low and flat.
   ○ B. We do not have a big enough river.
   ○ C. We do not have the labor to build ditches.
   ○ D. Our engineers do not have the skill to design that.

7. What is a reason why the ancient Greeks produced so much olive oil?
   ○ A. They could feed the olive oil to their pigs.
   ○ B. They could exchange the olive oil for nuts.
   ○ C. They could grow olive trees in a small space.
   ○ D. They could get olives from other countries in trade.

8. The ancient Greeks raised these animals on their farms because these animals

   ○ A. did not need flat land.
   ○ B. could drink sea water.
   ○ C. supplied oil for lamps.
   ○ D. did not eat much food.

9. Why did Greek communities sometimes fight each other?
○ A. They had too many soldiers.
○ B. They were crowded together.
○ C. They could not start colonies.
○ D. They each wanted more land.

10. What problem did ancient Greek communities try to solve by starting colonies?
○ A. too many ships
○ B. too much timber
○ C. shortage of people
○ D. shortage of farmland

11. A good location to start an ancient Greek colony would have had
○ A. tall mountains.
○ B. a high city wall.
○ C. a natural harbor.
○ D. strong local tribes.

12. How did colonies affect ancient Greek culture?
○ A. They spread the culture over a wide area.
○ B. They led the Greeks to adopt Asian culture.
○ C. They caused village cultures to develop in different ways.
○ D. They forced settlers to lose their culture and rights as Greeks.

13. Why did ancient Greek communities trade?
○ A. to stop having to farm
○ B. to get goods they needed
○ C. to enjoy adventures at sea
○ D. to give families work to do

14. Which choice of titles would **best** fit as column headings for the chart below?

Ancient Greece	
• Olive oil • Pottery	• Grain • Metal

○ A. *Wants* and *Needs*
○ B. *Farms* and *Villages*
○ C. *Goods* and *Services*
○ D. *Exports* and *Imports*

15. What did Greek sailors use to help them steer their ships?
○ A. stars
○ B. charts
○ C. radios
○ D. compasses

Applying Social Studies Skills

Use the map and your knowledge of history to answer the questions. Write the word or phrase in the space provided.

Ancient Greek Colonies and Trade Routes, About 500 B.C.E.

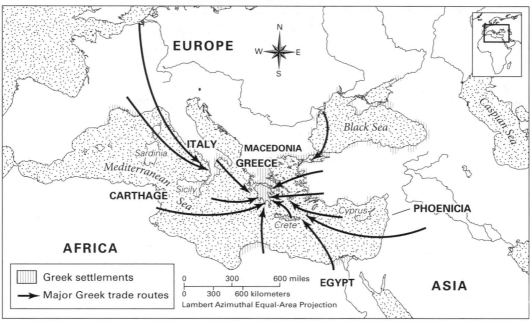

16. What are three places from which mainland Greece imported trade goods?

17. a. On the map, place an *X* in the location of the Aegean Sea.
    b. Now, describe the location of the Aegean Sea.

18. a. Most of the Greek settlements away from mainland Greece were located where?

    b. Why were such locations chosen?

19. a. Which form of transportation was used to carry most trade goods?
    Circle one:

        Donkeys   Horses   Ships   Wagons

    b. Explain why the ancient Greeks chose that form of transportation.

Exploring the Essential Question

How did geography influence settlement and way of life in ancient Greece?

Follow the directions to complete the item below.

20. Complete the spoke diagram. In each oval, write one way that this feature of Greek geography influenced settlement and way of life in ancient Greece.

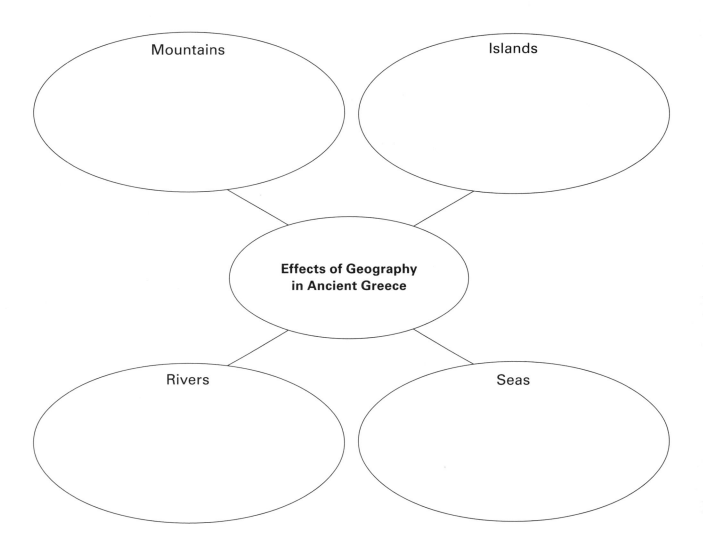

© Teachers' Curriculum Institute

Name_____ Date_____

Chapter 26 Assessment

Mastering the Content

Fill in the circle next to the best answer.

1. How was it possible that different parts of Greece had different forms of government?
   - A. Different languages made communication difficult.
   - B. Steep mountains kept people from different areas apart.
   - C. Colonies were started by groups from different countries.
   - D. Different kings made different rules about how to govern.

2. Which form of government in a Greek city-state usually came **first**?
   - A. tyranny
   - B. oligarchy
   - C. monarchy
   - D. democracy

3. How did most kings in ancient Greece come to power?
   - A. They inherited from a relative.
   - B. They were elected by the people.
   - C. They paid merchants for support.
   - D. They used soldiers to take control.

4. Who belonged to the councils of aristocrats?
   - A. rich men who had land from their families
   - B. merchants who became wealthy from trade
   - C. soldiers who were famous for their courage
   - D. popular leaders who won support from the poor

5. What happened to the king's advisers after the king lost power?
   - A. They were forced to be slaves.
   - B. They sailed away to start colonies.
   - C. They became the new ruling group.
   - D. They asked the people to elect them to office.

6. Which word in English comes from a Greek word meaning "few"?
   - A. *tyrant*
   - B. *oligarch*
   - C. *monarch*
   - D. *democrat*

7. What might an oligarch do on an ordinary day?
   - A. herd sheep and goats
   - B. work hard in the fields
   - C. sell goods in the market
   - D. take part in a chariot race

8. What kinds of laws did the oligarchs pass?
   - A. laws that meant nothing
   - B. laws that were fair to all
   - C. laws that helped the poor
   - D. laws that favored the rich

9. Oligarchs were thrown out of power by a partnership between
   - A. sailors and fishers.
   - B. foreign powers and kings.
   - C. army leaders and poor people.
   - D. merchants and skilled artisans.

10. Who would have **most** likely said these words?

    I was in the army when people began to complain about members of the government getting richer while everybody else was getting poorer. So I stepped forward, and with the people's help, I became the leader.

    ○ A. a king
    ○ B. a tyrant
    ○ C. a citizen
    ○ D. an aristocrat

11. In a tyranny, what allowed the leader to rule?

    ○ A. military force
    ○ B. family tradition
    ○ C. the law of the land
    ○ D. foreign partnerships

12. Which letter marks a time when many city-states were coming under the rule of tyrants?

1600 B.C.E	1400 B.C.E	1200 B.C.E	1000 B.C.E	800 B.C.E	600 B.C.E

    Ⓐ   Ⓑ   Ⓒ   Ⓓ

    ○ A. letter A
    ○ B. letter B
    ○ C. letter C
    ○ D. letter D

13. Why were some tyrants well liked?

    ○ A. They united the city-states.
    ○ B. They passed the throne to their sons.
    ○ C. They gave all men a voice in government.
    ○ D. They made laws that improved people's lives.

14. How was democracy in Athens different from other ancient forms of government?

    ○ A. People might vote unwisely.
    ○ B. Merchants made all the laws.
    ○ C. Slaves were equal to free men.
    ○ D. All citizens shared ruling power.

15. How was ancient Greek democracy different from democracy in the United States today?

    ○ A. Citizens voted directly on all issues.
    ○ B. Citizens gave their leaders total power.
    ○ C. Citizens elected representatives to make laws.
    ○ D. Citizens listened to the ideas of powerful speakers.

16. What idea that is important today came from ancient Athens?

    ○ A. Nobody should be a slave.
    ○ B. People should rule themselves.
    ○ C. Men and women should be equal.
    ○ D. Leaders should be both wise and good.

Applying Social Studies Skills

Use the flowchart and your knowledge of history to answer the questions. Write the word or phrase in the space provided.

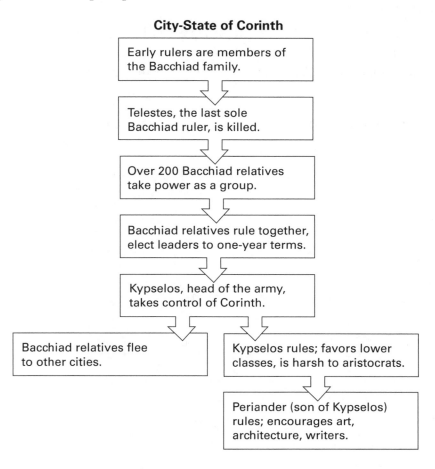

City-State of Corinth

Early rulers are members of the Bacchiad family.

Telestes, the last sole Bacchiad ruler, is killed.

Over 200 Bacchiad relatives take power as a group.

Bacchiad relatives rule together, elect leaders to one-year terms.

Kypselos, head of the army, takes control of Corinth.

Bacchiad relatives flee to other cities.

Kypselos rules; favors lower classes, is harsh to aristocrats.

Periander (son of Kypselos) rules; encourages art, architecture, writers.

17. Who was one tyrant of Corinth?

18. After the death of Telestes, what was the next form of government in Corinth?

19. What was the **most** likely reason the Bacchiad relatives left Corinth?

Exploring the Essential Question

How did democracy develop in ancient Greece?

Follow the directions to complete the item below.

20. Suppose that you write for a newspaper in ancient Athens. You have been sent to report on a meeting of the Athens Assembly. Use the questions below to take notes for your newspaper article. Write at least one full sentence under each question.

 a. What is happening at the Athens Assembly?

 b. What do you see?

 c. What do you hear?

 d. What do you feel (emotion), taste, or smell?

 e. What will be the first sentence of your article? The purpose of this sentence is to hook the reader's attention. For example, you might explain why this meeting of the Athens Assembly is important, or you might describe a detail that will make the readers want to find out more.

Placard Template

Section _____ : _____
        (number)   (title)

Section Question:

Key Details:
-
-
-

Challenge Question:

Creating Placards for Athens and Sparta

With your partner, follow these steps to create a placard describing one aspect of life in Athens or Sparta.

Step 1: Read your assigned section and complete the corresponding Reading Notes in your Interactive Student Notebook. (**Note:** You will create the challenge question later.)

Step 2: Use the information from the reading to complete Student Handout 27. Use these guidelines:

- Draw a simple visual and write a brief caption in each of the two metopes (squares) at the top of the temple.
- Write in the question from the Reading Notes for your assigned section.
- Summarize three or more key details that answer the question.
- Create a challenge question that can be answered only by carefully reading your assigned section.

Step 3: Make the answer key for your challenge question. Fold in half the piece of paper your teacher gives you. Write the answer on the inside of the folded paper so that it is covered.

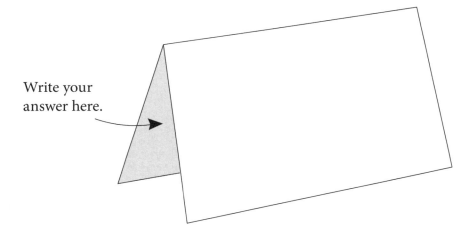

Write your answer here.

Step 4: Add color and creative touches to the temple on your placard to reflect life in your city-state. For example, you might use dull colors to decorate the temple of Sparta, or use a flowery design to decorate the triangle at the top of the Athenian temple.

Comparing and Contrasting Athens and Sparta

Use the graphic organizer below to compare and contrast life in Athens and Sparta.

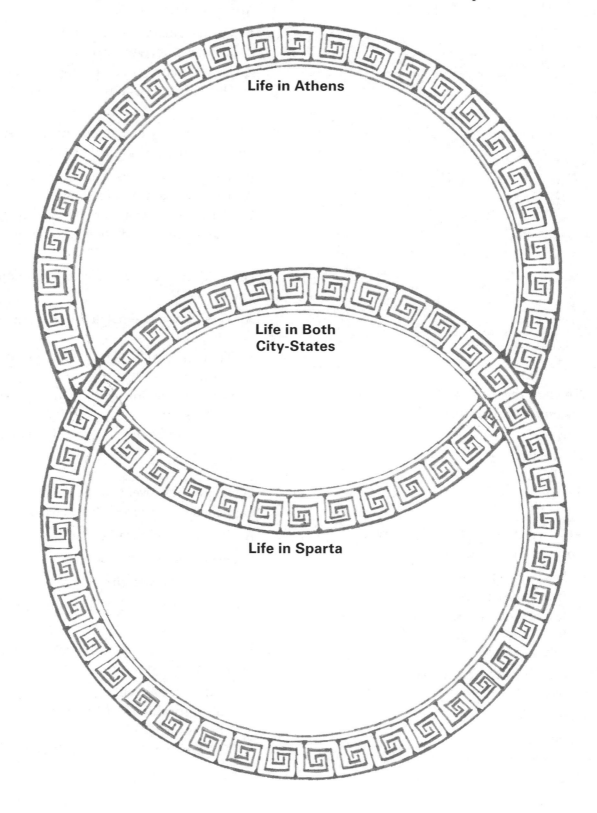

Life in Athens

Life in Both City-States

Life in Sparta

Chapter 27 Assessment

Mastering the Content

Fill in the circle next to the best answer.

1. Which of these city-states on the map was on the Peloponnesus?

   ○ A. Argos
   ○ B. Athens
   ○ C. Thebes
   ○ D. Delphi

2. Which feature of Athens's geography **most** affected its economy?

   ○ A. It was on a peninsula.
   ○ B. It was close to the sea.
   ○ C. It was built on rocky cliffs.
   ○ D. It was surrounded by fertile fields.

3. Which physical feature made Sparta somewhat isolated?

   ○ A. poor soil
   ○ B. broad rivers
   ○ C. major highways
   ○ D. surrounding mountains

4. How would a man become a member of Athens's Council of 500?

   ○ A. He inherited the position.
   ○ B. He was elected by citizens.
   ○ C. He was chosen in a drawing.
   ○ D. He overthrew a council member.

5. What is one way the Assembly of Athens differed from the Council of 500?

   ○ A. The Assembly was larger.
   ○ B. The Assembly met more often.
   ○ C. The Assembly had far less power.
   ○ D. The Assembly did not permit discussion.

6. How did the citizens of Athens get enough grain to eat?

   ○ A. They conquered neighboring farm villages.
   ○ B. They shipped local products to Egypt to trade.
   ○ C. Grasses good for making bread grew wild nearby.
   ○ D. Every family raised its own food behind the house.

7. Which of these events **most** likely happened in the agora of Athens?

   ○ A. People bought leather sandals.
   ○ B. People voted for their leaders.
   ○ C. Boys held a wrestling contest.
   ○ D. Girls played musical instruments.

8. Why did Athenian schoolboys have to memorize everything?

   ○ A. There were not enough books.
   ○ B. Public speaking was important.
   ○ C. They wanted to become citizens.
   ○ D. Examinations were very difficult.

9. A 12-year-old Athenian girl would **most** likely get her education

○ A. in another city.
○ B. in a day school.
○ C. from a priestess.
○ D. from her mother.

10. Why is Sparta said to have been an oligarchy?

○ A. Military strength was valued.
○ B. It was organized as a city-state.
○ C. The government had two kings.
○ D. A small group held the most power.

11. Who made the **most** important government decisions in Sparta?

○ A. the Assembly
○ B. the military leaders
○ C. the Council of Elders
○ D. the winners of sports games

12. Sparta used heavy iron bars as money. What conclusion does this suggest?

○ A. Sparta shipped most goods by boat.
○ B. Sparta discouraged trade with other city-states.
○ C. Spartan money was easier to use than Athenian money.
○ D. Spartan money was more valuable than Athenian money.

13. Which sentence **best** describes education in Sparta?

○ A. Children did not learn to read.
○ B. Children studied sculpture and painting.
○ C. Both boys and girls got military training.
○ D. Both boys and girls learned to cook and clean.

14. To become a full citizen, a Spartan man had to

○ A. pass a difficult test.
○ B. come from a rich family.
○ C. get elected by the people.
○ D. marry a citizen's daughter.

15. What happened after Sparta conquered a neighboring land?

○ A. The conquered people left by sea to start new colonies for Sparta.
○ B. The conquered people moved to Sparta to sell goods in the marketplace.
○ C. The Spartans made the conquered people leave so that Spartans could move there.
○ D. The Spartans made the conquered people give Sparta much of their food crops.

16. Unlike the women of Athens, the women of Sparta

○ A. could not vote.
○ B. could own a lot of property.
○ C. had most influence in the home.
○ D. served equally with men in the army.

Applying Social Studies Skills

Use the passage below and your knowledge of history to answer the questions. Write the word or phrase in the space provided.

Herodotus was an ancient Greek historian. He made up a conversation between a Greek man and the king of Persia. The king asked what would happen if the Persian army attacked Greece. Here is part of the Greek man's answer:

> All Greeks are brave, but what I am about to say does not concern all, but only the Spartans. . . . They are sure to join battle with you, even if all the rest of the Greeks surrendered to you. As for Spartan numbers, do not ask how many or few they are, hoping for them to surrender. For if a thousand of them should take the field, they will meet you in battle, and so will any other number, whether it is less than this, or more.

> One against one, they [the Spartans] are as good as anyone in the world. But when they fight in a body, they are the best of all. For, though they are free men, they are not entirely free. They accept Law as their master. And they respect this master, Law, more than your subjects respect you. Whatever he commands, they do. And his command never changes: It forbids them to flee in battle, whatever the number of their foes. It requires them to stand firm—to conquer or die.

17. Why does the speaker say not to ask how many Spartans there are?

18. What does the speaker mean by saying that the Spartans are not entirely free?

19. What do you think was Herodotus's opinion of the Spartans? Explain your answer.

Exploring the Essential Question

What were the major differences between Athens and Sparta?

Follow the directions to complete the item below.

20. In which city-state would you rather have lived—Athens or Sparta? In the spaces below, state your answer and give three reasons. Your reasons should include facts about both Athens and Sparta.

    City-state where you would rather have lived:

    Reason #1

    Reason #2

    Reason #3

A Greek Play

Excerpt from _The Persians_
by Aeschylus

Messenger: The bodies of men miserably slain
                   Lie heaped upon the shore of Salamis
                   And glut full many a creek and cove thereby.

Chorus: The bodies of the men that died
                   The breakers buffet, the billows beat!
                   Tinct with the azure of the sea-salt tide,
                   Rolled with the wreckage of a shattered fleet!

Glossary
slain killed
glut fill
cove a small inland curve of a shoreline
breakers small waves hitting the shore
buffet strike
billows large waves of the sea
tinct colored
azure blue

Performing a Greek Play

Follow these steps to perform a Greek play that describes the events leading up to a battle in the Persian wars.

Step 1: Know your part. You will be assigned to act as a character or to be a member of the chorus. Once assigned to your part, find and review your lines on your handout. Use the pronunciation guide below to help you.

Pronunciation Guide	
Darius	duh-RAHY-uhs
Hellespont	HEL-uh-spont
Leonidas	lee-ON-ih-duhs
Miltiades	mil-TAHY-uh-deez
Salamis	SAL-uh-mis
Themistocles	thuh-MIS-tuh-kleez
Thermopylae	ther-MOP-uh-lee
Xerxes	zurk-seez

Step 2: Find your place on stage. When directed by your teacher, performers playing characters should "step into" the projected image and assume the position of their assigned character. If your character is supposed to have a prop, act as though you are holding that item. Members of the chorus should stand together outside the projected image.

Step 3: Perform the play. Perform the scene written on the handout by reading your lines and executing any actions for your part.

Script for Battle of Marathon

Parts	Starting Positions
King Darius	Standing and holding a staff
Persian soldier	Standing behind Darius and holding a shield and a spear
Miltiades	Standing opposite Darius and holding a shield and a short sword
Greek runner	Standing next to Miltiades
Chorus	Standing together as a group

King Darius: *(shaking his staff in the air)* Those Greeks must pay! I am the king of a great empire, and I will conquer those little city-states.

Chorus: An angry Persian king commands
The Greeks give in to his demands
For gifts of earth and water.
They refused
To be ruled
By the mighty Persian Empire.

Persian soldier: *(making marching movements)* So we Persians sailed to Greece and marched on to the plain at Marathon. And there we waited with our noble king. *(stops marching)*

Chorus: The Athenian general Miltiades did see
He was greatly outnumbered.

Miltiades: *(looking around)* I have persuaded the other Greek commanders to fight the Persians here at Marathon. But where are they? *(turning to the Greek runner)* Brave runner, go as fast as you can to Sparta and ask for help.

Greek runner: *(nodding enthusiastically)* I will run day and night to get the help you seek. *(runs off stage)*

Chorus: He ran for two days and two nights.
He told the Spartans they were needed to fight.
They told him, "No."
They could not go
Until their festival ended.
Oh, what will Miltiades do?

Script for Battle of Thermopylae

Parts	Starting Positions
King Xerxes, son of Darius	Standing and holding a staff
King Leonidas, Spartan general	Standing opposite Xerxes and holding a shield and a spear
Greek soldier	Standing behind Leonidas and holding a shield and a short sword
Greek messenger	Standing next to the Greek soldier
Chorus	Standing together as a group

King Xerxes: I, King Xerxes of Persia, am the heir to noble Darius. I will finish what he did not. Greece will be mine! *(slaps hand to chest)*

Chorus: A huge army Xerxes did organize
To claim Greece as his prize.
From Asia to Europe
The Persians marched.
Then west and then south.
The Persians marched,
Attacking all in their path.

King Leonidas: *(looking worried)* Several of our Greek city-states have been captured! I, King Leonidas of Sparta, will use my great army to fight the Persians. *(uses his spear to point out the army standing behind him)*

Chorus: The Spartans could not fight alone,
For the Persians attacked by land and by sea.
The Athenians would fight the Persian navy.
And the Spartans would fight at Thermopylae.

Greek soldier: We Spartans make our stand in a narrow pass between the mountains and the sea. With only thousands of soldiers to their hundreds of thousands, we will stop those Persians. *(making fighting motions with his weapons)*

Greek messenger: *(quietly to the audience)* However, it will not be for long. *(sneaks over to King Xerxes and whispers in his ear)*

Chorus: What does this mean?
What will he do?
Is he a brave servant of Sparta
Or a traitorous fool?

Script for Battle of Salamis

Parts	Starting Positions
Athenian citizen	Standing on a ship and shaking his head in dismay
Themistocles, Athenian navy leader	Standing on a ship and scanning the horizon
King Xerxes	Standing on a ship opposite Themistocles and holding a staff
Greek messenger	Standing next to Xerxes
Chorus	Standing together as a group

Athenian citizen: The slaughter of those 300 Spartans leaves no hope for us in Athens. *(panicking)* We must leave before the Persians come!

Chorus: Those Athenians were very worried.
And so they hurried
Out of their city
And out of harm's way.
The small army left was no match
For King Xerxes and the Persian might.
He burned the city to the ground.

Themistocles: My beautiful Athens has been destroyed. *(in deep thought)* I think I know a way to defeat those Persians.

Chorus: The Athenian navy leader Themistocles
Had an idea.
If he set a trap with a clever trick
Maybe he could stop those Persian ships.

Themistocles: We will have a better chance to defeat the Persian navy if we can fight them in the narrow channels between the islands and the mainland. *(pointing to the horizon)* We just need to lure Xerxes in. I have sent my loyal servant to set the trap.

King Xerxes: *(questioning)* So Themistocles wants to join us?

Greek messenger: *(nodding)* Yes, if you follow the Greek ships toward Salamis and attack them now, half of the Greek sailors will surrender.

Chorus: Does Xerxes believe?
Will he leave?
And follow the Greeks
Into a channel
Where he will be trapped?

Script for Battle of Plataea

Parts	Starting Positions
King Xerxes	Standing and holding a staff
Persian leader	Standing next to Xerxes and holding a shield and a spear
Spartan leader	Standing opposite Xerxes and holding a shield and a short sword
Spartan messenger	Standing next to the Spartan leader
Chorus	Standing together as a group

King Xerxes: *(fearful)* The loss at Salamis was too much. I must go before the Greeks destroy our bridge crossing at the Hellespont.

Chorus: The defeated King Xerxes
He did flee
To cross his bridges
At the Hellespont,
But he did find
Nature was not kind.
His bridges were destroyed,
And he had to cross by boat.

Persian leader: *(proudly)* King Xerxes has left me in charge of the army that remains in Greece. And in the spring, those Greeks will know the full force of the mighty Persian army!

Spartan leader: *(looking worried)* Those Persians will surely try again when spring comes. Will my Spartan army be all that is left?

Chorus: Now you must remember
That Athens and Sparta
Had joined together to
Put up a fight.

Spartan leader: *(turning to the messenger)* Go, find our fellow Greeks.
Ask them if they will fight again.

Spartan messenger: *(nodding)* I will find our Athenian allies and seek their help.

Chorus: What hope is there,
With Athens destroyed?
Will they surrender to Persia?
Or fight alongside
Their Spartan brothers?

Chapter 28 Assessment

Mastering the Content
Fill in the circle next to the best answer.

1. What was an advantage that Greece had over the Persians?
   ○ A. more land
   ○ B. more people
   ○ C. better strategy
   ○ D. strong central leadership

2. The Persian Empire began in present-day
   ○ A. Iran.
   ○ B. Italy.
   ○ C. Russia.
   ○ D. North Africa.

3. How did the Persian Empire expand its territory?
   ○ A. by making friends
   ○ B. by establishing colonies
   ○ C. by paying others to join it
   ○ D. by conquering its neighbors

4. Why did the Greeks care about what happened to Ionia?
   ○ A. Greece belonged to the Turkish kingdom of Ionia.
   ○ B. Greeks had established wealthy settlements in Ionia.
   ○ C. Ionia was an island that had been conquered by Greece.
   ○ D. Ionia was a Greek city-state between Athens and Sparta.

5. What was the outcome of the Ionian Revolt?
   ○ A. The Ionians won their freedom.
   ○ B. The Ionians became part of Greece.
   ○ C. The Persians were defeated by Greece.
   ○ D. The Persian army punished the Ionians.

6. Why did King Darius ask for presents of Greek earth and water?
   ○ A. Greece was known for its fertile soil.
   ○ B. Much of the Persian Empire was desert.
   ○ C. Darius could not afford to pay money for those materials.
   ○ D. Such gifts would mean that the Greeks had accepted Persian rule.

7. What was one reason Persia attacked Greece?
   ○ A. Persia wanted revenge.
   ○ B. Persia wanted farmland.
   ○ C. Persia wanted Greek culture.
   ○ D. Persia wanted better schools.

8. When Darius sent cavalry across the sea by boat, what must have been in the boats?
   ○ A. horses
   ○ B. cannons
   ○ C. heavy armor
   ○ D. wooden rams

9. To defeat the Persians at Marathon, the Greeks made use of
   ○ A. a strong navy.
   ○ B. a narrow valley.
   ○ C. bows and arrows.
   ○ D. long-distance runners.

The Persian Wars

10. Why did Xerxes cross the Hellespont?
- ○ A. to get into the Aegean Sea
- ○ B. to go from Asia into Europe
- ○ C. to take the Greeks by surprise
- ○ D. to escape through the mountains

11. Suppose that an Athenian soldier wrote this passage, about 480 B.C.E.:

> *I will stand shoulder to shoulder with the brave men of Greece—Spartans as well as my fellow Athenians—and fight to the death, if that is what it takes to stop the Persians.*

What does this passage indicate?
- ○ A. Greece had never been invaded before.
- ○ B. Greek men had never fought without women before.
- ○ C. Athens and Sparta together would be stronger than Persia.
- ○ D. Athenians and Spartans would join to fight a common enemy.

12. What happened at the Battle of Thermopylae?
- ○ A. The Spartans defeated the Persians.
- ○ B. The Persians defeated the Spartans.
- ○ C. The Athenians defeated the Persians.
- ○ D. The Persians defeated the Athenians.

13. After the Persians burned Athens to the ground, how did the Athenians continue to fight?
- ○ A. They used their navy.
- ○ B. They agreed to surrender.
- ○ C. They attacked several islands.
- ○ D. They hid out in the mountains.

14. Which of these factors **most** affected the outcome of the Battle of Salamis?
- ○ A. Persian use of a Greek spy
- ○ B. Greek swords, spears, and armor
- ○ C. Greek knowledge of local waterways
- ○ D. Persian bridge made by roping boats together

15. Why was the Battle of Plataea important?
- ○ A. It let Greece rule Persia.
- ○ B. It caused Persia to attack.
- ○ C. It ended the Persian wars.
- ○ D. It destroyed the Persian navy.

16. What was an important result of the Persian wars?
- ○ A. They ended Greek independence.
- ○ B. They destroyed the city of Sparta.
- ○ C. They caused the Greeks to invent new gods.
- ○ D. They prevented Persia from conquering Greece.

Applying Social Studies Skills

Use the timeline and your knowledge of history to answer the questions.
Write the word or phrase in the space provided.

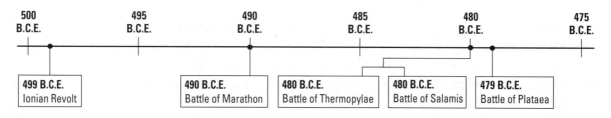

| 500 B.C.E. | 495 B.C.E. | 490 B.C.E. | 485 B.C.E. | 480 B.C.E. | 475 B.C.E. |

499 B.C.E.
Ionian Revolt

490 B.C.E.
Battle of Marathon

480 B.C.E.
Battle of Thermopylae

480 B.C.E.
Battle of Salamis

479 B.C.E.
Battle of Plataea

17. The Battle of Salamis took place about ten years after what event?

18. Athens was burned to the ground between the battles of Thermopylae and
    Salamis. As a result, many Athenian families lost their homes in what year?

19. In some periods, major events or battles are spread over a number of years.
    In other periods, several major events or battles occur close together in time.
    Find both kinds of periods on the timeline. From the spacing of events on the
    timeline, what can you conclude?

Exploring the Essential Question

What factors influenced the outcome of the Persian wars?

Follow the directions to complete the item below.

20. Suppose that you are making a speech in a Greek city-state during the period of the Persian wars. Complete the sentences below to offer and explain three pieces of advice about how the Greeks can defeat the Persians. Your advice should be related to events that actually happened during the wars, and to the factors that influenced their outcome.

a. Fellow Greeks, to defeat the Persians, you should . . .

    You should do this because . . .

b. In addition, to defeat the Persians, I recommend that you should . . .

    You should do this because . . .

c. Finally, to defeat the Persians, you should . . .

    You should do this because . . .

Station A: Religion

The Site: You are visiting the Temple of Apollo at Delphi, a town outside Athens, to learn about religion.

1. Examine the image on the placard on the wall at the station. Discuss the question with your partner and record your ideas in Section 29.3 of your Reading Notes.

2. Read Section 29.3 in your book and complete the corresponding Reading Notes for that section. Correct or add any details to your original response to the first question.

3. Read this paragraph to learn why you are visiting this site:

    You have been learning about Greek mythology. You told your teacher that you saw no point in studying this subject. Your teacher sent you to Delphi to ask the oracle if mythology would be important in the future. The oracle has said, "Greek mythology will be the origin of many words in a great language of the future. To learn a few words of this new language, play the game I have designed."

4. With your partner, play the game the oracle has designed. Follow these guidelines:
    *   The goal of the game is to get as many matches as possible. A match is made when a player finds both a Myth Card and a Word Card that are clearly related. A match is not made if a player finds two Myth Cards, two Word Cards, or a Myth Card and a Word Card that are not related.
    *   One partner begins the game by flipping over two cards. If there is a match, that player keeps the two cards and takes another turn. If there is not a match, the player returns the cards to their facedown positions, and the other partner takes a turn.
    *   The winner of the game is the player who collects the most cards.

5. Return the station to the condition in which you found it, and have the teacher check your work.

Myth Cards

Myth Card

Pan

Pan was half man and half goat. His bright red face, his flat nose, and the two horns growing from his head made him very frightening.

Myth Card

Tantalus

The gods punished Tantalus by placing him in a lake. When he tried to drink the water in the lake, the water level dropped. When he tried to eat the fruit that hung above him, the branches blew away.

Myth Card

Hercules

As punishment for killing his children, Hercules had to do 12 difficult jobs. One job was to kill a vicious lion.

Myth Card

Narcissus

Narcissus was very handsome and very conceited. He treated badly the people who loved him. Narcissus fell in love with his reflection in a pool of water and died staring at himself.

Myth Card

Titans

The Titans were huge creatures who ruled the world until they were defeated by Zeus and the other Olympian gods.

Myth Card

Stentor

Stentor was in the Greek army during the Trojan War. He shouted announcements to the soldiers. His voice was as loud as 50 men shouting together.

Myth Card

Nemesis

Nemesis was the goddess who judged men. She caused unhappiness in the lives of people she thought were too happy. Nemesis punished those who were conceited or guilty of crimes.

Myth Card

Muses

The Muses were nine daughters of Zeus. They ruled over the arts of history, poetry, music, dance, and drama.

Myth Card

Echo

Hera was Zeus's wife. One day, Hera punished the forest nymph Echo. Echo's punishment was that she could speak only when spoken to, but even then, she could only repeat what was said.

Word Cards

Word Card

Panic

Definition:
extreme fear

Example:
There was panic in the audience when the fire broke out.

Word Card

Tantalize

Definition:
to tease or torment someone with something he or she cannot have.

Example:
Please don't tantalize me with candy when I'm on a diet.

Word Card

Herculean

Definition:
something needing great strength or courage

Example:
It was a herculean task to lift the car off the trapped boy.

Word Card

Narcissism

Definition:
too much pride in oneself or one's appearance

Example:
His narcissism prevents him from thinking of anyone but himself.

Word Card

Titanic

Definition:
great in size or strength

Example:
The artist created a titanic sculpture for the town square.

Word Card

Stentorian

Definition:
very loud

Example:
His stentorian commands leave a ringing in my ears.

Word Card

Nemesis

Definition:
something or someone that causes failure or harm

Example:
I don't do well in school because taking tests is my nemesis.

Word Card

Museum

Definition:
a place where valuable objects of art and science are displayed

Example:
The Greek statues are kept in a museum.

Word Card

Echo

Definition:
a repeated sound

Example:
When you speak in an empty room, you sometimes hear an echo.

Architecture

The Site: You are standing among the grand temples on the acropolis in Athens to learn about architecture.

1. Examine the image on the placard on the wall at the station. Discuss the question with your partner and record your ideas in Section 29.4 of your Reading Notes.

2. Read Section 29.4 in your book and complete the corresponding Reading Notes for that section. Correct or add any details to your original response to the first question.

3. Read this paragraph to learn why you are visiting this site:

    You are participating in a design contest for a new temple on the acropolis in Athens. The best design will be built next to the Parthenon. This temple will celebrate the naming of Athens. According to Greek myth, the goddess Athena battled her uncle Poseidon to be the protector of Athens. Poseidon offered the people a gift of a saltwater spring. Athena offered the gift of an olive tree. Athena won, and the city was named for her. The daughter of Zeus, she is the goddess of wisdom, war, and the arts.

4. With your partner, design your temple on one copy of the temple blueprint. Follow these guidelines:
    *   Color in the pediment with your choice of color.
    *   Draw one metope for the frieze.
    *   Pick one type of column (Doric, Ionian, or Corinthian) and sketch your choice.
    *   Mark an *X* on the bird's-eye view of the temple to show where you will place your statue of Athena.
    *   Complete the sentences explaining your design.
    *   Tape your design on the wall near the station.

5. Return the station to the condition in which you found it, and have your teacher check your work.

Template Blueprint

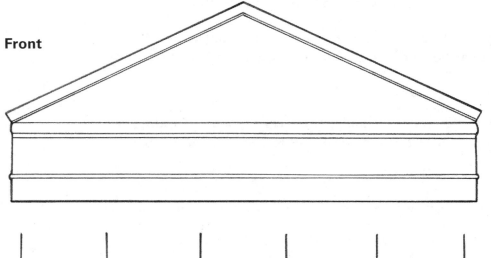

Front

We chose this color for the pediment because...

We drew the metope for the frieze because...

We chose this style of column because...

Bird's Eye View

Back

Front

We placed our statue here because...

Sculpture

The Site: You are visiting a marble workshop to learn about sculpture.

1. Examine the image on the placard on the wall at the station. Discuss the question with your partner and record your ideas in Section 29.5 of your Reading Notes.

2. Read Section 29.5 in your book and complete the corresponding Reading Notes for that section. Correct or add any details to your original response to the first question.

3. Read this paragraph to learn why you are visiting this site:

   There has been an accident in the marble workshop. Two statues were broken into several pieces. The sculptor apprentices need to reassemble the pieces so the master sculptor can repair the statues. The apprentices, however, still have much to learn about sculpture, so they need your help to reassemble the statues correctly. The apprentices tell you that one of these statues was carved many years before the other.

4. With your partner, correctly assemble the pieces of each statue. Since one statue was carved much earlier, the assembled statues should clearly differ in style.

5. Return the station to the condition in which you found it, and have your teacher check your work.

Egyptian Statue Puzzle

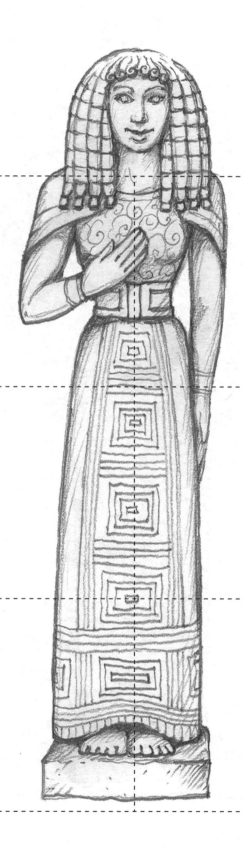

Greek Statue Puzzle

Drama

The Site: You are visiting the Theater of Dionysus to learn about drama.

1. Examine the image on the placard on the wall at the station. Discuss the question with your partner and record your ideas in Section 29.6 of your Reading Notes.

2. Read Section 29.6 in your book and complete the corresponding Reading Notes for that section. Correct or add any details to your original response to the first question.

3. Read this paragraph to learn why you are visiting this site:

    The city of Athens is the host for several days of drama competitions at the Theater of Dionysus. The playwright Sophocles has submitted a tragedy for the competition. In a tragedy, the main character meets his or her downfall at the end. Sophocles has asked for your help in rehearsing part of the play.

4. With your partner, help rehearse part of Sophocles' play, *Antigone*. Follow these guidelines:
    *   Take a copy of the script for *Antigone* and assign one part to each person.
    *   Perform the selection from *Antigone* by reading your character's part.
    *   On the lined paper, write your names and the answer to this question: Will Antigone break the law, and what do you think will happen to her?

5. Return the station to the condition in which you found it, and have your teacher check your work.

Antigone Script

Background

The play opens with two sisters, Antigone (an-TIH-guh-nee) and Ismene (is-MEE-nee), discussing the tragic events of their family. Their two brothers, Eteocles (ih-TEE-uh-kleez) and Polyneices (pol-uh-NIE-seez), had agreed to share power by alternating as King of Thebes. When Eteocles refused to give up power, Polyneices attacked Thebes with a foreign army. The brothers end up killing each other in battle. The new king, Creon (KREE-on), has honored Eteocles with a funeral because Eteocles had to defend the city. But Creon has forbidden anyone to properly bury Polyneices because he attacked the city.

Selection from *Antigone*

by Sophocles

Antigone: Now, dear Ismene, my own blood sister, do you have any sense of all the troubles Zeus keeps bringing on the two of us, as long as we're alive?

Ismene: What is it? The way you look makes it seem you're thinking of some dark and gloomy news.

Antigone: Look—what is Creon doing with our two brothers? He's honoring one with a full funeral and treating the other one disgracefully!

Ismene: Oh, my poor sister, if that's what is happening, what can I say that would be any help to ease the situation or resolve it?

Antigone: Think whether you will work with me in this and act together.

Ismene: In what kind of work? What do you mean?

Antigone: Will you help these hands take up Polyneices' corpse and bury it?

Ismene: What? You're going to bury Polyneices, when that has been made a crime for all in Thebes?

Antigone: Yes. I'll do my duty to my brother—and yours as well, if you're not prepared to. I won't be caught betraying him.

Ismene: You're too rash. Has Creon not expressly banned the act?

Antigone: Yes. But he is not right to keep me from what is mine.

Ismene: Oh, dear. Think, Antigone. Think how we'll die far worse than all the rest, if we defy the law and move against the king's decree, against his royal power.

Philosophy

The Site: You are standing in the agora in Athens to learn about philosophy.

1. Examine the image on the placard on the wall at the station. Discuss the question with your partner and record your ideas in Section 29.7 of your Reading Notes.

2. Read Section 29.7 in your book and complete the corresponding Reading Notes for that section. Correct or add any details to your original response to the first question.

3. You are visiting this site to talk with Socrates. Play CD Track 18 to meet him. Stop the CD player when he pauses to let you think about his first idea.

4. With your partner, think about Socrates' ideas. Follow these guidelines:
   - Find the handout for Socrates' first quotation.
   - In the first column, write your names.
   - In the second column, briefly describe what you think Socrates means.
   - In the third column, write down whether you agree or disagree with Socrates.
   - Continue playing CD Track 23 and complete the handouts for the second and third quotations.

5. Return the station to the condition in which you found it, and have your teacher check your work.

Socrates' First Quotation

THE UNEXAMINED LIFE
IS NOT WORTH LIVING.

Names	We think Socrates means . . .	We agree/disagree with Socrates.

Socrates' Second Quotation

THE ONLY GOOD IS KNOWLEDGE, AND THE ONLY EVIL IS IGNORANCE.

Names	We think Socrates means . . .	We agree/disagree with Socrates.

Socrates' Third Quotation

BAD MEN LIVE THAT THEY MAY EAT AND DRINK, WHEREAS GOOD MEN EAT AND DRINK THAT THEY MAY LIVE.

Names	We think Socrates means . . .	We agree/disagree with Socrates.

Sports

The Site: You are watching the Panathenaic Games, a series of athletic events and competitions, to learn about sports.

1. Examine the image on the placard on the wall at the station. Discuss the question with your partner and record your ideas in Section 29.8 of your Reading Notes.

2. Read Section 29.8 in your book and complete the corresponding Reading Notes for that section. Correct or add any details to your original response to the first question.

3. Read this paragraph to learn why you are visiting this site:

   The city of Athens is celebrating the festival of Panathenaea. As part of the festival, superb athletes are competing in a series of events. You are going to compete in three of those events. In the javelin event, you will test your throwing ability. In the broad jump event, you will test your jumping ability. In the book hold event, you will test your strength. The athlete with the best distance or time in each of these events will be recognized as the winner of that event.

4. With your partner, compete in the three events. Follow these guidelines:
   - Find the Judge's Score Sheet and write your names in the first column.
   - Stand on the masking tape. Throw the javelin (straw) as far as you can. Have your partner use the yardstick to measure your distance, and record it on the Judge's Score Sheet.
   - Stand on the masking tape. With your feet together, jump as far as you can. Have your partner use the yardstick to measure your distance, and record it on the Judge's Score Sheet.
   - Stand with one arm extended out in front of you, with your palm facing down. Balance a copy of *History Alive! The Ancient World* on the back of your hand. Have your partner time how many seconds you can hold the book, and record the time on the Judge's Score Sheet.

5. Return the station to the condition in which you found it, and have your teacher check your work.

Judge's Score Sheet

Athlete Name	Javelin Throw	Broad Jump	Book Hold
	_____ inches	_____ inches	_____ seconds
	_____ inches	_____ inches	_____ seconds
	_____ inches	_____ inches	_____ seconds
	_____ inches	_____ inches	_____ seconds
	_____ inches	_____ inches	_____ seconds
	_____ inches	_____ inches	_____ seconds
	_____ inches	_____ inches	_____ seconds
	_____ inches	_____ inches	_____ seconds
	_____ inches	_____ inches	_____ seconds
	_____ inches	_____ inches	_____ seconds
	_____ inches	_____ inches	_____ seconds
	_____ inches	_____ inches	_____ seconds

Writing a Persuasive Speech About Athens

During your walking tour of Athens, you learned about six aspects of Greek culture that thrived during the Golden Age. On a separate sheet of paper, write a speech for the Athenian leader Pericles, using information that you learned on your tour. Your speech should clearly convince Athenians and Greeks from other city-states that Athens is a great city.

Your speech must be at least four paragraphs and include these elements:

- a brief introduction to Athens and the Golden Age
- a statement explaining why Athens is a great city
- a description of two or more relevant examples from your walking tour of Athens
- an appeal to any listeners who might say that Athens is not a great city
- a brief conclusion that restates your position and reminds listeners of your main points

Chapter 29 Assessment

Mastering the Content

Fill in the circle next to the best answer.

1. Why did Athenians start new construction after the Persian wars?
   ○ A. The wars had made them wealthy.
   ○ B. They had conquered other city-states.
   ○ C. Their city had been totally destroyed.
   ○ D. Most of their soldiers had been killed.

2. Why was Pericles famous?
   ○ A. He was the author of important plays.
   ○ B. He was the architect of a major temple.
   ○ C. He led the army during the Persian wars.
   ○ D. He led the government during the Golden Age.

3. Athens paid salaries to men who held public office. How did that affect the growth of democracy?
   ○ A. It hurt democracy by making government workers rich.
   ○ B. It helped democracy by enabling people who were not rich to work for the government.
   ○ C. It helped democracy by rewarding each of the people who came to vote in the Assembly.
   ○ D. It hurt democracy by encouraging the leader of Athens to surround himself with his friends.

4. Which phrase **best** describes public buildings in Athens?
   ○ A. made of stone
   ○ B. one story high
   ○ C. on narrow streets
   ○ D. outside the city walls

5. Why was the Parthenon built?
   ○ A. to foretell the future
   ○ B. to honor the goddess Athena
   ○ C. to reward the chief of the navy
   ○ D. to hold meetings by city leaders

6. The oracle of Delphi was a priestess whose words were believed to come from
   ○ A. Zeus.
   ○ B. Apollo.
   ○ C. Demeter.
   ○ D. Aphrodite.

7. Why was Mount Olympus important to the Greeks?
   ○ A. They built a theater on its side.
   ○ B. They grew olives on its slopes.
   ○ C. They thought the gods lived there.
   ○ D. They watched athletes compete below it.

8. How can you tell that this is a Doric column?
   ○ A. It is simple.
   ○ B. It has a frieze.
   ○ C. It sits on a base.
   ○ D. It is very decorative.

9. Which part of the temple is the pediment?

- ○ A. the platform for standing
- ○ B. the triangle at the top front
- ○ C. the inside part with sculptures
- ○ D. the band that runs above the columns

10. One of the greatest achievements of Greek sculptors was

- ○ A. creating a vast terra-cotta army.
- ○ B. carving tiny figures in amazing detail.
- ○ C. making lifelike statues in natural poses.
- ○ D. building huge monuments of solid gold.

11. What was one reason that actors wore masks in ancient Greek theater?

- ○ A Women played male characters.
- ○ B. Men played all characters.
- ○ C. It honored Dionysus, the god of masks.
- ○ D. Women played male roles and men played female roles.

12. What was the main purpose of a Greek chorus?

- ○ A. to satisfy the angry gods
- ○ B. to train children to sing well
- ○ C. to keep workers moving quickly
- ○ D. to help people understand the play

13. The word *philosophy* comes from Greek words meaning

- ○ A. "see from afar."
- ○ B. "sad and happy."
- ○ C. "near the market."
- ○ D. "love of wisdom."

14. For what crime was Socrates arrested?

- ○ A. telling state secrets to enemy powers
- ○ B. refusing to teach the children of the rich
- ○ C. living on the streets with no means of support
- ○ D. asking questions that seemed to dishonor the gods

15. What does the Greek love of sports show about ancient Greeks?

- ○ A. They valued physical fitness.
- ○ B. They forced their slaves to fight.
- ○ C. They treated men and women as equals.
- ○ D. They cared more about winning than fairness.

16. Why did the Greeks agree every four years to stop fighting for a brief period?

- ○ A. to allow their soldiers to rest
- ○ B. to pull a ship through the city
- ○ C. to let athletes go to the Olympics
- ○ D. to hold a festival for all their gods

Applying Social Studies Skills

Use the map and your knowledge of history to answer the questions. Write the word or phrase in the space provided.

Ancient Athens

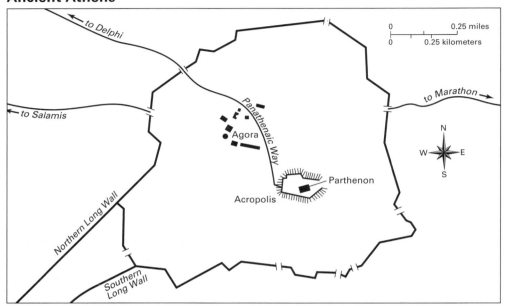

17. The Northern Long Wall and the Southern Long Wall protected the route between Athens and its main seaport. The map suggests that the seaport was in which direction from Athens?

18. Suppose that you were an ancient tourist who wanted to visit famous sites from the Persian wars.

    If you traveled east out of Athens, what could you visit?

    If you traveled west out of Athens, what could you visit?

19. Suppose that you were a visitor from Delphi who came to Athens to visit the acropolis. Using information on the map, identify the road you would take, and describe one thing you would see after you entered the city, before you reached the acropolis.

Exploring the Essential Question

What were the major cultural achievements of Athens?

Follow the directions to complete the item below.

20. Design a travel poster advertising a visit to the city-state of Athens during its Golden Age. Include the following in your poster:

    • Four drawings that represent places or objects a visitor should see, or activities a traveler should participate in.

    • A caption that explains why the visitor should do each of the four things suggested on the poster. For example, a caption might read, "Learn your future. Visit Delphi."

Group Spectrum

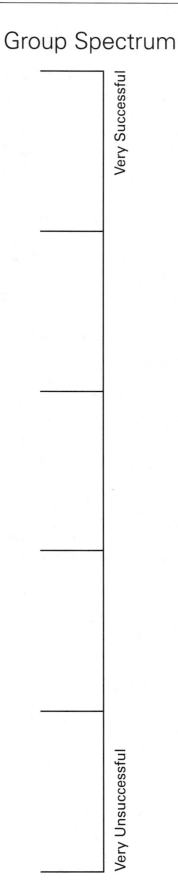

Chapter 30 Assessment

Mastering the Content

Fill in the circle next to the best answer.

1. What was an outcome of the Peloponnesian War?
   - ○ A. Persia defeated Sparta.
   - ○ B. Sparta defeated Athens.
   - ○ C. Athens conquered Egypt.
   - ○ D. Greece conquered Macedonia.

2. What made it possible for Philip II to succeed in Greece?
   - ○ A. his interest in philosophy
   - ○ B. a peace agreement with Persia
   - ○ C. conflict among his scattered tribes
   - ○ D. divisions between Greek city-states

3. How did Alexander show the influence of his teacher, Aristotle?
   - ○ A. in his hatred of cities
   - ○ B. in his warlike ambition
   - ○ C. in his love of Greek culture
   - ○ D. in his skill at Asian languages

4. What did Alexander do to help unite the Greeks under his rule?
   - ○ A. took away their freedoms
   - ○ B. taught them a new religion
   - ○ C. had their leaders take turns
   - ○ D. gave them a common enemy

5. What happened to the government officials of towns that surrendered to Alexander?
   - ○ A. They got to stay in office.
   - ○ B. They were sold into slavery.
   - ○ C. They were taken away and killed.
   - ○ D. They became officers in his army.

6. Why is Alexander called "Great"?
   - ○ A. He conquered a huge area.
   - ○ B. He created a lasting empire.
   - ○ C. He spread new kinds of farming.
   - ○ D. He set up independent city-states.

7. What was Alexander's goal for his empire?
   - ○ A. to make Athens the biggest capital city
   - ○ B. to require everyone to follow one religion
   - ○ C. to make conquered towns and cities independent
   - ○ D. to bring different cultures under one government

8. Alexander built cities to
   - ○ A. train loyal soldiers.
   - ○ B. spread Greek culture.
   - ○ C. preserve local customs.
   - ○ D. move away from Macedonia.

9. Why was the city of Alexandria, in Egypt, especially famous?

○ A. Its library helped make it a center of learning.

○ B. Its army helped make it feared by other cities.

○ C. Its pyramids helped make it a tourist attraction.

○ D. Its roads across the desert helped make it a trade center.

10. How did Alexander use religion to help him rule the Egyptians?

○ A. He gained their loyalty by honoring their gods.

○ B. He frightened them by capturing their priests.

○ C. He took control by making them accept Greek gods.

○ D. He destroyed opposition by tearing down their temples.

11. Alexander told the Greeks that he was the son of

○ A. Aristotle.

○ B. the god Zeus.

○ C. the king of Persia.

○ D. a Macedonian giant.

12. In Persia, Alexander allowed the Persians to

○ A. treat him as a personal equal.

○ B. hold the top offices in the army.

○ C. control the taxes that they collected.

○ D. run the day-to-day business in their lands.

13. Why did Alexander receive visitors in a tent?

○ A. Tents were a Greek tradition.

○ B. He moved from place to place.

○ C. It was a custom of Persian kings.

○ D. He was showing a lack of respect.

14. When Alexander reached northern India, what made him turn back?

○ A. His home was far away.

○ B. He married a local princess.

○ C. He developed a serious illness.

○ D. His soldiers refused to go any farther.

15. What happened to Alexander's empire after he died?

○ A. It was defeated by the Greeks.

○ B. The capital moved to Babylon.

○ C. His generals fought for control.

○ D. His son Philip became the ruler.

16. What was the lasting influence of Alexander's conquests?

○ A. the rise of a new religion

○ B. the spread of Greek culture

○ C. the growth of a nomadic way of life

○ D. the political unity of Asia and Egypt

Applying Social Studies Skills

Use the map and your knowledge of history to answer the questions. Write the word or phrase in the space provided.

Alexander the Great's Empire

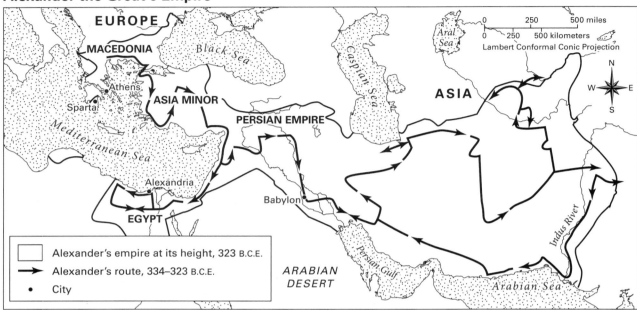

17. Find the easternmost point to which Alexander's army traveled. What body of water is there?

18. What two other bodies of water named on the map did Alexander travel near?

19. Find the route that Alexander followed from Egypt to Babylon. What is a likely reason he took that route rather than a more direct route?

Exploring the Essential Question

How did Alexander build his empire?

Follow the directions to complete the item below.

20. Suppose that you are a soldier in the army of Alexander the Great. Write a letter home to a friend or family member in Macedonia. Your letter should include the following:

   • Sensory details and concrete language about your experiences.

   • The place where you are writing from. You may use the map on the preceding page for ideas.

   • Events or descriptions that illustrate at least two methods that Alexander used to build his empire.

   • Your feelings about what you have seen, heard, or done.

Legacy Cards

Section 31.2

Literature and History

Today, schoolchildren around the world learn how to write. Some languages use symbols that stand for things or ideas. Other languages, like English, use symbols that stand for sounds. There are 26 symbols, or letters, in the English alphabet. People in many nations enjoy reading works of literature and studying history.

Section 31.3

Government

In the United States today, all citizens over the age of 18 have the right to vote. The method they use to vote varies by state. Some citizens use computers. Some use paper ballots that are read by machines. And some citizens still place a paper ballot in a ballot box.

Section 31.4

Medicine

Today, when people become sick, they may visit a doctor. Doctors examine their patients and observe their symptoms. Then, they may recommend a test. Doctors can determine the causes of and treatments for many types of diseases.

Section 31.5

Mathematics

Geometry is a type of mathematics that involves the shapes and sizes of things. People use geometry in many ways today. For example, engineers and carpenters use it to construct buildings. Landscapers use it to design gardens. Even people who develop games use it to create video games.

Legacy Cards

Section 31.6

Astronomy

Scientists today know that Earth is part of a system of planets that revolve around the sun. As Earth revolves around the sun, it also rotates on an axis. By studying the sky, scientists can see evidence of Earth's rotation, in the way that stars seem to move from one side of the sky to the other.

Section 31.7

Geography

A flat map of Earth is difficult to make because our planet is a sphere. When geographers draw Earth on a flat map, the places farthest from the equator appear larger than they really are. Today's mapmakers have developed many different styles of maps to try to fix this problem.

Section 31.8

Biology

Today, plant growers in nurseries know many ways to create new plant growth. They plant seeds and bulbs, take cuttings from roots and stems, and grow flowers that are pollinated by insects.

Section 31.9

Architecture

The two wings of the U.S. Capitol building, in Washington, D.C., have beautifully carved pediments above finely decorated friezes. Tall, slender columns, topped by detailed leaf carvings, are under the pediments and friezes.

Legacy Cards

Section 31.10

Theater

Many theaters today are designed to give audiences the best possible viewing experience. Everyone wants to have a seat with a clear view, especially to see extraordinary theatrical stunts, such as flying. Good acoustics enable theatergoers to hear special sound effects.

Section 31.11

Sports

Every four years, athletes from around the world participate in the Olympic Games. The Winter Games include competitions in sports like skiing and hockey. The Summer Games include such track and field events as the discus throw and the javelin toss.

Identifying Greek Contributions to Modern Life

With your partner, follow the steps below to identify Greek contributions to modern life.

Step 1: Read your legacy card to learn about a part of modern life.

Step 2: Locate the placard showing the Greek achievement that contributed to this aspect of modern life.

Step 3: In the Reading Notes in your Interactive Student Notebook, find the appropriate section and heading in the first column of the matrix and write the placard letter in the column next to it.

Step 4: Return to your desk and read the appropriate section of Chapter 31 in your book. Complete the corresponding Reading Notes in your Interactive Student Notebook.

Step 5: Check your answers with your teacher and then get a new legacy card.

Chapter 31 Assessment

Mastering the Content
Fill in the circle next to the best answer.

1. The word *alphabet* comes from
   - ○ A. the ideas of Aristotle.
   - ○ B. the work of the writer Thucydides.
   - ○ C. the first two letters of the Greek alphabet.
   - ○ D. the Greek words meaning "word" and "parts."

2. Which of these words **best** belongs in the empty box in this chart?

Two Kinds of Greek Drama	
Comedy	

   - ○ A. Festival
   - ○ B. Musical
   - ○ C. Theater
   - ○ D. Tragedy

3. Why is Herodotus called the "father of history"?
   - ○ A. He had many children.
   - ○ B. He taught in the agora.
   - ○ C. He wrote about the past.
   - ○ D. He was an important leader.

4. Which of the choices below is a part of American democracy that comes from the ancient Greeks?
   - ○ A. juries of citizens
   - ○ B. a Council of Elders
   - ○ C. one official religion
   - ○ D. independent city-states

5. How was ancient Greek democracy different from American democracy today?
   - ○ A. Everyone did not always agree.
   - ○ B. All citizens voted on every issue.
   - ○ C. People could speak their opinions.
   - ○ D. Strong speakers influenced others.

6. Hippocrates is called the "father of medicine." Which statement would he **most** likely have made?
   - ○ A. "I will tell everybody about your illness."
   - ○ B. "I see that you got sick after eating that meat."
   - ○ C. "You must let me try this experiment on you."
   - ○ D. "You are sick because the gods are angry at you."

7. Which one of these lists of items would Pythagoras and Euclid **most** likely have written about?
   - ○ A. rocks, stones, and dirt
   - ○ B. skin, blood, and bones
   - ○ C. lines, circles, and squares
   - ○ D. actors, costumes, and stages

8. Which of these ideas was **first** introduced in ancient Greece?
   - ○ A. Earth moves around the sun.
   - ○ B. The planets affect human lives.
   - ○ C. It is good to study the night sky.
   - ○ D. The moon seems to change shape.

9. How did Greek scientists make their most important discoveries?

○ A. They got the citizens to vote.
○ B. They translated Egyptian texts.
○ C. They built complicated machines.
○ D. They observed and asked questions.

10. Who would be the most likely to use lines of latitude and longitude?

○ A. a painter
○ B. an architect
○ C. a mapmaker
○ D. an astronomer

11. How did the philosopher Aristotle affect the modern study of plants and animals?

○ A. He invented a machine for measuring growth.
○ B. He created a system to divide them into groups.
○ C. He discovered that the heart pumps blood through the body.
○ D. He suggested cutting people open to see how the body works.

12. What influence from ancient Greece is visible in this picture of the Lincoln Memorial in Washington, D.C.?

○ A. the use of columns
○ B. the honoring of heroes
○ C. the effect of bright lights
○ D. the importance of religion

13. In what way are many theaters today like the ones in ancient Greece?

○ A. The back of the theater is open.
○ B. People pay more for the best seats.
○ C. The stage is built into the side of a hill.
○ D. The rows rise so people can see and hear.

14. What was the purpose of the first Olympics?

○ A. to honor a Greek god
○ B. to choose military leaders
○ C. to decide who would be king
○ D. to reach the top of Mount Olympus

15. What is one way the modern Olympics are like those of ancient Greece?

○ A. The location changes.
○ B. An athlete lights a flame.
○ C. Games are held every year.
○ D. Many countries send athletes.

Applying Social Studies Skills

Use the chart and your knowledge of history to answer the questions. Write the word or phrase in the space provided.

16. The Athenians built temples on a special hill. Why did they call that hill the "acropolis"?

17. Geometry began as a system for measuring areas of land. How can that origin be seen in the word *geometry*?

Greek Root	Meaning
acro-	high, height
auto-	self
bio-	life, living
dem-	people
geo-	earth
micro-	small
philo-	love of
tele-	far away
-cracy	rule, power
-graph, -graphy	writing
-logy	science, study
-meter, -metry	measure, measuring
-phone	sound
-polis	city
-scope	device for viewing
-soph, -sophy	wisdom

18. Write each of these words next to its meaning below.

autobiography   *microbiology*   *philosophy*
democracy   *microscope*   *telescope*

   a. _____ love of wisdom

   b. _____ rule by the people

   c. _____ writing about one's own life

   d. _____ study of very small living things

   e. _____ device for looking at things far away

   f. _____ device for looking at very small things

19. Identify one additional word that can be made from the Greek roots in the chart. Write the word here.

Exploring the Essential Question

How did ancient Greece contribute to the modern world?

Follow the directions to complete the item below.

20. Plan a tour of a town, either real or made-up, in the United States today. The tour stops will reflect three different forms of Greek influence, from this list.

Literature and History	Astronomy	Architecture
Government	Geography	Theater
Medicine	Biology	Sports
Mathematics		

Write the text for a flier or brochure for your tour. It should include the following:

- a description of each of the three stops on the tour

- an explanation of how each site shows the influence of ancient Greece

- a reason why visitors interested in Greek contributions would visit that site

Unit 5 Timeline Challenge Cards

Oligarchies Replace Monarchies
By 800 B.C.E.

Oligarchies replace monarchies as the form of government in most Greek city-states.

Tyrannies Replace Oligarchies
By Mid-600s B.C.E.

Tyranny becomes the form of government in many Greek city-states.

Greek City-States Flourish
About 500 B.C.E.

Greek city-states establish colonies and conduct trade in the wider Mediterranean region.

Democracy Develops in Athens
By 500 B.C.E.

Democracy develops in Athens and gives shared ruling power to all citizens.

Unit 5 Timeline Challenge Cards

Persian Wars
499–479 B.C.E.

The Persian wars end with a Greek victory aided by the alliance of Athens and Sparta.

Golden Age of Athens
479–431 B.C.E.

The Golden Age of Athens makes the city-state the artistic and cultural center of Greece.

Peloponnesian War
431–404 B.C.E.

The Peloponnesian War between Athens and Sparta, each with its own allies, weakens the Greek city-states.

Pericles' Funeral Oration
431 B.C.E.

Pericles praises the greatness of Athens in his Funeral Oration honoring Athenian soldiers killed in the Peloponnesian War.

Unit 5 Timeline Challenge Cards

Death of Thucydides
About 400 B.C.E.

The historian Thucydides writes about the history of the Peloponnesian War.

Death of Socrates
399 B.C.E.

A jury finds the philosopher Socrates guilty and sentences him to death.

Empire of Alexander the Great
334–323 B.C.E.

Alexander the Great builds a vast empire and spreads Greek culture to Asia and Africa.

Euclid Writes About Geometry
About 300 B.C.E.

The mathematician Euclid writes *The Elements,* a collection of 13 books about geometry.

Etruscan and Greek Influence Cards

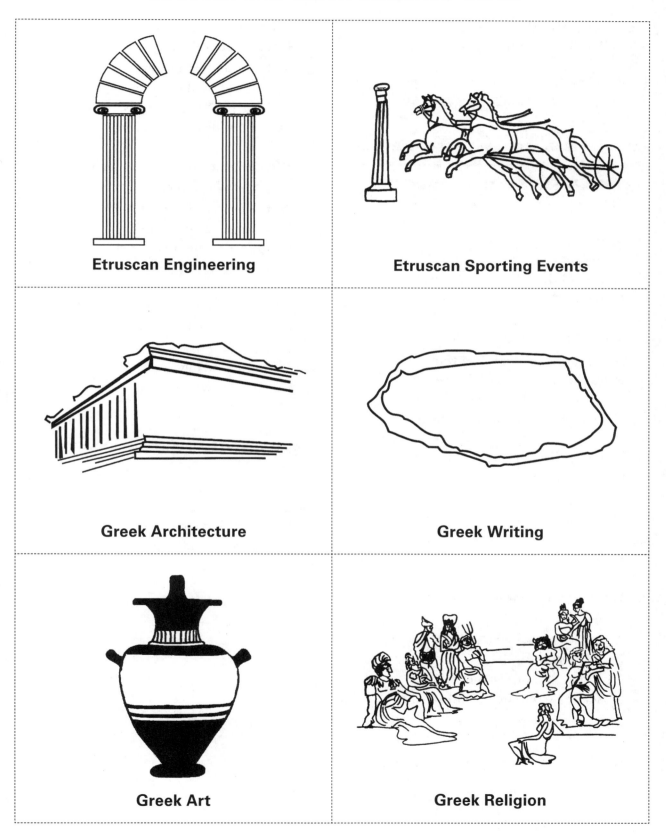

Etruscan Engineering

Etruscan Sporting Events

Greek Architecture

Greek Writing

Greek Art

Greek Religion

Chapter 32 Assessment

Mastering the Content
Fill in the circle next to the best answer.

1. Based on the timeline, in which period was Roman civilization active?

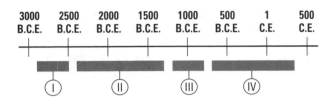

○ A. period I
○ B. period II
○ C. period III
○ D. period IV

2. Who were Romulus and Remus?

○ A. opposing generals in a war
○ B. explorers on a famous river
○ C. the mythical founders of Rome
○ D. colonists from ancient Greece

3. Who first lived in the area that would become Rome?

○ A. Latins
○ B. Greeks
○ C. Etruscans
○ D. Macedonians

4. What landscape would an early visitor to Rome have seen?

○ A. a plain by the sea
○ B. a hill beside a river
○ C. a mountainous island
○ D. a lake surrounded by hills

5. What tourist sights in Rome show Etruscan influence?

○ A. buildings with arches
○ B. fields of bright flowers
○ C. large public courtyards
○ D. windmills to water crops

6. What was one reason why the Etruscans might build a cuniculus?

○ A. to entertain the people
○ B. to farm on steep hillsides
○ C. to carry water to their cities
○ D. to conquer neighboring tribes

7. Which dangerous sport did the Romans adapt from the Etruscans?

○ A. long jumping
○ B. chariot racing
○ C. pole throwing
○ D. bear wrestling

8. Slaves who became gladiators were required to fight to

○ A. train war horses.
○ B. protect the city.
○ C. establish colonies.
○ D. amuse an audience.

9. How did Romans learn about Greek culture?
- ○ A. They moved to Greece.
- ○ B. They sold slaves to Greece.
- ○ C. Greek colonists had settled nearby.
- ○ D. Greek leaders met with Roman leaders.

10. What does this building in Rome show about Roman architecture?

- ○ A. It was influenced by the Greeks.
- ○ B. Etruscan styles influenced it.
- ○ C. It used keystones for support.
- ○ D. Slaves worked to construct it.

11. How did the Romans get their alphabet?
- ○ A. directly from the Greeks, who invented it
- ○ B. directly from the Etruscans, who invented it
- ○ C. from the Etruscans, who got it from the Greeks
- ○ D. from the Greeks, who got it from the Etruscans

12. Unlike our writing today, both Greek and Roman writing
- ○ A. served to record laws.
- ○ B. used only capital letters.
- ○ C. was rarely seen in public.
- ○ D. represented words with pictures.

13. Why do historians use the term "Greco-Roman art"?
- ○ A. Roman art shows a strong influence from Greece.
- ○ B. The same artists worked in both Greece and Rome.
- ○ C. Greeks admired Roman styles and tried to imitate them.
- ○ D. Scholars cannot tell whether a work is Greek or Roman.

14. What was a **major** difference between Greek and Roman art?
- ○ A. Greek art showed leaders. Roman art showed gods.
- ○ B. Greek art showed events. Roman art showed landscapes.
- ○ C. Greek art showed daily life. Roman art showed celebrations.
- ○ D. Greek art showed ideal people. Roman art showed realistic people.

15. What does the chart below show about Greek and Roman gods?

Greek Gods	Roman Gods
Zeus	Jupiter
Aphrodite	Venus
Aries	Mars

- ○ A. They had the same rituals.
- ○ B. They had different names.
- ○ C. They had the same worshippers.
- ○ D. They had different personalities.

16. Regarding the gods, the Romans cared more than the Greeks about
- ○ A. telling their stories.
- ○ B. seeing plays about them.
- ○ C. honoring them with sports.
- ○ D. performing the correct rituals.

Applying Social Studies Skills

Use the map and your knowledge of history to complete the sentences.

17. The three cultures shown on the map are located mostly

Italian Peninsula, 6th Century B.C.E.

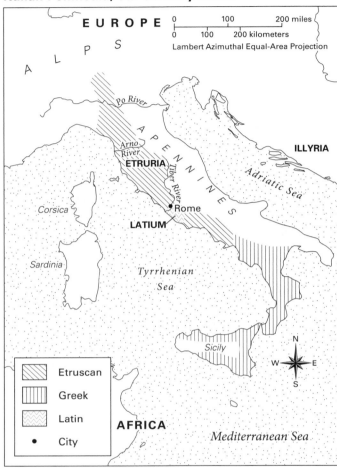

18. The form of transportation mostly likely used by Greek colonists is reflected by the fact that

19. A likely reason why the Etruscans were able to rule Rome for a time is that

Exploring the Essential Question

How did the Etruscans and Greeks influence the development of Rome?

Follow the directions to complete the item below.

20. Suppose you are a Roman planning a museum exhibit about how Rome was influenced by Etruscan and Greek cultures. Draw a picture in each frame below, one for an Etruscan influence and the other for a Greek influence. Write a specific caption of one or two sentences to explain how each influence was adapted by the Romans.

Etruscan Influence

Greek Influence

Caption:

Caption:

Role Cards for Pats

You are assigned the role of a "Pat."

- Elect two Pats to be spokespersons.
- Make decisions for the class about how to make a large, colorful mosaic.
- Make sure your group of Plebs cuts out the correct tiles.
- Direct the Plebs to work quickly.
- Relax in the Forum when you want to take a break from supervising.

You are assigned the role of a "Pat."

- Elect two Pats to be spokespersons.
- Make decisions for the class about how to make a large, colorful mosaic.
- Make sure your group of Plebs cuts out the correct tiles.
- Direct the Plebs to work quickly.
- Relax in the Forum when you want to take a break from supervising.

You are assigned the role of a "Pat."

- Elect two Pats to be spokespersons.
- Make decisions for the class about how to make a large, colorful mosaic.
- Make sure your group of Plebs cuts out the correct tiles.
- Direct the Plebs to work quickly.
- Relax in the Forum when you want to take a break from supervising.

You are assigned the role of a "Pat."

- Elect two Pats to be spokespersons.
- Make decisions for the class about how to make a large, colorful mosaic.
- Make sure your group of Plebs cuts out the correct tiles.
- Direct the Plebs to work quickly.
- Relax in the Forum when you want to take a break from supervising.

You are assigned the role of a "Pat."

- Elect two Pats to be spokespersons.
- Make decisions for the class about how to make a large, colorful mosaic.
- Make sure your group of Plebs cuts out the correct tiles.
- Direct the Plebs to work quickly.
- Relax in the Forum when you want to take a break from supervising.

You are assigned the role of a "Pat."

- Elect two Pats to be spokespersons.
- Make decisions for the class about how to make a large, colorful mosaic.
- Make sure your group of Plebs cuts out the correct tiles.
- Direct the Plebs to work quickly.
- Relax in the Forum when you want to take a break from supervising.

Chapter 33 Assessment

Mastering the Content

Fill in the circle next to the best answer.

1. Who first ruled early Rome?
   ○ A. Etruscan kings
   ○ B. military consuls
   ○ C. Roman senators
   ○ D. plebeian assemblies

2. According to legend, events on a visit to the oracle at Delphi determined
   ○ A. where Rome should be built.
   ○ B. who would govern Rome next.
   ○ C. how Rome could start colonies.
   ○ D. when Rome would write its laws.

3. In the Roman Republic, *patricians* referred to
   ○ A. every adult male citizen.
   ○ B. everyone except slaves.
   ○ C. wealthy landowning families.
   ○ D. people with Greek ancestors.

4. Why were plebeians unhappy when the Roman Republic was first set up?
   ○ A. They had lost the right to vote.
   ○ B. They preferred living in an empire.
   ○ C. They had no say in making the laws.
   ○ D. They preferred being ruled by a king.

5. Who set up the Roman Republic?
   ○ A. plebeians
   ○ B. patricians
   ○ C. Greek settlers
   ○ D. Etruscan princes

6. How did plebeians serve the republic during its early years?
   ○ A. as priests
   ○ B. as soldiers
   ○ C. as foreign advisers
   ○ D. as government officials

7. In the Roman Republic, who might have spoken these words?

   I was elected to the group that holds most of the power. I will keep this office all my life. I help make laws and serve as a judge.

   ○ A. a scribe
   ○ B. a consul
   ○ C. a tribune
   ○ D. a senator

8. What was one major job of the consuls?
   ○ A. to command the army
   ○ B. to choose the lawmakers
   ○ C. to perform religious rituals
   ○ D. to construct public buildings

9. What event belongs in the blank space on the timeline?

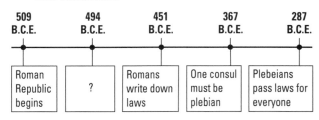

509 B.C.E.	494 B.C.E.	451 B.C.E.	367 B.C.E.	287 B.C.E.
Roman Republic begins	?	Romans write down laws	One consul must be plebian	Plebeians pass laws for everyone

   ○ A. Roman Empire falls
   ○ B. Plebeians elect a leader
   ○ C. Plebeians refuse to fight
   ○ D. Etruscans return to power

10. What was a result of the Conflict of the Orders?

   ○ A. Plebeians lost the right to vote.
   ○ B. Patricians gave up some power.
   ○ C. Romans defeated the Greek navy.
   ○ D. Etruscans won control over Rome.

11. How could a Roman become a tribune?

   ○ A. have a consul appoint him
   ○ B. win the favor of the senators
   ○ C. inherit the job from his father
   ○ D. get the plebeians to elect him

12. The power of the tribunes increased when they gained the right to

   ○ A. make laws for the plebeians.
   ○ B. appoint a special dictator.
   ○ C. lead the army in wartime.
   ○ D. veto actions by the Senate.

13. Why did the plebeians want laws to be written?

   ○ A. so the patricians could not change laws whenever they wished
   ○ B. so their land would be protected by the government
   ○ C. so the government could not pass new laws too quickly
   ○ D. so their children could learn to read in Roman schools

14. What changed as a result of the action in the image below?

   ○ A. Patricians had less power than before.
   ○ B. Plebeians followed more laws than before.
   ○ C. Priests became the wealthiest people in Rome.
   ○ D. Scribes became the most powerful people in Rome.

15. Plebeians became nearly equal to patricians when they won the right to

   ○ A. put laws in writing.
   ○ B. choose their own king.
   ○ C. pass laws for all Romans.
   ○ D. serve as priests and soldiers.

16. Why are both the Roman Republic and the United States today considered republics?

   ○ A. All the citizens vote directly on all the laws.
   ○ B. Any citizen can voice an opinion about the laws.
   ○ C. The people give a leader the right to veto some laws.
   ○ D. The people elect representatives to make laws for them.

Applying Social Studies Skills

Use the passage and your knowledge of history to complete the sentences.

Gaius Terentilius Harsa . . . spent several days in haranguing [making a scolding speech to] the plebeians on the overbearing arrogance [pride] of the patricians. In particular he [complained] against the authority of the consuls as excessive [too much] and intolerable in a free commonwealth, for while in name it was less invidious [unpleasant], in reality it was almost more harsh and oppressive [crushing] than that of the kings had been, for now, he said, they had two masters instead of one, with uncontrolled, unlimited powers . . .

—Livy, *The History of Rome,* Volume I, 3.

---

17. In saying that now Rome had two masters instead of one, Harsa meant that in place of one _____, Rome now had two _____.

18. A likely effect of Harsa's speeches may have been to

19. Harsa would likely have favored a change in government to

Exploring the Essential Question

What were the characteristics of the Roman Republic and how did they change over time?

Follow the directions to complete the item below.

20. If the Roman Republic existed today, its people would probably use the Internet. On the computer screen below, do the following:

- Design a home page for a plebeian Web site during the Conflict of the Orders. Include a few sentences about plebeian goals during this conflict.
- Make up two other Web sites that would interest plebeians. Add "links" to those two sites at the bottom of the screen.

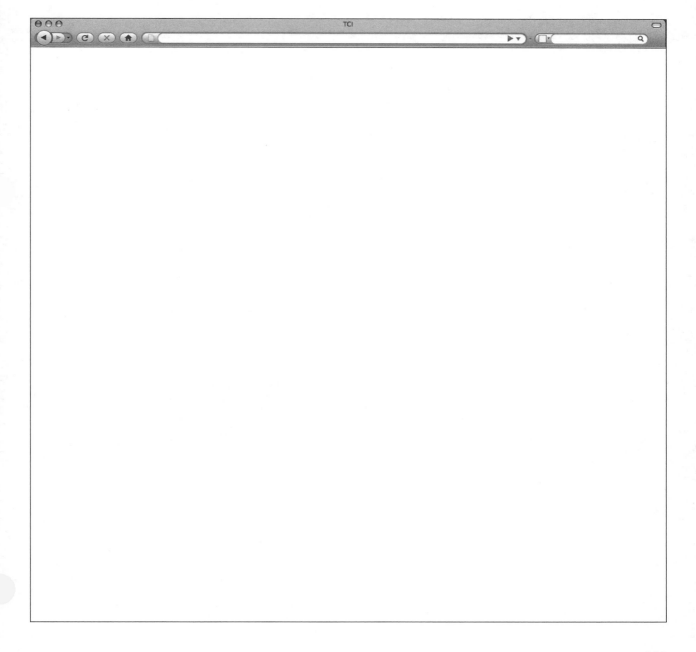

Creating a Column About Roman Expansion

Circle the topic your teacher assigns to your group. Then follow the steps below to create a column that commemorates the period of growth in the Roman Empire.

Rome's Conquest of the Italian Peninsula, 509 to 264 B.C.E.

Overseas Expansion During the Punic Wars, 264 to 146 B.C.E.

Expansion During the Final Years of the Republic, 145 to 44 B.C.E.

Rome Becomes an Empire, 44 B.C.E. to 14 C.E.

_____ **Step 1: Assign roles**. Review the roles and divide them among the members of your group. Make sure everyone understands his or her responsibilities.

Historian: You will lead the group during Step 2 to make sure everyone understands key historical information about your assigned topic.

Editor: You will lead the group during Step 3 to write four appropriate inscriptions for the column.

Sculptor: You will lead the group during Step 4 to make sure appropriate visuals are created to illustrate the inscriptions.

Engineer: You will lead the group during Step 5 to make sure the group works cooperatively to assemble the elements of the column.

_____ **Step 2: Learn about the topic of your column.** Take turns reading aloud the section of Chapter 34 in *History Alive! The Ancient World* that corresponds to your topic. When you finish, the Historian will make sure everyone in the group has completed the Reading Notes (map and column) that correspond to your section.

_____ **Step 3: Write inscriptions for your column.** The Editor will give each group member a blank sheet paper. The paper should then be held vertically, like a column. At the bottom of the paper, each group member will write a simple inscription that describes a key event or development in your assigned period of Roman expansion. For example, an inscription might say, "Rome signs a treaty with Latin tribes in 493 B.C.E." Another example is, "Pax Romana begins under Caesar Augustus." When you are finished, you must have four different inscriptions for your column. The Editor will make sure the inscriptions are written in each person's own words, are historically accurate, and are free of spelling and grammatical errors.

Under the direction of Augustus, the Romans began to rebuild their city.

_____ **Step 4: Illustrate your column.** Above each inscription, each group member will make a sketch to represent the inscription. The Sculptor will verify that the sketches clearly represent the ideas in the inscriptions.

Under the direction of Augustus, the Romans began to rebuild their city.

_____ **Step 5: Assemble your column.** The Engineer will make sure the group works cooperatively to assemble the column. Follow these steps:

- Tape your papers together vertically to create a "column," as shown to the right. The inscriptions should be in chronological order, starting from the bottom of the column.

- Place a copy of *Student Handout 34B: Top of a Roman Column* on top of your column.

- On another sheet of paper, write a title for your column based on your assigned topic. This will be the plaque for your column's base. Attach it, horizontally, at the bottom of your column, as shown to the right.

- Add color and other creative touches to make your column visually appealing.

Top of a Roman Column

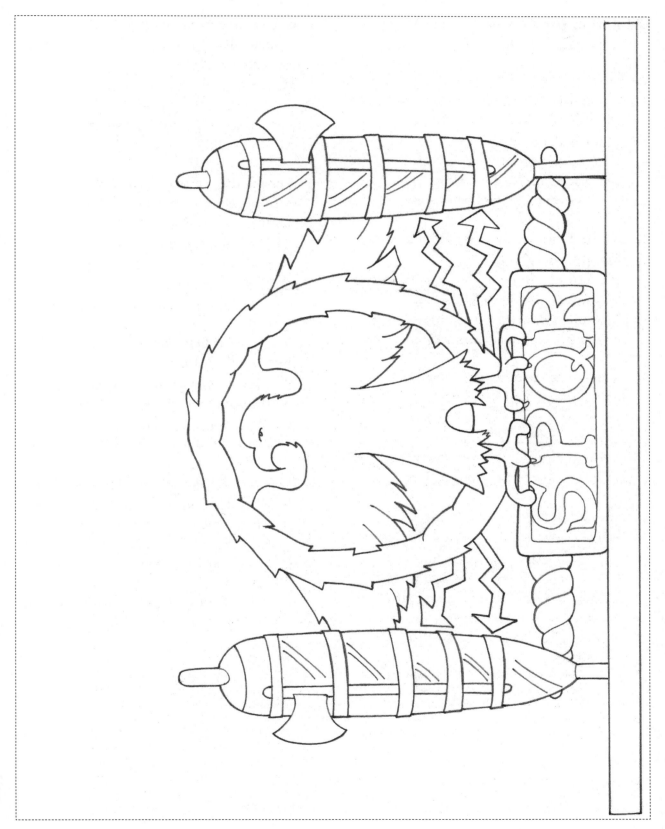

Chapter 34 Assessment

Mastering the Content

Fill in the circle next to the best answer.

1. Which of the following did Rome do during the first period of expansion, before 264 B.C.E.?
   - ○ A. surrender to Etruscans
   - ○ B. conquer most of Europe
   - ○ C. expand into North Africa
   - ○ D. take over the Italian peninsula

2. Why did most of the city of Rome burn down in 390 B.C.E.?
   - ○ A. It was set on fire during a civil war.
   - ○ B. It was attacked by Gauls.
   - ○ C. Romans destroyed it to unite the Latins.
   - ○ D. Hill tribes threw flaming torches into it.

3. What made the dictator Cincinnatus a hero of the Roman Republic?
   - ○ A. He chose to give up his power.
   - ○ B. He built roads from city to city.
   - ○ C. He won the support of the army.
   - ○ D. He conquered neighboring lands.

4. How did Rome's expansion affect the plebeians?
   - ○ A. The plebeians got more land.
   - ○ B. The plebeians got more slaves.
   - ○ C. More plebeians had to serve in the army.
   - ○ D. More plebeians had to establish colonies.

5. A city conquered by Rome might become a Roman ally. What was a **disadvantage** for the conquered city?
   - ○ A. It had to pay Roman taxes.
   - ○ B. Its citizens were taken to Rome.
   - ○ C. Its people became Roman citizens.
   - ○ D. It was allowed to trade with Rome.

6. During the Punic Wars in Rome's second period of expansion, Rome's **main** enemy was
   - ○ A. mainland Greece.
   - ○ B. the Egyptian pharaoh.
   - ○ C. a city-state in North Africa.
   - ○ D. a nomadic tribe in Europe.

7. Which issue first led to war between Rome and Carthage?
   - ○ A. the ability to get wheat from Egypt
   - ○ B. the right to start colonies in Spain
   - ○ C. the use of chariots in warfare
   - ○ D. control of trade in the Mediterranean

8. How did the Romans build a strong navy?
   - ○ A. They drew on ancient Latin traditions.
   - ○ B. They copied ship designs from Carthage.
   - ○ C. They were influenced by Etruscan culture.
   - ○ D. They adopted ideas from Greek settlers in Italy.

9. How did the general Hannibal surprise the Romans?

○ A. He burned their city to the ground.
○ B. He crossed the Alps with elephants.
○ C. He attacked their ships in the harbor.
○ D. He hired spies to pretend to be citizens.

10. Look at the map. Rome gained this territory as a result of

Roman Territory, About 146 B.C.E.

○ A. the Punic Wars.
○ B. conquering the Gauls.
○ C. defeating the Greek navy.
○ D. victory over the Egyptians.

11. How did taking prisoners as slaves lead to unemployment?

○ A. Roman citizens were not allowed to keep slaves.
○ B. People who supported slave revolts lost their jobs.
○ C. Landowners put slaves to work instead of paying free workers.
○ D. Soldiers who captured slaves were released from the army.

12. How did expansion make civil wars larger and more harmful?

○ A. Rome adopted other cultures.
○ B. New technology was invented.
○ C. Romans moved to distant lands.
○ D. Powerful generals led big armies.

13. What was one cause of the end of the Roman Republic?

○ A. Rome built long roads.
○ B. Caesar defeated Pompey.
○ C. Spartacus freed the slaves.
○ D. Rome set up new colonies.

14. The people who murdered Julius Caesar wanted to give power back to the Senate. Instead, their action began

○ A. a civil war.
○ B. an era of trade.
○ C. the Punic Wars.
○ D. Rome's expansion.

15. How did Octavian become Rome's first emperor, Caesar Augustus?

○ A. He was crowned by Julius Caesar.
○ B. He was elected by the people.
○ C. He defeated his rivals in battle.
○ D. He married Cleopatra of Egypt.

16. How did the Praetorian Guard cause problems for the emperors?

○ A. Although they took part in parades, they had few military skills.
○ B. Although its members were farmers, they also liked to fight.
○ C. Although they were stationed in Spain, they sometimes marched into Italy.
○ D. Although their job was to protect the emperor, sometimes they plotted against him.

Applying Social Studies Skills

Use the map and your knowledge of history to complete the sentences.

Roman Territory, 509 B.C.E. to 14 C.E.

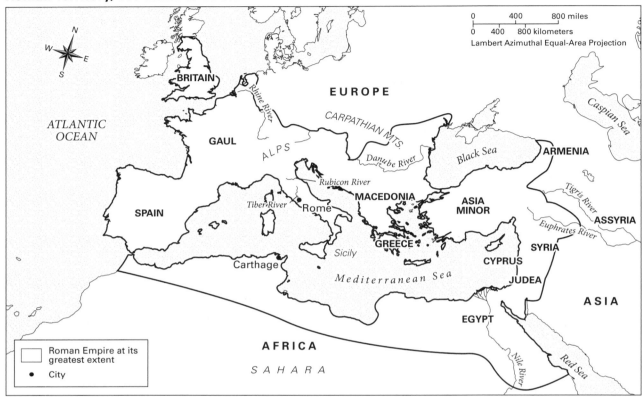

17. A ship carrying goods from Carthage to Greece might stop at the island of

18. Natural barriers limited Roman expansion to the north and south.

    a. A natural barrier to the north was

    b. A natural barrier to the south was

19. Travelers from Rome to Britain might go either by land or by sea.

    a. A land route on Roman roads would cross _____

      and _____.

    b. A sea route would follow the coasts of _____

      and _____.

    c. A trader traveling between Rome and Britain would be more likely to travel

      by _____ because

Exploring the Essential Question

Did the benefits of Roman expansion outweigh the costs?

Follow the directions to complete the item below.

20. For each period of Roman expansion, think of some benefits and costs. Some examples from different periods are listed below. You may think of others.

   - For each period, if you think expansion mostly harmed Romans, on the spectrum mark an X toward the left. If it mostly helped, mark your X toward the right. An X in the middle means you think that the costs and benefits were about the same.

   - Then, write a brief explanation of your rating.

Benefits	Costs
• Exposure to other cultures	• Civil wars
• Good roads	• Farmlands destroyed
• Pax Romana	• Replacement of republic with empire
• Strong central leadership	• Required military service
• Use of many slaves	• Slave revolts
• Wealth	• Unemployment

First period of expansion, 509–264 B.C.E.

High Cost _____|_____High Benefit

Explanation:

Second period of expansion, 264–146 B.C.E.

High Cost _____|_____High Benefit

Explanation:

Third period of expansion, 145–44 B.C.E.

High Cost _____|_____High Benefit

Explanation:

Fourth period of expansion, 44 B.C.E.–14 C.E.

High Cost _____|_____High Benefit

Explanation:

Station A: Law and Order

1. Read Section 35.3 in *History Alive! The Ancient World* and complete the corresponding Reading Notes in your Interactive Student Notebook.

2. Review the following information to learn how a teenager might have experienced law and order in ancient Rome.

> In Rome, if a poor teenager were convicted of a crime, he got a worse punishment than a wealthy teenager did. Punishments depended on a person's status or wealth. During a trial, judges placed each defendant (the person on trial) in one of two categories: *honestiores* or *humiliores*. The humiliores were usually poorer and received harsher punishments. Punishments also varied according to the crime. For example, the punishment for not paying a debt was a fine.
>
> The punishment for a serious crime might be crucifixion (death on a wooden cross), flogging, beheading, or drowning. Humiliores who were sentenced to death often had to fight as a gladiator or against a wild animal, such as a lion or bear, in front of thousands at the Colosseum.

3. On Student Handout 35, use the information you just read to complete the picture of a Roman teenager who has been sentenced to death. Write a caption for your picture that includes the term *Colosseum*.

4. Have your teacher check your work, and then move to another station.

Station B: Religion

1. Read Section 35.4 in *History Alive! The Ancient World* and complete the corresponding Reading Notes in your Interactive Student Notebook.

2. Review the following information to learn how a teenager might have experienced religion in ancient Rome.

> Roman teenagers heard special music at religious ceremonies and festivals. This music was often played on instruments called the *lute* (a guitarlike instrument) and the *lyre* (a harplike instrument). The lyre was a popular instrument in Rome. Often, a large lyre was played in public performances. It was called the *kithara* and is the origin of the word guitar. A double-piped instrument called the *aulos* was also popular.
>
> Some wealthy boys learned to play the lyre. As teenagers, if they played well enough, they could take part in music contests for amateurs. When they performed, they wore flowing robes and a wreath of flowers on their heads.

3. On Student Handout 35, use the information you just read to complete the picture of a Roman teenager playing the lute. Write a caption for your picture that includes the term *religious*.

4. Have your teacher check your work, and then move to another station.

Station C: Family Life

1. Read Section 35.5 in *History Alive! The Ancient World* and complete the corresponding Reading Notes in your Interactive Student Notebook.

2. Review the following information to learn how a teenager might have experienced family life in ancient Rome.

Romans, especially girls, often married when they were teenagers. On their wedding day, Roman teenagers celebrated with their families. In the evening, after the ceremony, there was a great feast at the bride's father's house. Afterward, the new couple would lead a parade of guests, musicians, and torchbearers to the groom's house. There, the bride would put oil on the door and hang ribbon on the doorpost. The groom would then carry her over the threshold (through the front door). This was so the bride would not stumble, which was thought to be unlucky. Once inside the house, the bride was given a lighted torch and water, which represented purity.

3. On Student Handout 35, use the information you just read to complete the picture of Roman newlyweds entering their new home. Write a caption for your picture that includes the term *marriage*.

4. Have your teacher check your work, and then move to another station.

Station D: Food and Drink

1. Read Section 35.6 in *History Alive! The Ancient World* and complete the corresponding Reading Notes in your Interactive Student Notebook.

2. Review the following information to learn how a teenager might have experienced food and drink in ancient Rome.

> The family of a wealthy Roman teenager entertained often at home. Typically, they hosted long, fancy dinner parties with live music. While eating, people reclined on low couches set around the table. They propped themselves up on their elbows and usually ate with their fingers.
>
> A slave brought a bowl of water so the guests could wash their fingers between courses. A banquet menu might include water and honey with a first course of boiled eggs with pine-nut sauce, a main course of boiled flamingo, and roses for dessert.

3. On Student Handout 35, use the information you just read to complete the picture showing Roman teens eating a banquet meal. Write a caption for your picture that includes the term *dinner party*.

4. Have your teacher check your work, and then move to another station.

Station E: Housing

1. Read Section 35.7 in *History Alive! The Ancient World* and complete the corresponding Reading Notes in your Interactive Student Notebook.

2. Review the following information to learn how a teenager might have experienced housing in ancient Rome.

> If a Roman teenager were from a poor family, he or she would likely live in a cramped, dingy apartment building. If the family were especially poor, they lived on the top floor of the building in a small, dark apartment without heat or running water.
>
> There was no garbage collection, either. To get rid of garbage or leftover food in slop bowls, a Roman teenager would likely dump it out the window into the street below.

3. On Student Handout 35, use the information you just read to complete the picture of a Roman teenager getting rid of garbage from her top floor apartment. Write a caption for your picture that includes the term *house*.

4. Have your teacher check your work, and then move to another station.

Station F: Education

1. Read Section 35.8 in *History Alive! The Ancient World* and complete the corresponding Reading Notes in your Interactive Student Notebook.

2. Review the following information to learn how a teenager might have experienced education in ancient Rome.

> Most Romans completed their education by age 12. But, if a Roman teenager wanted to become a politician or lawyer, he would start studying rhetoric, the art of public speaking, when he was 13 or 14. He would study the subject with a special teacher called a *rhetor*. The rhetor taught students how to write speeches. Students wrote them with a pen, called a *stylus,* on a wax-covered board. The stylus was made of reed or bronze. It had a pointed end for writing and a blunt end for erasing mistakes. The rhetor also taught students how to present their speeches. They learned how to speak with passion and how to persuade people with their ideas.
>
> If a teenager were from a very rich family, his parents might even send him to Athens or Rhodes (in Greece) to learn public speaking from the very best Greek teachers.

3. On Student Handout 35, use the information you just read to complete the picture of the Roman teenager writing a political speech. Write a caption for your picture that includes the term *writing*.

4. Have your teacher check your work, and then move to another station.

Station G: Recreation

1. Read Section 35.9 in *History Alive! The Ancient World* and complete the corresponding Reading Notes in your Interactive Student Notebook.

2. Review the following information to learn how a teenager might have experienced recreation in ancient Rome.

> Young Roman men and women spent lots of time chatting, playing games, and bathing at public bathhouses. They bathed separately, but did the same things. Before going into the pools, a teenager would first work up a sweat. To do so, he would exercise (lift weights, play ball, wrestle, or do gymnastics) or sit in a warm, moist room called a *sudarium*. Then, he would head for the *caldarium*—the hottest room of all—to break into a cleansing sweat. Next, he might cool off in the *tepidarium*, a warm room with a small bathing pool.
>
> To get clean, he would rub oil from a small pot into his skin. He would then scrape off the oil, sweat, and dirt with a long, flat blade called a *strigil*. Afterward, he might take a plunge in a cold pool before ending the day with a relaxing massage.

3. On Student Handout 35, use the information you just read to complete the picture of the Roman teenager cleaning with a strigil. Write a caption for your picture that includes the term *bathing*.

4. Have your teacher check your work, and then move to another station.

Station H: Country Life

1. Read Section 35.10 in *History Alive! The Ancient World* and complete the corresponding Reading Notes in your Interactive Student Notebook.

2. Review the following information to learn how a teenager might have experienced country life in ancient Rome.

A wealthy Roman teenager would spend much of the summer at the family's estate, or villa, in the countryside. These splendid country homes were on large plots of land outside the city, but they often provided the comforts of town life. They had gardens, fountains, pools, and maybe even a bathhouse. Sometimes, a wealthy teenager's father might make him spend time in the country farming. Some fathers thought that working hard on the land would make their sons tougher. For pleasure, a wealthy Roman teenager might ride a horse, go hunting, or have a picnic.

On a particularly hot day, he might just cool off and relax by the pool in a large, shady garden at the family's villa.

---

3. On Student Handout 35, use the information you just read to complete the drawing of a wealthy Roman teenager relaxing and cooling off at a villa on a hot summer's day. Write a caption for your picture that includes the term *villa*.

4. Have your teacher check your work, and then move to another station.

Daily Life of a Roman Teenager

Station A: Law and Order

Caption:

Station B: Religion

Caption:

Station C: Family Life

Caption:

Station D: Food and Drink

Caption:

Station E: Housing

Caption:

Station F: Education

Caption:

Station G: Recreation

Caption:

Station H: Country Life

Caption:

Chapter 35 Assessment

Mastering the Content
Fill in the circle next to the best answer.

1. What could a foreign visitor to Rome expect to see in the Forum?
   - ○ A. a track for chariot races
   - ○ B. a central gathering place
   - ○ C. a wealthy country house
   - ○ D. a site of fights with lions

2. What was a common way to become a Roman slave?
   - ○ A. having skill at a craft
   - ○ B. doing poorly in school
   - ○ C. being captured in a war
   - ○ D. losing a political election

3. Why did the Roman emperors give the poor "bread and circuses"?
   - ○ A. so the poor would not rebel
   - ○ B. so the poor could learn to read
   - ○ C. so the poor would not eat meat
   - ○ D. so the poor could make more money

4. What is one example of the rule of law in the Roman Empire?
   - ○ A. The emperor had to obey the Senate.
   - ○ B. Senators carried an ax to protect themselves.
   - ○ C. The punishments were the same for rich and poor.
   - ○ D. Any Roman could accuse someone of a crime.

5. Who made the decisions at Roman trials?
   - ○ A. a jury
   - ○ B. a senator
   - ○ C. the victim
   - ○ D. the emperor

6. Why would a Roman family throw a small cake into the fire?
   - ○ A. They considered burned cakes a treat.
   - ○ B. They did not have enough wood to use as fuel.
   - ○ C. They thought only large cakes were worth eating.
   - ○ D. They were making an offering to the goddess of the hearth.

7. Why did Rome have many different forms of worship?
   - ○ A. There was an altar in each home.
   - ○ B. The emperors claimed to be gods.
   - ○ C. Foreigners brought their religions.
   - ○ D. Festivals were popular with the poor.

8. When did a man become a *paterfamilias*?
   - ○ A. when he got married
   - ○ B. when his own father died
   - ○ C. when he became a grandfather
   - ○ D. when he gave his toys to the gods

9. The poor often ate food that was
   - ○ A. bought at "fast-food" shops.
   - ○ B. prepared for them by slaves.
   - ○ C. cooked in their kitchen at home.
   - ○ D. from a fancy, expensive market.

10. Where would one **most** likely see the foods listed below?
    - mice cooked in honey
    - roasted parrots stuffed with dates
    - salted jellyfish
    - snails dipped in milk
    - ○ A. in a major offering to the gods
    - ○ B. at a poor Roman's breakfast
    - ○ C. at a wealthy Roman's dinner
    - ○ D. in the stands at a chariot race

11. Why was the home of a wealthy Roman unlikely to burn down?
    - ○ A. It had a chimney.
    - ○ B. It did not have kitchen.
    - ○ C. It had small rooms.
    - ○ D. It was built of stone.

12. What was a typical home for a poor Roman city-dweller?
    - ○ A. a villa outside the city walls
    - ○ B. a house made of mud bricks
    - ○ C. a large room with thick walls
    - ○ D. an apartment in a tall building

13. Which of these teens might have been a student in ancient Rome?
    - ○ A. a slave girl training to be a midwife
    - ○ B. a rich boy studying leatherworking
    - ○ C. a 16-year-old girl going to school
    - ○ D. a poor boy studying science

14. Why was fighting a regular event in the Colosseum?
    - ○ A. to protect the city from raids
    - ○ B. to entertain the audience
    - ○ C. to express the anger of the poor
    - ○ D. to decide who should be emperor

15. Why did thousands of Romans go to the Circus Maximus?
    - ○ A. to eat a free meal
    - ○ B. to watch chariot races
    - ○ C. to enjoy the dancing bears
    - ○ D. to shop for everyday clothing

16. What did many wealthy Romans do when the city got hot in the summer?
    - ○ A. covered their skin with fresh mud
    - ○ B. slept in rooms below ground level
    - ○ C. moved to their estates in the country
    - ○ D. limited their diet to bread and milk

Applying Social Studies Skills

Use the letter below and your knowledge of history to complete the sentences.

Pliny (PLIN-ee) the Younger lived from 61/62 to 113 C.E. He wrote this letter after visiting a wealthy friend.

I do not think I have ever spent a more delightful time than during my recent visit to Spurinna's house; indeed I enjoyed myself so much that if it is my fortune to grow old, there is no one whom I should prefer to take as my model in old age . . . For while one is young a little disorder and rush—so to speak—is not unbecoming; but for old folks . . . a [peaceful] and well-ordered life is highly suitable. That is the principle upon which Spurinna acts . . .

In the morning . . . at the second hour [after sunrise] he calls for his shoes and walks three miles, exercising mind as well as body. If he has friends with him, the time is passed in conversation on the noblest of themes, otherwise a book is read aloud . . . Then he sits down, and there is more talk . . . ; afterward he enters his carriage, taking with him either his wife . . . or one of his friends . . .

After riding seven miles he walks another mile, then resumes his seat, or betakes himself to his room and his pen; for he composes, both in Latin and Greek, the most scholarly [poems]. . . Then he plays at ball for a long spell, throwing himself heartily into the game, for it is by means of this kind of active exercise that he battles with old age. . .

After his bath he lies down and waits a little while before taking food . . . The dinner is often relieved by actors of comedy, . . . Even in the summer the meal lasts well into the night, but no one finds it long, for it has kept up with such good humor and charm.

17. Spurinna exercises his body by _____ and _____.
    He exercises his mind by _____ and _____.

18. Guests do not find the dinner too long because

19. Pliny hopes that when he gets old, he can imitate his friend by

Exploring the Essential Question

How did wealth affect daily life in the Roman Empire?

Follow the directions to complete the item below.

20. Write a response to Pliny's letter on the previous page. Your response should include the following:
    - How Spurinna's daily life is affected by his wealth.
    - How Pliny's views about his friend may be affected by Pliny's own wealth or social class.
    - How a poor Roman visiting the same house might feel about at least two of Spurinna's activities.
    - Whether you admire Spurinna's life, and the reasons for your opinion.

Literature of the New Testament: Parables

Parable of the Fig Tree

Jesus told this story: "A man had a fig tree planted in his vineyard. He came looking for some fruit on the tree, but he found none. So the man said to his gardener, 'I have been looking for fruit on this tree for three years, but I never find any. Cut it down. Why should it waste the ground?' But the servant answered, 'Master, let the tree have one more year to produce fruit. Let me dig up the dirt around it and put on some fertilizer. If the tree produces fruit next year, good. But if not, you can cut it down.'"

—Luke 13:6–9, New Century Version Bible

Parable of the Lost Sheep

"Be careful. Don't think these little children are worth nothing. I tell you that they have angels in heaven who are always with my Father in heaven. If a man has a hundred sheep but one of the sheep gets lost, he will leave the other ninety-nine on the hill and go to look for the lost sheep. I tell you the truth, if he finds it he is happier about that one sheep than about the ninety-nine that were never lost. In the same way, your Father in heaven does not want any of these little children to be lost."

—Matthew 18:10–14, New Century Version Bible

Parable of the Rich Fool

Then Jesus told this story: "There was a rich man who had some land, which grew a good crop. He thought to himself, 'What will I do? I have no place to keep all my crops.' Then he said, 'This is what I will do: I will tear down my barns and build bigger ones, and there I will store all my grain and other goods. Then I can say to myself, "I have enough good things stored to last for many years. Rest, eat, drink, and enjoy life!"' But God said to him, 'Foolish man! Tonight your life will be taken from you. So who will get those things you have prepared for yourself?' This is how it will be for those who store up things for themselves and are not rich toward God."

—Luke 12:16–21, New Century Version Bible

Parable of the Tower Builder

"If you want to build a tower, you first sit down and decide how much it will cost, to see if you have enough money to finish the job. If you don't, you might lay the foundation, but you would not be able to finish. Then all who would see it would make fun of you, saying, 'This person began to build but was not able to finish.'"

—Luke 14:28–30, New Century Version Bible

Parable of the Lost Son

In this parable, Jesus tells of a wasteful son. Jesus says that a rich man had two sons. The younger son took his inheritance money and traveled to a faraway land. He spent all his money on friends and parties. The older son stayed home and helped his father work.

Before long, the younger brother ran out of money and all his friends left him. A famine spread throughout the land, and the young son could only find work taking care of pigs. He became so hungry that he wanted to eat the scraps that he fed the pigs. Finally, the young son decided that the servants in his father's house were better off than he was, so he began the long journey back home.

When the younger son returned, his father forgave him and held a great feast to celebrate his return. The older brother was very angry, but the father told him that he must forgive his younger brother and rejoice. They should be thankful because the younger brother had been lost, but now he was found.

—Luke 15:11–32 (Paraphrased)

Parable of the Good Samaritan

A man who was listening to Jesus preaching asked Jesus, "Who is my neighbor?" Jesus answered by telling a story about a man who was on his way from Jerusalem to Jericho. Robbers attacked him. They tore off his clothes, beat him, and left him to die by the side of the road.

Two local people passed by and saw the man, but they did not stop to help him. Then a Samaritan, who was a stranger, came along. When he saw the man, he felt sorry for him. He took care of the injured man, put him on his donkey, and took him to an inn to rest. The Samaritan paid for everything.

When Jesus finished the parable, he asked, "Which of the three men was a neighbor?" Jesus's listener responded, "The one who showed him mercy." Jesus said, "Go and do likewise."

—Luke 10:25–37 (Paraphrased)

Analyzing Parables as Literature

Follow the steps below to analyze Jesus's parables.

For each parable:

- List the characters.
- Summarize the plot.
- Explain the moral lesson you think Jesus was trying to teach.

Parable	Characters	Plot	Moral Lesson
Parable of the Fig Tree			
Parable of the Lost Sheep			
Parable of the Rich Fool			
Parable of the Tower Builder			
Parable of the Lost Son			
Parable of the Good Samaritan			

Chapter 36 Assessment

Mastering the Content

Fill in the circle next to the best answer.

1. Why did the Jews distrust King Herod?
   - ○ A. He believed in many gods.
   - ○ B. He persecuted their followers.
   - ○ C. He was controlled by the Romans.
   - ○ D. He rebuilt the Temple of Jerusalem.

2. What did many Jews hope that a Messiah would do?
   - ○ A. free them from a foreign power
   - ○ B. attract other people to their faith
   - ○ C. teach people how to live in peace
   - ○ D. warn them of the end of the world

3. What is the main source of early information about the life of Jesus?
   - ○ A. the Latin writings of Roman historians
   - ○ B. Egyptian scrolls found near the Dead Sea
   - ○ C. Gospels written in Greek by his followers
   - ○ D. scribes who recorded his deeds in Hebrew

4. Jesus probably grew up in the family of
   - ○ A. a carpenter in Nazareth.
   - ○ B. a shoemaker in Jerusalem.
   - ○ C. an innkeeper in Bethlehem.
   - ○ D. a fisherman by the Sea of Galilee.

5. According to the New Testament, which event introduced Jesus's years of public preaching?
   - ○ A. One of the disciples asked him a question.
   - ○ B. John the Baptist identified him as the Messiah.
   - ○ C. The rabbis in Jerusalem asked him to teach them.
   - ○ D. King Herod passed a harsh law that made him angry.

6. Why did Jesus preach mostly outdoors?
   - ○ A. He taught his followers to respect nature.
   - ○ B. His disciples were too shabby to go inside.
   - ○ C. The Romans would not let him preach indoors.
   - ○ D. The crowds were too big to fit in the buildings.

7. According to the earliest written accounts, what did Jesus emphasize in his teachings?
   - ○ A. love
   - ○ B. justice
   - ○ C. revenge
   - ○ D. obedience

8. According to Jesus, what would the kingdom of God be like?
   - ○ A. The Roman Empire would end.
   - ○ B. A new emperor would be crowned.
   - ○ C. People would destroy the old temples.
   - ○ D. People would live according to God's will.

9. One example of a parable is a story about
   ○ A. Jesus rising from the dead.
   ○ B. the birth of a baby in a stable.
   ○ C. Paul telling others about Jesus.
   ○ D. a traveler helping an injured man.

10. According to the New Testament, why did Jesus go to Jerusalem a few days before his execution?
   ○ A. to pray in a beautiful garden
   ○ B. to give out food to his followers
   ○ C. to celebrate the festival of Passover
   ○ D. to drive the Romans from the city

11. The New Testament tells that the rulers of Jerusalem had Jesus arrested because they
   ○ A. wanted to conquer the Jews.
   ○ B. feared he might lead a revolt.
   ○ C. had told him to stay in Galilee.
   ○ D. said he should worship the emperor.

12. How was Paul important to the early development of Christianity?
   ○ A. He asked converts to come and visit him.
   ○ B. He spread Christianity to people who were not Jews.
   ○ C. He preached Christianity in the Temple in Jerusalem.
   ○ D. He led the disciples who traveled with Jesus.

13. How did Paul continue to have influence while in jail?
   ○ A. by writing letters
   ○ B. by persecuting Christians
   ○ C. by converting fellow prisoners
   ○ D. by preaching through the window

14. What was one result of the actions listed below?

   ┌───┐
   │ **Actions Taken by Christians**   │
   │   │
   │ did not worship Roman gods   │
   │ did not want great wealth   │
   │ did not believe the emperor was a god   │
   │ did not serve in the army   │
   └───┘

   ○ A. Jesus was crucified.
   ○ B. Paul became a Christian.
   ○ C. Christians were persecuted.
   ○ D. Constantine freed Roman slaves.

15. Which teaching helped to spread Christianity in the Roman Empire?
   ○ A. Believers would not feel pain or hunger.
   ○ B. Citizens had the right to overthrow evil rulers.
   ○ C. People could sacrifice to any gods they wanted.
   ○ D. Slaves and the poor could hope for a better life after death.

16. How did Emperor Constantine affect the spread of Christianity?
   ○ A. He banned Christianity from Judea.
   ○ B. He freed Christians to worship openly.
   ○ C. He ordered Christians to be killed by wild animals.
   ○ D. He made Christianity the official religion of Rome.

Applying Social Studies Skills

Use the timelines and your knowledge of history to complete the sentences.

Rome

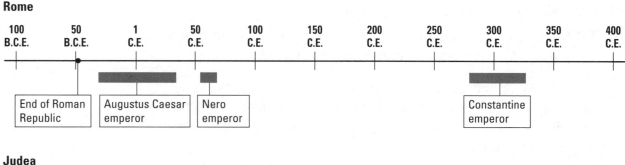

Judea

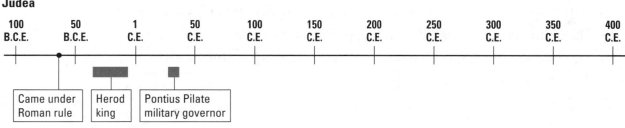

Christianity

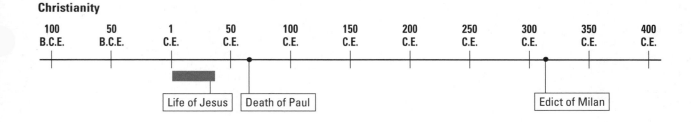

17. Jesus was born when the Roman emperor was _____ .

   and the local ruler of Judea was _____ .

18. When Judea came under Roman rule, the form of government in Rome was

19. A difference in policy toward Christians between the emperors Nero and
   Constantine can be seen in the contrast between which two events on
   the timeline?

   •

   •

   This contrast shows a policy change in the direction of

Exploring the Essential Question

How did Christianity originate and spread?

Follow the directions to complete the item below.

20. Christianity spread in the Roman Empire in spite of, and partly because of, how Roman officials treated Christians for many years.

    Write a dialogue between two Romans who have just witnessed the death of a Christian for his or her beliefs. The two Romans should have different reactions to the event. In the words of your characters, your dialogue should include:

    - a description of what happened, with supporting details and precise words.
    - the opinions of one character who approves of the government's action.
    - the opinions of another character who admires or sympathizes with the Christian.

Chapter 37 Assessment

Mastering the Content

Fill in the circle next to the best answer.

1. What do Christians around the world have in common?
    ○ A. the form of worship
    ○ B. the teachings of Jesus
    ○ C. the style of church building
    ○ D. the *Book of Common Prayer*

2. What do Christians mean by "the Holy Trinity"?
    ○ A. the period leading up to Easter
    ○ B. Joseph, Mary, and the baby Jesus
    ○ C. the church on different continents
    ○ D. three beings that make up one God

3. Christian art often uses a dove as a symbol for God's power at work in the world today. What do Christians call this power?
    ○ A. the Bible
    ○ B. Jesus Christ
    ○ C. the Holy Spirit
    ○ D. God the Father

4. *Salvation* means "saving." Christians believe that faith in Jesus can save them from
    ○ A. sin.
    ○ B. pain.
    ○ C. sorrow.
    ○ D. poverty.

5. A *schism* is a division or separation. Who were divided by the Great Schism of 1054?
    ○ A. Greece and Russia
    ○ B. Catholics and Protestants
    ○ C. the pope and the emperor
    ○ D. eastern and western churches

6. What is the job of a patriarch?
    ○ A. to assist the pope in Rome
    ○ B. to plan the Christian calendar
    ○ C. to head an Eastern Orthodox church
    ○ D. to start a new Protestant denomination

7. Why did Martin Luther get in trouble with the Roman Catholic Church?
    ○ A. He refused to stop calling for reforms.
    ○ B. He studied the religions of Africa and Asia.
    ○ C. He insisted that Earth travels around the sun.
    ○ D. He asked Church leaders to move to Germany.

8. Which of these is an example of a Christian *denomination*?
    ○ A. Jews
    ○ B. Hindus
    ○ C. Baptists
    ○ D. Buddhists

9. On which point about baptism do Christian churches differ?
   - ○ A. the idea that it is a sacrament
   - ○ B. the age when it should happen
   - ○ C. whether it should involve water
   - ○ D. whether it makes one a Christian

10. Which event in the life of Jesus is remembered in Holy Communion?
    - ○ A. the Last Supper
    - ○ B. the Resurrection
    - ○ C. his baptism
    - ○ D. his birth in a stable

11. Where do most Christian churches meet for worship?
    - ○ A. in the streets of the city
    - ○ B. in the homes of members
    - ○ C. in beautiful places outdoors
    - ○ D. in buildings made for the purpose

12. Which image is the **most** widely recognized symbol of Christianity?
    - ○ A.
    - ○ B.
    - ○ C.
    - ○ D.

13. What Christian belief explains why most Christian churches meet on Sunday?
    - ○ A. Jesus was baptized on a Sunday.
    - ○ B. Businesses should close on Sunday.
    - ○ C. Jesus rose from the dead on Sunday.
    - ○ D. The Old Testament specifies Sunday.

14. Christians sing special songs called *carols* at Christmas. Most Christmas carols tell parts of a story about the
    - ○ A. birth of Jesus in Bethlehem.
    - ○ B. persecution of Christians in Rome.
    - ○ C. way Jesus appeared to the disciples.
    - ○ D. formation of the first Christian church.

15. How do many Christians observe the 40 days before Easter?
    - ○ A. by going out into the wilderness
    - ○ B. by giving up something they like
    - ○ C. by watching children act in plays
    - ○ D. by giving presents to one another

16. Why are palm leaves often part of Christian services on the Sunday before Easter?
    - ○ A. Palm trees grow on almost every continent.
    - ○ B. Palms are a traditional symbol for eternal life.
    - ○ C. The Messiah was said to be anointed with palm oil.
    - ○ D. Crowds welcomed Jesus to Jerusalem with palm branches.

Applying Social Studies Skills

Use the graph and your knowledge of history to complete the sentences or answer the questions.

Largest Christian Denominations in the United States

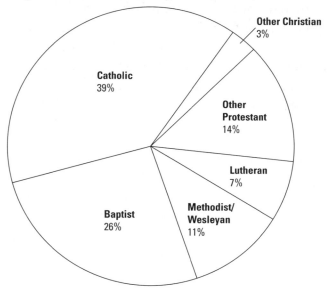

17. The largest Protestant group shown on the graph is

18. The earliest Protestant denomination was begun by Martin Luther and is named for him. Today, that denomination makes up about _____ percent of American Christians.

19. The graph shows only Christians, not Americans of other religions or Americans who do not practice a religion. If a new pie graph were made to include all Americans, the percentage shown as Catholic would be (circle one):

    less than 39%   the same 39%   more than 39%

Exploring the Essential Question

How are Christians' lives shaped by the beliefs and practices of Christianity?

Follow the directions to complete the item below.

20. The word *church* has three different meanings for Christians. In each box below, write a paragraph of two to four sentences correctly using the meaning of the word *church*. Each paragraph should reflect information you have learned in this chapter about Christian beliefs and practices.

Church: a group of religious believers

Church: a building used for religious services

Church: an organized branch of a religion

The "Rome to Home" Game

Follow the steps below to play "Rome to Home." The winning team is the one with the most points after Round 4.

Round 1 Art

Step 1: Read Section 38.3, and complete the corresponding part of your Reading Notes.

Step 2: In three minutes, identify in your magazines modern examples—such as sculptures and mosaics—that show the influence of Roman art on modern life. Put sticky notes on the pages where you find examples.

Step 3: List the five unique examples you identified. You will score 1 point for every example that only your group identifies.

Step 4: Presenters from each group will share their answers. After each Presenter shares, those groups that identified the same example must cross it off their lists.

Step 5: Count the examples you have not crossed off your list. Make sure you are awarded the appropriate number of points.

Round 2 Architecture and Engineering

Step 1: Read Section 38.4, and complete the corresponding Reading Notes.

Step 2: In three minutes, identify in your magazines modern examples—such as domes and stadiums—that show the influence of Roman architecture and engineering on modern life. Put sticky notes on the pages where you find examples.

Step 3: List the five unique examples you identified. You will score 1 point for every example that only your group identifies.

Step 4: Presenters from each group will share their answers. After each Presenter shares, those groups that identified the same example must cross it off their lists.

Step 5: Count the examples you have not crossed off your list. Make sure you are awarded the appropriate number of points.

Round 3 Language

Step 1: Read Section 38.5, and complete the corresponding part of your Reading Notes.

Step 2: In three minutes, identify in your magazines words that have Latin prefixes or roots, such as words starting with *pre-* or *re-,* and examples of Roman numerals. Put sticky notes on the pages where you find examples.

Step 3: List the five unique words or Roman numerals you identified. You will score 1 point for every example that only your group identifies.

Step 4: Presenters from each group will share their answers. After each Presenter shares, those groups that identified the same word must cross it off their lists.

Step 5: Count the words you have not crossed off your list. Make sure you are awarded the appropriate number of points.

Round 4 Philosophy and Law

Step 1: Read Section 38.6, and complete the corresponding part of your Reading Notes.

Step 2: In three minutes, identify in your magazines modern examples that show the influence of Roman philosophy and law on modern life. The examples should emphasize good character and justice. Put sticky notes on the pages where you find examples.

Step 3: List the five unique examples you identified. You will score 1 point for every example that only your group identifies.

Step 4: Presenters from each group will share their answers. After each Presenter shares, those groups that identified the same example must cross it off of their lists.

Step 5: Count the examples you have not crossed off your list. Make sure you are awarded the appropriate number of points.

Chapter 38 Assessment

Mastering the Content

Fill in the circle next to the best answer.

1. Why was the Roman Empire hard to defend?
   - ○ A. It had a very long border.
   - ○ B. It lacked harbors for ships.
   - ○ C. Its population was very small.
   - ○ D. Its rulers were unwilling to fight.

2. What happened in 476 C.E., often considered to mark the fall of Rome?
   - ○ A. Rome surrendered to Persian invaders.
   - ○ B. The last emperor in Rome was removed.
   - ○ C. Rome ceased to be a republic.
   - ○ D. Carthage defeated Rome.

3. What became of the eastern empire after 476 C.E.?
   - ○ A. It was conquered by nomads.
   - ○ B. It lasted another thousand years.
   - ○ C. It fell apart under local warlords.
   - ○ D. It shared the same fate as the west.

4. Which of the following was a **main** weakness that led to the fall of Rome?
   - ○ A. The Romans never developed a good way to transfer ruling power.
   - ○ B. The emperor was too far away from Rome to rule well.
   - ○ C. The plebeians did not understand how to make new laws.
   - ○ D. Romulus Augustus was allowed to have a private army.

5. How did patrons support the arts?
   - ○ A. They sold the art.
   - ○ B. They made the art.
   - ○ C. They paid the artists.
   - ○ D. They trained the artists.

6. What is the **most** likely reason why Americans made statues of George Washington in the Roman style?
   - ○ A. to give Washington nobility
   - ○ B. to give Washington godlike status
   - ○ C. to identify Washington as a general
   - ○ D. to identify Washington as an emperor

7. Which kind of art did Romans wear as jewelry?
   - ○ A. fresco
   - ○ B. cameo
   - ○ C. mosaic
   - ○ D. clay

8. What was the name of the cultural flowering in Europe based on Greek and Roman ideas?
   - ○ A. New Age
   - ○ B. Dark Age
   - ○ C. Renaissance
   - ○ D. Enlightenment

9. How were the Romans able to build bigger arches than anyone before them?
   - ○ A. by placing domes on top of their vaults
   - ○ B. by capturing skilled builders to work as slaves
   - ○ C. by designing outdoor stadiums for sports events
   - ○ D. by mixing stone and sand with cement to make concrete

10. Which statement is true of Rome's roads, bridges, and aqueducts?
  ○ A. They were usually made of wood.
  ○ B. They were weak and fell apart quickly.
  ○ C. They were copied from those of the Greeks.
  ○ D. They were the greatest in the ancient world.

11. Look at the chart below. Which is another word in the list that uses the Latin prefix meaning "eight"?
  ○ A. sextet
  ○ B. octagon
  ○ C. novice
  ○ D. decimal

English Word	Latin Meaning
September	seventh month
October	eighth month
November	ninth month
December	tenth month

12. Which modern languages developed from Latin?
  ○ A. Greek and Turkish
  ○ B. Dutch and German
  ○ C. Polish and Russian
  ○ D. Spanish and French

13. The Roman numeral I means 1, V means 5, and X means 10. What is this number? XVII
  ○ A. 6
  ○ B. 12
  ○ C. 17
  ○ D. 25

14. Which quality would a Stoic consider **most** important?
  ○ A. love
  ○ B. anger
  ○ C. pleasure
  ○ D. dignity

15. Which Roman ideal of justice is based on natural law?
  ○ A. All people are wise.
  ○ B. The ruler knows best.
  ○ C. All people have rights.
  ○ D. The strongest should rule.

Applying Social Studies Skills

Use the map and your knowledge of history to complete the sentences.

The Remains of the Roman Empire, About 500 C.E.

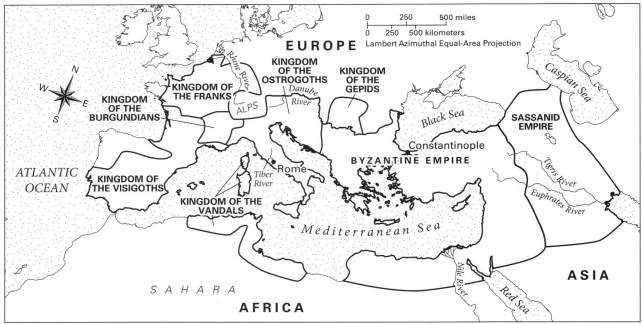

16. In the time period covered by this map, the Germanic tribe that ruled the Italian peninsula was the

17. Emperor Constantine named his capital city for himself. By 500 C. E. it was the capital of the

18. The word *vandalism* comes from the Vandals, a Germanic tribe whose raids involved destruction of property. By 500 C.E., they ruled islands in the _____ and territory on the continent of _____.

19. Only one of the Germanic tribes established a kingdom that grew and survived into modern times, as the nation called France. Its name reflects its origins. In 500 C.E. it was the Kingdom of the

Exploring the Essential Question

To what extent does ancient Rome influence us today?

Follow the directions to complete the item below.

20. Which Roman influence do you think is most important? Write a number beside each item below to rank them in order of importance to you, from 1 to 6. (The 1 means "most important," and the 6 means "least important.")

_____ Roman influence on architecture

_____ Roman influence on art

_____ Roman influence on engineering

_____ Roman influence on language

_____ Roman influence on philosophy

_____ Roman influence on law

Next, complete each item below for the three influences that you ranked the highest.

1. Most important influence: the Roman influence on _____
   a. What is an example of this influence?

   b. Why did you rank it as most important?

2. Second most important influence: the Roman influence on _____
   a. What is an example of this influence?

   b. Why did you rank it as second most important?

3. Third most important influence: the Roman influence on _____
   a. What is an example of this influence?

   b. Why did you rank it as third most important?

Unit 6 Timeline Challenge Cards

Rome Founded
About 753 B.C.E.

The Latins found the city of Rome in central Italy. Myth claims that Romulus and Remus begin the settlement.

Roman Republic Formed
About 509 B.C.E.

Roman patricians create a republic, in which elected officials govern the people.

Plebeians Rebel
494–287 B.C.E.

The government of the Roman Republic becomes more democratic as laws are written that protect plebeians' rights.

Roman Conquest of Italy
509–264 B.C.E.

Romans fight Latin neighbors and Etruscans to win control of the Italian peninsula.

Unit 6 Timeline Challenge Cards

First Roman Road
312 B.C.E.

The Roman military builds the Appian Way, first of the Roman roads. About 50,000 miles of paved roads are built by the Romans, setting the standard of road building for the next 2,000 years.

Punic Wars
264–146 B.C.E

In a series of three wars, Rome defeats Carthage to become the greatest power in the Mediterranean region.

Julius Caesar Named Dictator
49 B.C.E.

Julius Caesar becomes dictator of Rome, institutes reforms, and grants citizenship to Gaul and Spain.

Reign of Emperor Augustus
31 B.C.E.–14 C.E

After Caesar's death in 44 B.C.E., Augustus begins the Roman Empire and expands its boundaries during the Pax Romana.

Unit 6 Timeline Challenge Cards

Life of Jesus
About 6 B.C.E.–30 C.E.

Jesus and his teachings lay the foundations of Christianity.

Missionary Work of Paul
About 47 C.E.

Paul begins his missionary work, traveling throughout the Greek-speaking world and spreading Christianity.

Edict of Milan
313 C.E.

Emperor Constantine gives Christians the freedom to practice their religion openly. By 395 C.E., Christianity becomes the official religion of the Roman Empire.

Fall of Western Roman Empire
476 C.E.

The western part of the Roman Empire falls. The eastern part of the empire continues as the Byzantine Empire.

TCI's mission is to empower educators to help all learners succeed in the diverse classroom. Recognizing that some students may benefit from extra support, the following writing, reading, critical thinking skills, and map skills toolkits provide information and practice exercises to build student competence and confidence in these areas. Handouts with samples and graphic organizer templates will guide students in applying their skills for success in all their studies.

To the Teacher

Essay writing is an essential skill for success in school. This Writing Toolkit provides basic tools for supporting students who need help writing a five-paragraph expository or persuasive essay. It includes the following:

- graphic organizers for planning five-paragraph essays
- a sample persuasive essay
- instructional pages on the parts of a five-paragraph essay
- an overview of the writing process
- instructional pages on the writing process
- an essay scoring rubric

Using the Graphic Organizer to Improve Student Writing

Graphic organizers are useful for generating, organizing, and evaluating ideas at various stages of the writing process. The graphic organizers in this Toolkit are easy-to-follow templates that can be applied to a variety of expository and persuasive writing assignments. The organizers follow the standard five-paragraph essay format—introduction, three body paragraphs, and conclusion—and contain prompts to remind students of the essential elements of each type of essay.

Tips for Teaching Students to Use the Graphic Organizer

- On a blank transparency, demonstrate how to construct the graphic organizer while students draw and label one in their notebooks. Discuss each part of an essay.
- Use color to help students differentiate between the parts of an essay. Project a transparency of the graphic organizer and circle or highlight each part of the essay using a different color. Suggest that when drafting their essays, students might want to write or highlight the various parts of the essay in different colors.
- Remind students that they can use a graphic organizer at any stage of the writing process. They should not worry about filling it in with polished prose or even complete sentences.
- Have students identify the type of essay in this toolkit. As needed, remind students that letters to the editor are persuasive. Review writing purposes, including the differences between writing that explains and writing that persuades.
- Project or hand out the sample essay to pairs of students. Have students use the essay to complete the Organizer for a Five-Paragraph Essay That Persuades.

Organizer for a Five-Paragraph Essay That Explains

Topic:

Paragraph 1 Introduction	Thesis statement:
Paragraph 2 Body	Topic sentence/Main idea 1: Support (Evidence/Explanation):
Paragraph 3 Body	Topic sentence/Main idea 2: Support (Evidence/Explanation):
Paragraph 4 Body	Topic sentence/Main idea 3: Support (Evidence/Explanation):
Paragraph 5 Conclusion	Summary:

Organizer for a Five-Paragraph Essay That Persuades

Topic:

Paragraph 1 Introduction	Thesis statement or Opinion:
Paragraph 2 Body	Topic sentence/Reason 1: Support (Evidence/Explanation):
Paragraph 3 Body	Topic sentence/Reason 2: Support (Evidence/Explanation):
Paragraph 4 Body	Topic sentence/Reason 3: Support (Evidence/Explanation):
Paragraph 5 Conclusion	Call to Action:

Sample Five-Paragraph Essay

JOIN THE MICROLENDING CLUB

What would your life be like if you had to live on less than two dollars a day? Two years ago, that's all that Ameena Iqbal earned. On that money, she had to feed, clothe, and shelter herself and three children in a small village in Bangladesh. Luckily, Iqbal had a talent and a dream. She could sew, and she dreamed of having a sewing machine. Her dream came true when a microlending club in Lewiston, North Carolina, lent her $200. That sum covered the cost of buying a sewing machine and renting space in a small shop with electricity. With that loan, Iqbal and her children were on their way out of poverty. Would you like to help people like Ameena Iqbal in leaving poverty behind? You can! Just join the Willow Glen Middle School Microlending Club.

You should join the Willow Glen Microlending Club because we help poor people around the world. Here's how it works. We raise money to lend. The money goes into a fund managed by an investment company. The money manager makes loans to poor people in other countries. Most of them are women who want to start or improve small businesses. The women get the money, along with a schedule for repaying it slowly over time. As the money is repaid, it goes back into the fund, little by little, with interest. Then our club uses the same money, plus other money we raise, to help more people. So far our club has helped six people, including a woman in India who started a bakery and a woman in Bolivia who improved her weaving business. In both these cases, the women's lives have changed completely. They have gone from barely being able to feed their children to paying their bills and making small improvements in their lives. Perhaps best of all, their children have a better chance in life as a result.

Some people aren't sure they want to join our club because they have to fundraise. Don't let that stop you! The fundraising part of our work is easy. We sell a terrific product: rain barrels. The rain barrels collect rain, and people use them in their yards and gardens. Rain barrels are a great way to cut down on outdoor water use. We actually help our environment at the same time that we help people around the world. Best of all, the rain barrels just about sell themselves. People see what a good idea they are, as well as what a good cause they support. After some of our members sold two rain barrels on Alameda Street, they got three orders for barrels from neighbors on the same street just by word of mouth. People in our town want these barrels.

Another reason to join our club is that it's fun to be a member. We work in teams or small groups to sell the rain barrels. No one has to do the work alone, and you get to know people as you earn money for the club. Also, every time we make a loan, we have a small party to celebrate. That helps you make new friends in the club at the same time that you help poor people around the globe. The best part of all is seeing pictures of the people we help. You have no idea how good it can feel to see a picture of a small bakery in India that your efforts helped to start!

If you want to help others and have fun, too, come to the next meeting of the Microlending Club. We meet in Room 216 on Wednesday right after school. Find out why our club already has 26 members and is growing bigger every month. Find out how easy it is to be a member. Most of all, find out how you can start helping to make the world a better place.

Camila Suarez, President
Jaquon Washington, Treasurer

Developing a Thesis Statement

Developing a Thesis Statement for Writing That Explains

When you write to explain, your **thesis statement** should summarize the central idea of your entire essay. A thesis statement is usually one sentence. It often appears at the end of your introduction.

You can develop a thesis statement before you begin drafting or afterward. For example, you may be asked to explain why a period of time is called a golden age. You come up with these reasons: (1) There was peace; (2) There was prosperity; (3) Many great accomplishments were made in the arts and sciences. You might then put your reasons together to write your thesis: This period was known as the golden age because it was a time of peace and prosperity, and many great accomplishments were made in the arts and sciences.

Here are some suggestions to help you develop a thesis statement for writing that explains:

- If the essay assignment asks a question, make your answer the thesis statement.
- Take some notes on the essay topic before developing your thesis statement.
- Be sure that your thesis statement presents an overview of what you will say in your body paragraphs.

Developing a Thesis Statement for Writing That Persuades

In a persuasive essay, your purpose is to convince the reader to agree with your thesis. To develop a thesis, consider your topic carefully: what do you think about it and why? You might need to do some research, since forming an opinion on an issue or topic requires that you know something about it. Your thesis statement should clearly state the position you plan to argue.

Here are some suggestions to help you develop a thesis statement for writing that persuades:

- Take some notes on the issue before developing your thesis statement.
- Avoid stating a fact as a thesis. Your thesis should be a judgment you make about an issue.
- Avoid making an all-or-nothing or exaggerated claim that is difficult to support. Use qualifying words such as *almost, often, rarely, usually,* or *most.*

Writing the Introduction

The **introduction,** or opening paragraph, prepares the audience for reading your essay. It "hooks" the reader's interest, gives background information on the issue or topic you plan to discuss, and presents your **thesis statement** or opinion statement.

The introduction is your chance to get the reader's attention. The way you do this depends on your purpose for writing. For a persuasive essay or editorial, consider these possibilities:

- a quotation
- a brief story
- a striking statistic
- a question
- an interesting or shocking fact

This first sentence creates interest by asking a question and using a striking statistic.

> What would your life be like if you had to live on less than two dollars a day? Two years ago, that's all that Ameena Iqbal earned. On that money, she had to feed, clothe, and shelter herself and three children in a small village in Bangladesh. Luckily, Iqbal had a talent and a dream. She could sew, and she dreamed of having a sewing machine. Her dream came true when a microlending club in Lewiston, North Carolina, lent her $200. That sum covered the cost of buying a sewing machine and renting space in a small shop with electricity. With that loan, Iqbal and her children were on their way out of poverty. Would you like to help people like Ameena Iqbal in leaving poverty behind? You can! Just join the Willow Glen Middle School Microlending Club.

The **thesis** (or **opinion statement**) states your opinion.

Use this checklist when writing your introduction:
- Does my introduction create interest in the topic of my essay?
- Does my introduction summarize the arguments I plan to make?
- Does my introduction contain a clear statement of my thesis?

Writing Body Paragraphs

Use the body of your essay to support your thesis. In an essay that explains, each body paragraph presents a main idea that supports the thesis, as well as explanation and evidence. In a persuasive essay, each body paragraph gives a reason to support your proposition or opinion and explains and supports it.

The key elements of a body paragraph are the **topic sentence** and **support**. Support takes two main forms. The first form is **evidence,** such as facts, statistics, examples, or quotations that back up your thesis or help prove your proposition. The second form of support is **explanation,** statements that make your main ideas and evidence more understandable to your audience.

> The **topic sentence** states the main idea or argument.

> **Explanation** helps the audience understand how the club works.

> **Evidence** tells whom the club has already helped and how the club has helped them.

You should join the Willow Glen Microlending Club because we help poor people around the world. Here's how it works. We raise money to lend. The money goes into a fund managed by an investment company. The money manager makes loans to poor people in other countries. Most of them are women who want to start or improve small businesses. The women get the money, along with a schedule for repaying it slowly over time. As the money is repaid, it goes back into the fund, little by little, with interest! Then our club uses the same money, plus other money we raise, to help more people. So far our club has helped six people, including a woman in India who started a bakery and a woman in Bolivia who improved her weaving business. In both these cases, the women's lives have changed completely. They have gone from barely being able to feed their children to paying their bills and making small improvements in their lives. Perhaps best of all, their children have a better chance in life as a result.

Use this checklist when writing the body of your essay:
- Does each body paragraph include a topic sentence and support?
- Does each body paragraph focus on one main idea (if you are explaining) or one reason (if you are persuading)?
- Does each topic sentence relate clearly to the thesis statement?
- Do you fully explain all your ideas so that the audience can follow them?

Writing a Topic Sentence

The **topic sentence** states the main idea of a paragraph. A good topic sentence is clear and provides an overview of the sentences that will follow in the paragraph.

The topic sentence is usually, but not always, the first sentence of a paragraph. In a paragraph that explains, the topic sentence states a main idea. In a paragraph that persuades, the topic sentence states a reason.

> Some people aren't sure they want to join our club because they have to fundraise. Don't let that stop you! The fundraising part of our work is easy. We sell a terrific product: rain barrels. The rain barrels collect rain, and people use them in their yards and gardens. Rain barrels are a great way to cut down on outdoor water use. We actually help our environment at the same time that we help people around the world. Best of all, the rain barrels just about sell themselves. People see what a good idea they are, as well as what a good cause they support. After some of our members sold two rain barrels on Alameda Street, they got three orders for barrels from neighbors on the same street just by word of mouth. People in our town want these barrels.

The **topic sentence** states a reason why students should join the club.

The supporting sentences tell how the club fundraises and why the fundraising is easy.

Use this checklist when writing your topic sentences:
- If I am writing to explain, does my topic sentence state the main idea of the paragraph?
- If I am writing to persuade, does my topic sentence state a reason that supports my thesis, or opinion?

Developing Body Paragraphs: Supporting Evidence

Always support your ideas. In each body paragraph, you must present **evidence** to support each of your topic sentences and, therefore, your main point. Your evidence may include facts, statistics, examples, and quotations from various sources. In persuasive writing, you might also include stories, eyewitness accounts, or personal accounts. The following types of evidence appear in the letter to the editor about joining the microlending club:

Fact: The money goes into a fund managed by an investment company.

Statistic: So far our club has helped six people.

Examples: . . . a woman in India who started a bakery business and a woman in Bolivia who improved her weaving business.

Personal account: After some of our members sold two rain barrels on Alameda Street, they got three orders for barrels from neighbors on the same street just by word of mouth.

Use this checklist when presenting your supporting evidence:
- Do I provide evidence to support each topic sentence?
- Is my supporting evidence clear? If I am writing to persuade, is my supporting evidence convincing?

Developing Body Paragraphs: Explanation

Always explain your ideas. You are writing for an audience that probably does not know everything you know about your topic. Even if your readers do know something about the topic, they may not understand every statement you make about it. Furthermore, no matter how good your support is, it will usually be better if you explain it.

In the paragraph below, suppose the writer simply said, "It's fun to be a member." Why should the audience believe it? Why wouldn't the audience ask, "What kind of fun do you have?" By giving explanations, the writer anticipates what the audience will want to know.

> Another reason to join our club is that it's fun to be a member. We work in teams or small groups to sell the rain barrels. No one has to do the work alone, and you get to know people as you earn money for the club. Also, every time we make a loan, we have a small party to celebrate. That helps you make new friends in the club at the same time that you help poor people around the globe. The best part of all is seeing pictures of the people we help. You have no idea how good it can feel to see a picture of a small bakery in India that your efforts helped to start!

In a persuasive essay, you can also explain by considering the reader's objections and addressing them. In the paragraph below, notice how the writer considers and then addresses an objection a reader might raise: that fundraising is hard.

> Some people aren't sure they want to join our club because they have to fundraise. Don't let that stop you! The fundraising part of our work is easy. We sell a terrific product, rain barrels. The rain barrels collect rain, and people use them in their yards and gardens. Rain barrels are a great way to cut down on outdoor water use. We actually help our environment at the same time that we help people around the world. Best of all, the rain barrels just about sell themselves. People see what a good idea they are, as well as what a good cause they support. After some of our members sold two rain barrels on Alameda Street, they got three orders for barrels from neighbors on the same street just by word of mouth. People in our town want these barrels.

In a persuasive essay, explanation can help persuade the reader.

Use this checklist when writing your explanation:
- Do I anticipate questions the reader might have and answer them?
- If I am writing to persuade, do I consider the reader's objections or opposing views and then address them?

Writing the Conclusion

The last paragraph of your essay is the **conclusion**. Your goal in this paragraph is to leave your reader feeling that you have pulled everything together in a convincing way. If you are writing to explain, end with a summary of your main ideas, but do not use the exact same words you have already used. If you are writing to persuade, end with a **call to action**.

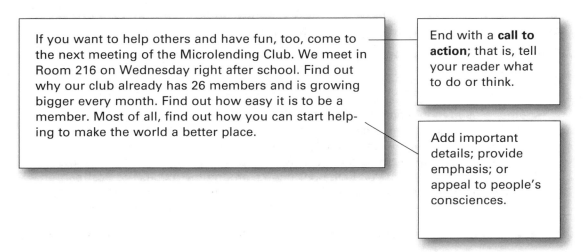

If you want to help others and have fun, too, come to the next meeting of the Microlending Club. We meet in Room 216 on Wednesday right after school. Find out why our club already has 26 members and is growing bigger every month. Find out how easy it is to be a member. Most of all, find out how you can start helping to make the world a better place.

End with a **call to action**; that is, tell your reader what to do or think.

Add important details; provide emphasis; or appeal to people's consciences.

To be effective, a conclusion must do more than simply summarize and restate. It should also contain something new—a fresh idea or connection, an additional piece of information, some striking language—to keep readers engaged to the very end.

Here are some other ideas for crafting an effective conclusion:
- End with a question that will keep readers thinking.
- Acknowledge a final opposing viewpoint and argue against it convincingly.
- End with a fitting quotation.
- Appeal to your reader's sense of what is right and good.

Use this checklist when writing your conclusion:
- Did I remind the reader of my central idea and purpose for writing without using the exact same words?
- Did I pull everything together in a convincing way?

Overview of the Writing Process

Good writing is the result of a multistep process that takes time and practice. The writing process can be divided into stages: **prewriting, drafting, revising,** and **finalizing**. Each stage consists of several steps. You can adjust the writing process to suit your writing assignment. Feel free to backtrack to an earlier stage or rearrange the order of steps as you write. Here is one way to look at the writing process.

Stage 1: Prewriting

- Come up with a topic or gather ideas about a topic you were assigned.
- Develop a thesis about that topic.
- Research and gather information to support your thesis.
- Evaluate your sources.
- Plan your essay using a graphic organizer.

Stage 2: Drafting

- Use the graphic organizer as a guide but add or change ideas as you go along.
- Write an engaging introduction that includes your thesis.
- Use each body paragraph to develop one main idea or one reason related to your thesis.
- Use your conclusion to sum up in fresh words or to issue a call to action.

Stage 3: Revising

- Reread your draft and identify places that need improvement.
- Rewrite, reorganize, and add or delete material if necessary.
- Edit your writing for accurate content, clear sentences, helpful transitions, and effective word choices.
- Consult with peer reviewers.
- Evaluate suggested changes and make revisions.

Stage 4: Finalizing

- Proofread for errors in spelling, grammar, usage, and mechanics.
- Make corrections.
- If needed, make a bibliography or source list.
- Use correct formatting. Your paper should have margins on all sides. Paragraphs should be indented. Everything should appear orderly and consistent on the page.
- Create a final copy.

Prewriting: Using Primary and Secondary Sources

Historians and researchers divide historical sources into two types: primary and secondary.

Primary sources are documents or recordings that were created at the same time that the events being described were taking place. An example of a primary source about the Civil War is a letter written by a soldier to his family during the Civil War. Artifacts and printed material from a historical era, such as sheet music and advertisements, are also considered primary sources.

Secondary sources are documents or recordings that were created after the events being described were over. Secondary sources interpret and synthesize primary sources and other types of information. An example of a secondary source about the Civil War is a television documentary created by a 20th-century filmmaker.

Other kinds of primary and secondary sources are listed below.

Primary Sources
Diaries, journals, and logs
Letters
Speeches
Interviews and oral histories
Memoirs
Autobiographies
Magazine and newspaper articles
Photographs
Home movies
Field notes
Sheet music
Paintings
Artifacts

Secondary Sources
Biographies
Government and organizational records
Statistical records
Editorials
Magazine and newspaper articles
Encyclopedias, almanacs,
    and other reference works
Nonfiction books
Television and film documentaries
Public opinion polls

Prewriting: Taking Notes and Citing Sources

If you research your topic, take notes. Be sure to record the sources of your information. If you are using Internet resources, print out relevant material from the Web sites. If you are using print resources, take notes. Always keep track of the title, author, publisher, date of publication, page numbers, and Web address of any source you use.

Use a copy of this page for each source. Use the bottom (and the back if necessary) to take notes.

Title: _____

Author(s): _____

Publisher and copyright date: _____

Pages used: _____

Internet address: _____

Is it a primary or a secondary source? _____

What information does this source provide about my topic?

Prewriting: Evaluating Evidence

To be persuasive in your essay, you will need to provide relevant and accurate evidence to back up your position. You can use facts, statistics, examples, reasons, quotations, and anecdotes. To recognize useful evidence, ask these questions:

Is the information **relevant**?
- How closely is the information related to the topic of my essay?
- Does the information help me support my opinion?

Is the information **complete**?
- Does the author appear to tell only part of the story or only some of the facts?

Is the information **accurate**?
- Who wrote it? Is that person an expert? When was it written?
- Can I find this same information in books and on Web sites that are made by the government, by museums, and by people who are experts in their field?

Prewriting: Evaluating Sources

As you conduct research on your essay topic, you may come across sources that are not completely accurate. Keep the following in mind:

Is the author or publication biased? A biased source lacks objectivity and displays a slanted point of view. An author's viewpoint can be influenced by many factors, such as politics, gender, and ethnic background. Publications can be similarly influenced. Here are questions to help you determine the extent to which bias may affect the accuracy of your source:

- Why was this source created? Is it meant to inform, entertain, or persuade?
- Do the author and publisher have a reputation for accuracy?
- Does the author or publisher provide a bibliography of sources?
- Does the source include all relevant facts?
- Does the source include statements of opinion?
- Does the source use questionable claims as supporting evidence?
- Does the source use loaded language to try to provoke an emotional response?
- Does the source make broad generalizations that cannot be supported by evidence?
- Does the source acknowledge other points of view?

Is the source out of date? Older sources, particularly primary sources, are often extremely valuable because they take you back in time and provide details that only someone there at the time could have known. Still, they may contain inaccuracies. Recent sources are usually better for essays on current topics or fast-moving issues. Find out when your source material was written or published. Be sure the date is appropriate for your purpose.

Prewriting: Planning Your Essay

Before you draft your essay, you need to plan how you will arrange your main ideas or your reasons. In an essay that explains, you will usually want to select the most logical order. For example, you might sequence according to chronological order or state a cause and then each of its effects. In an essay that persuades, writers often present their best, or most important, reason first or save their best, or most important, reason for last.

Here are other questions to consider as you arrange the order of your paragraphs, as well as your support:

- How are my main ideas related? Present them in a logical order that makes the relationship clear.
- Does the reader have to understand one idea in order to understand another? If so, present the most fundamental idea first.
- Are my main ideas or reasons obvious, or are they difficult to understand? Consider placing the idea or reason that is easiest for the reader to grasp first. Then draw the reader into more difficult ideas.

Once you have decided on a plan, use the appropriate graphic organizer to map out exactly what you are going to say in each paragraph. You do not have to fill it in with complete sentences if you don't want to. But do include enough information to make the order of your reasons or main ideas, as well as your support, clear.

Drafting: Writing Clearly

Good writing is always clear and easy to follow. The first step in clear writing is always thinking about your audience. Ask yourself what your audience already knows. You do not have to repeat familiar ideas. Also ask yourself what your audience doesn't know or might want to know about your topic. In addition, focus on the following points:

To write clearly and to make your writing easy to read,
- develop one idea at a time. Follow your graphic organizer.
- make sure each sentence in a paragraph relates to the main idea or reason.
- make sure each paragraph relates to the thesis.
- leave out unnecessary details.
- use transitions to show how your ideas relate to one another.
- don't be afraid to repeat key words and phrases.
- be aware of your tone. Tone reflects your attitude toward your subject.
- use the passive voice only when the doer of the action is not known or is not important. The active voice is generally stronger, more concise, and easier to understand.
- use specific, concrete language.
- use a variety of sentence lengths and types.

Revising: Improving Your Essay

Once you have finished your draft, it is time to step back and evaluate your work. Follow these steps for revision:

- Take a break after writing the draft. Come back to it with fresh eyes.
- Remember the purpose of your essay by rereading your assignment.
- Reread your essay. Read it silently and then read it aloud.
- Mark the places that seem to need improvement.
- Rewrite and edit, making all necessary changes. Use the checklist and writing tips below.
- Proofread for errors in spelling, grammar, usage, and punctuation.

Essay Checklist

- Does my essay include a well-written introduction and conclusion?
- Do I state my thesis clearly in the introduction?
- Does each body paragraph have a topic sentence that supports my thesis?
- Does each body paragraph explain and support the topic sentence?

Writing Tips

- If your essay seems disorganized, go back to your graphic organizer. Did you follow your plan? If so, then think about how to reorganize your material to make your essay more orderly and logical. Move, add, or delete material as necessary.
- Look for places to add or improve transitions. Transitional words and phrases include *before, after, finally, most of all, first, last, like, unlike, likewise, nevertheless, in contrast, because, therefore, since, for that reason, and, also, furthermore, for example,* and *in other words*. Use transitions to link paragraphs and to link sentences.
- Look for places to vary your sentence length and structure. Use both short and long sentences. Insert an occasional question if it works. Begin your sentences in different ways.
- Vary your word choice. Replace dull words such as *good, great, bad, awful, terrific, awesome, excellent, really,* and *very* with more precise words. Replace state of being verbs (such as *is, are, was,* and *were*) with action verbs.

Revising: Giving and Getting Feedback from Peers

A helpful way to get feedback on your writing is by sharing your work with a classmate. Peer review works best when both individuals know their roles.

Writer's Role	Reviewer's Role
• Bring a copy of your revised draft. • Don't explain your purpose or your plan before the reader has read your paper. • Share any concerns you have about your writing. • Respond thoughtfully. Try not to be defensive since that might keep your reader from providing complete or honest feedback. • If you want more feedback, be sure to ask for it.	• Read carefully. Write your comments on the draft for the writer to keep. • Ask thoughtful questions. • Try to address the particular concerns the writer has expressed. • Be as positive and truly helpful as you can be. Give praise as well as suggestions for improvement. • Be honest.

Tips for Reviewing

- Ask questions that require more than a "yes" or "no" answer. This will help the writer to say more about his or her writing.
- If you like something about the essay, say so. Positive feedback shows the writer what he or she has done well. This is as helpful as criticism in learning to improve one's writing.
- Be specific. For example, "When I got to this sentence, I got confused" is more helpful than "This part is confusing."
- Criticize the writing, not the writer. Begin your comments with "I," not "You" or "Your essay." This helps keep the writer from feeling hurt or defensive.
- Write your comments on the draft, but don't edit or make changes. It is the writer's decision whether to incorporate your suggestions or not.

Essay Rubric

Use this rubric to help you evaluate your own and others' essays.

Criteria	Score			
	4	**3**	**2**	**1**
Purpose	Essay achieves its purpose (to persuade or explain).	Essay achieves its purpose reasonably well.	Essay struggles to achieve its purpose.	Essay does not achieve its purpose.
Organization	Ideas are clear and logically organized.	Ideas are reasonably clear and logically organized.	Ideas are somewhat unclear and disorganized.	Ideas are unclear and disorganized.
Content	Essay provides rich and detailed support for its main ideas or reasons.	Essay provides detailed support for its main ideas or reasons.	Essay provides support for its main ideas or reasons.	Essay does not provide support for its main ideas or reasons.
Style and Conventions	Writing varies word choice and sentence structure appropriately. It has no grammar, spelling, or mechanical errors.	Writing generally varies word choice and sentence structure appropriately. It has few grammar, spelling, or mechanical errors.	Writing does not vary word choice or sentence structure. It has some grammar, spelling, or mechanical errors.	Writing misuses words or has faulty sentences. It has many grammar, spelling, or mechanical errors.

SCORE:

To the Teacher

Reading skills are critical to students' success in all areas of study. In social studies, students will have great difficulty learning and understanding history if they struggle with reading comprehension.

This Reading Toolkit provides basic tools for supporting students who need additional guidance and structure. It includes

- a Prereading Guide that can be used before any chapter.
- instructional pages on understanding organizational text patterns.
- instructional pages that develop comprehension strategies.
- instructional pages that focus on vocabulary development.

Make the following pages available to your students as an independent tutorial, for class instruction, or for use with peer tutoring.

Prereading Guide

What is the **title** of the chapter?

List the section heads and the key terms below.

Section Heads   **Key Terms**

Quickly sketch or describe three **images** from the chapter. Write a one-sentence caption that explains how you think the image relates to the chapter.

Based on the information above, what predictions can you make about the main idea of the chapter?

Read the **chapter summary**. Write one sentence that explains what you think is the main idea of the chapter.

Ask questions to help focus and guide your reading.

Organizational Text Patterns

Expository texts, such as chapters in textbooks, have different organizational patterns. These patterns, or structures, can often be identified by **signal words**.

Text Pattern: Cause and Effect

What is it? Text organized to show cause and effect identifies the reasons that events occur and their results.

How to do it. Signal words that help identify a cause and effect pattern include the following:

as a result	because	consequently	due to
effects of	for	for this reason	hence
how	if . . . then	in order to	is caused by
leads to	may be due to	so	so that
thereby	therefore	thus	when . . . then

Try it. Read the following passage. Then list causes and effects in a graphic organizer like the one below.

> *As a result of the Civil War, many Americans began thinking of the United States as one country, rather than as a collection of sovereign states. Slavery no longer existed because of the war. There were terrible costs, though. Due to the war, more than 620,000 soldiers lay dead. Croplands lay in ruins. It would take generations for the South to recover.*

Graphic Organizer: Cause and Effect

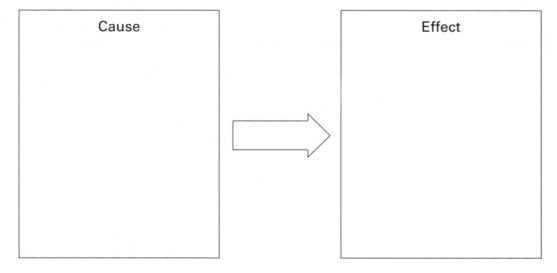

Cause   →   Effect

Organizational Text Patterns

Expository texts, such as chapters in textbooks, have different organizational patterns. These patterns, or structures, can often be identified by **signal words**.

Text Pattern: Compare and Contrast

What is it? Text with a compare and contrast organizational pattern tells about the similarities and differences of two or more objects, places, events, or ideas.

How to do it. Signal words that help identify a compare and contrast pattern include the following:

although	as well as	as opposed to	both
but	by contrast	compared with	different from
either . . . or	even though	however	instead of
in comparison	in the same way	just as	like
more . . . than	on the other hand	otherwise	similar to
similarly	still	unlike	yet

Try it. Read the following passage. Then list similarities and differences in a graphic organizer like the one below.

> Both the Union and the Confederacy had advantages and disadvantages going into the Civil War. The North had a larger population and more factories and railroads than the South, but it lacked strong military leadership. The South had serious economic problems, but it had capable generals and the advantage of fighting a defensive war.

Graphic Organizer: Compare and Contrast

Write characteristics of Topic 1 here.

Write characteristics of both topics here.

Write characteristics of Topic 2 here.

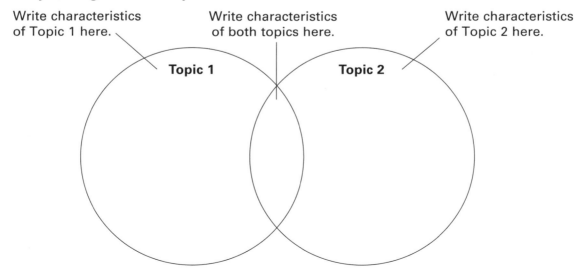

Topic 1   Topic 2

Organizational Text Patterns

Expository texts, such as chapters in textbooks, have different organizational patterns. These patterns, or structures, can often be identified by **signal words**.

Text Pattern: Proposition and Support
What is it? Text with a proposition and support organizational pattern presents an argument with supporting examples.

How to do it. Signal words that help identify a proposition and support pattern include the following:

additionally	because	believe	clearly
conclusively	consider	first	for example
for instance	furthermore	generally	however
if . . . then	in fact	it could be argued	most convincing
never	not only . . . but	often	this means

Try it. Read the following passage. Then list a proposition and supporting examples in a graphic organizer like the one below.

> *The Articles of Confederation did not establish an effective form of government because Congress's powers were limited. Not only was Congress not allowed to impose taxes, but Congress had to ask the states for funds to do anything. Too often, the states ignored the requests. Additionally, Congress could not intervene to resolve disputes between individual states. It could be argued that Shays' Rebellion best shows the weaknesses of the Articles of Confederation. When a group of farmers seized the weapons at a national arsenal, Congress did not have an army to stop them. The state militia had to restore order.*

Graphic Organizer: Proposition and Support

Proposition:

Support:

Support:

Support:

Organizational Text Patterns

Expository texts, such as chapters in textbooks, have different organizational patterns. These patterns, or structures, can often be identified by **signal words**.

Text Pattern: Sequencing
What is it? Text organized to show sequencing relates a series of events or steps in a process in time order.

How to do it. Signal words that help identify the sequencing pattern include the following:

after	afterward	before	during	earlier
finally	first	following	initially	last
later	meanwhile	next	not long after	now
previously	second	since	soon	then
third	today	until	when	

Try it. Read the following passage. Then show the sequence of events in a graphic organizer like the one below.

Article V of the U.S. Constitution lays out several methods for amending the Constitution. All but one of the Constitution's 27 amendments have followed the same process. First, a bill to amend the Constitution is proposed in Congress. Next, the amendment needs approval of a two-thirds majority of the House of Representatives. If it does not receive a two-thirds majority, the amendment process does not continue. After the House of Representatives has approved the amendment, the Senate must approve the amendment by a two-thirds major-ity. In some cases, amendments have passed the House of Representatives, but have not received enough votes in the Senate. If successful in both the House and the Senate, the amendment is then sent to the states for approval. At this point, three-quarters of the state legislatures must ratify the amendment in order for it to become law.

Graphic Organizer: Sequencing

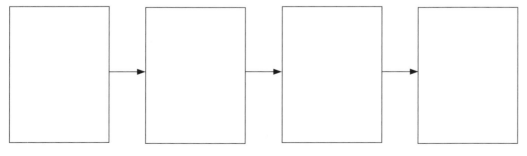

Comprehension Strategy

Comprehension strategies help you better understand and remember what you read.

KWL: Know/ Want / Learned

Follow these steps to fill in the graphic organizer:

Step 1: Brainstorm what you know about the topic of the chapter.

Step 2: Create questions that show what you want to find out when you read this chapter.

Step 3: Read the chapter. Make a list of the important details that you learned.

What I Know	What I Want to Find Out	What I Learned

Comprehension Strategy

Comprehension strategies help you better understand and remember what you read.

REAP: Read / Encode / Annotate / Ponder
Follow these steps to complete the graphic organizer below as you read the chapter:

Step 1: Read (R) the text. Write the title of the chapter.

Step 2: Encode (E) the text. Use your own words to describe the main idea of the chapter.

Step 3: Annotate (A) the text. Summarize at least three important points from the chapter.

Step 4: Ponder (P) the text. Write down at least one question that you now have after reading this chapter.

R	E
A	P

Comprehension Strategy

Comprehension strategies help you better understand and remember what you read.

SQ3R: Survey / Question / Read / Recite / Review
Follow these steps to read the chapter:

Step 1: Survey the chapter by looking at the title, subheads, captions, and illustrations. Read the introduction.

Step 2: Question. Turn the title and subheads into questions to focus your reading. Look up the meaning of any new vocabulary.

Step 3: Read. Search for answers to your questions.

Step 4: Recite. Recite the answers to your questions aloud or in writing. Reread if you have any unanswered questions.

Step 5: Review. Look over the chapter and summarize what you have learned.

Vocabulary Development

Illustrated Dictionary

Chapter _____

Follow these steps to create an Illustrated Dictionary for your Key Content Terms.

Step 1: Choose a Key Content Term.

Step 2: Draw a diagram, word map, or other graphic organizer that shows how the term relates to something you already know or to another key term in this chapter or in a previous chapter. Write the term in bigger or darker letters than you use for any other words.

Step 3: Find the definition of each term and summarize its meaning in your own words.

Step 4: Write a sentence that uses the term.

Step 5: Repeat for all the other Key Content Terms.

Sketch/Diagram	In Your Own Words	In a Sentence

Vocabulary Development

Rate Your Knowledge

Follow these steps to rate your knowledge of the Key Content Terms.

Step 1: Use one spectrum for each Key Content Term. Rate your knowledge of each term by marking the appropriate place on the spectrum. Below the spectrum, write anything you know about the term.

Step 2: Find out what others know about each term by asking another person (for example, a classmate, friend, parent, or teacher). Write down what you learn on the back of this sheet or on a separate sheet of paper.

Step 3: Find the definition of each term. Then, on the back of this sheet or on a separate sheet of paper, write a sentence that uses each term.

Term:

1	**2**	**3**	**4**	**5**

Unfamiliar   Very familiar

Term:

1	**2**	**3**	**4**	**5**

Unfamiliar   Very familiar

Term:

1	**2**	**3**	**4**	**5**

Unfamiliar   Very familiar

Term:

1	**2**	**3**	**4**	**5**

Unfamiliar   Very familiar

Vocabulary Development

Word Grids

Follow these guidelines to create a Word Grid for each of your Key Content Terms.

Box 1: List a Key Content Term from the chapter.

Box 2: Find the definition of the term and summarize its meaning in your own words.

Box 3: Add *related* information, such as examples, facts, synonyms, sayings, or a category to which the word belongs.

Box 4: Add *contrasting* information, such as antonyms, or words with opposite meanings.

1. Key Content Term	**2.** In Your Own Words
3. Related Words/Ideas	**4.** Contrasting Words/Ideas

1. Key Content Term	**2.** In Your Own Words
3. Related Words/Ideas	**4.** Contrasting Words/Ideas

Vocabulary Development

Word Pyramid   **Chapter** _____

Follow these guidelines to create a Word Pyramid for each of your Key Content Terms.

Row 1: List a Key Content Term from the chapter.

Row 2: Describe the term in your own words.

Row 3: Compare the term to one thing it is similar to and contrast the term with one thing it is different from.

Row 4: Draw or list things that the word brings to mind. That is, "associate" the word with things you already know.

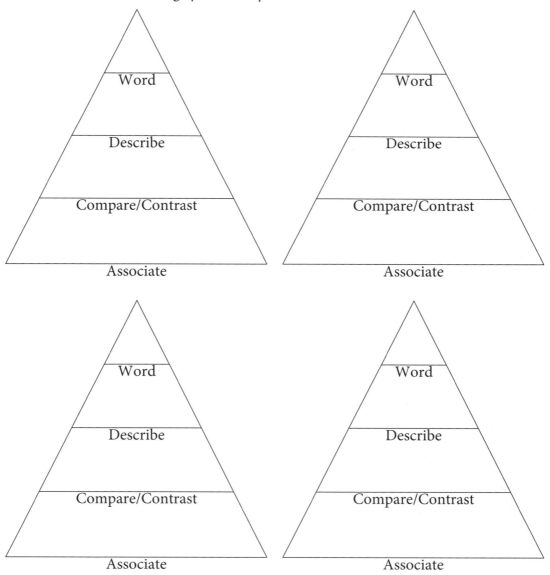

To the Teacher

Success in social studies depends on proficiency with fundamental critical thinking and reading skills. However, students may come into your class with varying levels of ability in comprehending social studies texts. Without fluency in skills such as recognizing cause and effect, students will have great difficulty in understanding history. You can use the pages in this booklet to bring your students up to speed.

First check the skills correlation chart for your program in the back of the Lesson Guide to see which skill or skills are part of the lesson you plan to teach. If you believe that your class would benefit from direct instruction in that skill, plan to dedicate some class time to the corresponding skill page of this toolkit. This extra bit of time will pay dividends in the success of the TCI activity and also in the long term, as these skills appear in state standards and are tested in state and national assessments.

Many teachers may want to make an overhead transparency of the page and work through the exercise together with the class. Whole class instruction such as this will give you the chance to model the skill for your students as well as provide them with the opportunity to practice it. You can also photocopy the page and distribute it to students for classwork or for homework.

As you review students' work with them, be sure to ask them to explain how they reached their answers. This sort of "thinking out loud" will help students to become more conscious of their own thought processes. Listening to their classmates' explanations will also show students other ways to read for meaning.

Comparing and Contrasting

What is it? When you **compare** things, you look for ways that they are alike. When you **contrast** things, you look for ways that they are different.

How to do it. As you read, first identify the things that you want to compare. Next, list all the ways that they are alike. These similarities may be stated or they may be implied. Then list all the ways in which the things differ. These too may be state or implied. Organizing similarities and differences in a Venn diagram will let you compare and contrast at a glance.

Try it. Read the passage below. Identify the similarities and differences. Write the similarities in the overlapping area of a Venn diagram. Write the differences in the spaces on either side.

Athens and Sparta were both city-states of ancient Greece. Yet they differed greatly. Located near the sea, Athens grew large and powerful through trade. Athenians were eager to travel and exchange ideas with others. They made their city a center of art and culture.

Sparta, on the other hand, was an inland city. Spartans did not trust out-siders or their ideas. Instead of trade, they used their armies to take what they needed from their neighbors. Spartans valued strength and simplicity. They produced soldiers rather than artists and thinkers.

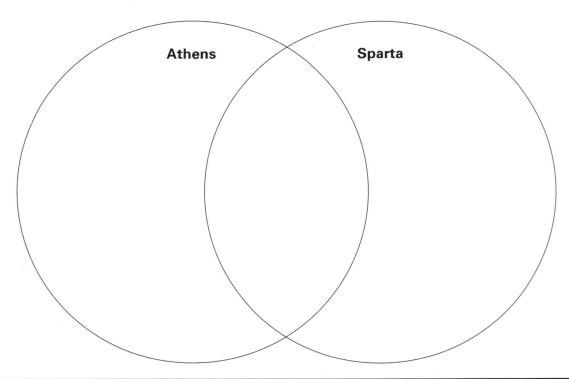

Sequencing Events

What is it? **Sequencing** events means listing them in the order they occurred. Organizing events in time order will help you understand why things happened as they did.

How to do it. As you read, look for words that signal time relationships between events. These words include *first, next, then, during, later, finally, before, after, at the same time,* and *meanwhile*. Then say the order of events to yourself. Recording events in a flow chart will help you clarify the sequence.

Try it. Read the passage below and spot the words that signal time relationships. Then sequence the events in a flow chart.

It took many years to become a knight in Europe in the Middle Ages. At age seven, a boy left home to live in the castle of a lord. He then became a page. During this time, he learned to ride a horse. After about seven years, he became a squire and took care of his lord's horse and weapons. At the same time, he also trained to become a warrior and served his lord in battle.

In his early 20s, a worthy squire would become a knight. Before receiving this honor, a squire often spent a night in prayer, and then dressed in white to show purity. In a ceremony, the young man promised loyalty to his lord. The lord then tapped him on each shoulder with a sword to make him a knight.

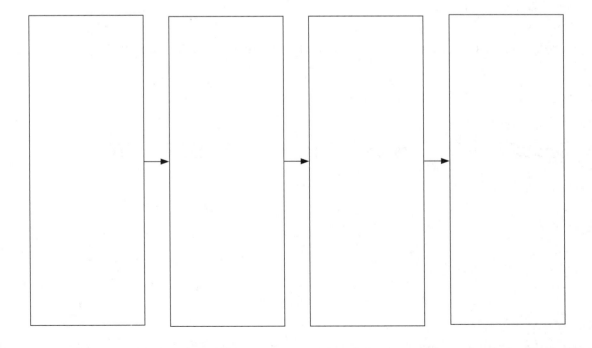

Creating a Timeline

What is it? A **timeline** shows when, and in what order, past events happened. Organizing events along a timeline helps you see how the events are related to one another in time. Understanding this relationship can also help you remember the sequence of events.

How to do it. First, locate the dates in your reading. Find the earliest and latest dates you want to record. Then choose beginning and end dates for your timeline. For example, if your dates range from 1812 to 1926, your timeline might begin at 1800 and end at 1930. Using a ruler, divide the line into equal units of time. Finally, place the other dated events from the reading along your timeline.

Try it. Read this passage and list dates to show on a timeline.

"All roads lead to Rome." This ancient saying dates back more than two thousand years. For 500 years, from about 27 B.C.E. to 476 C.E., Rome was the capital of the greatest empire the world had ever seen. At its height, around 117 C.E., the Roman Empire spanned the entire Mediterranean world.

However, the empire did not last. Power struggles, border threats, and economic and social problems led to its fall. In 330 C.E., the emperor Constantine moved his capital east to Byzantium. After that, power was divided between two emperors, one in Rome and the other in Byzantium. A Germanic tribe invaded Rome in 410 C.E. and looted the city. In 476 C.E., the last emperor in Rome was driven from his throne.

From your list of dates, create a timeline for the history of the Roman Empire.

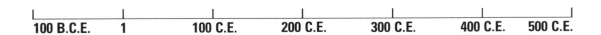

| 100 B.C.E. | 1 | 100 C.E. | 200 C.E. | 300 C.E. | 400 C.E. | 500 C.E. |

Analyzing Cause and Effect

What is it? A **cause** is something that brings about a particular result, which is called an **effect**. An event may have more than one cause and/or more than one effect. Analyzing cause and effect can help you understand why historical events happened.

Both causes and effects can be either **immediate** or **long-term**. An immediate cause or effect happens shortly before or after an event. Long-term causes and effects generally unfold over many months or years.

How to do it. To identify cause and effect, consider the following questions:
- What was the trigger that made an event happen? (immediate cause)
- What were the conditions that contributed to the event? (long-term cause)
- What was the direct result of an action? (immediate effect)
- What were some lasting consequences? (long-term effect)

Try it. Read this passage about the Boston Tea Party.

After the French and Indian War, British actions increasingly angered the American colonists. To pay for military costs, the British Parliament passed laws that chipped away at colonial rights. One such law, the Tea Act, set off a chain reaction that soon carried the colonies to open rebellion. To protest the Tea Act, a group of colonists dumped a shipload of tea into Boston Harbor. The outraged British clamped down with even harsher laws. Colonists called these laws the Intolerable Acts. These acts helped to build colonial resistance to the British government. This resistance led to the American Revolution.

Fill in a chart to show the causes and effects of the Boston Tea Party.

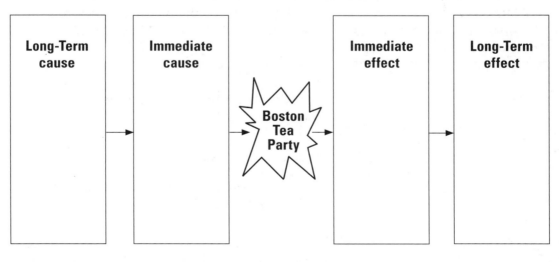

Making Predictions

What is it? By analyzing cause and effect, you can often make **predictions**. Making predictions means making an educated guess about the likely outcome of certain events or actions.

How to do it. Here are three ways to make predictions:
1. Look for patterns. Do the causes and effects over time follow a regular pattern?
2. Consider what might come next in a sequence. Where does this chain of events seem to be leading?
3. Look for correlations (connections) between historical events. Are there other events in history or other places in the world with a similar situation?

Try it. Often new inventions trigger a chain of events with a variety of outcomes. Consider the example of the cotton gin.

> *In 1793, the United States produced about 180,000 pounds of cotton. Seventeen years later, the harvest had grown to an astounding 93 million pounds. What spurred this incredible change? It was the invention of the cotton gin by Eli Whitney in 1793.*
>
> *The cotton gin is a machine that removes the seeds from cotton. Before the gin, one person took all day to clean one pound of cotton. In contrast, one small cotton gin could clean 50 pounds in a day. Later horse-driven gins could clean thousands of pounds per week. With cotton in high demand by textile mills in the North and in Britain, it quickly became very profitable for southern farmers.*

Answer the questions to predict other impacts of the cotton gin.

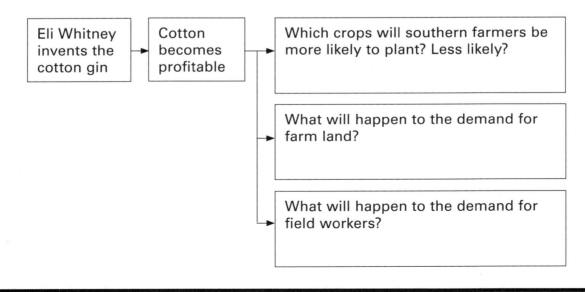

© Teachers' Curriculum Institute

Recognizing the Role of Chance, Error, and Oversight in History

What is it? Many things affect the course of history, even accidents and mistakes. **Chance** is an unexpected or accidental event. **Errors** are mistakes people make. **Oversight** occurs when someone does not pay close attention to what is important.

How to do it. Look for examples of chance, error, and oversight in your reading. What was the effect or outcome of each accident or error?

Try it. Read the following passage about the American War of Independence. Notice any chance happenings, errors, or oversights.

> In 1777, the British planned to capture Albany, New York. Three British armies were to attack from different directions to take the city. By controlling Albany, they could prevent colonial forces from joining together.
>
> General Burgoyne to the north and Lieutenant Colonel St. Leger to the west set off as planned. However, General Howe to the south decided to attack Philadelphia before heading to Albany. Once his troops occupied Philadelphia, he stayed there. While he enjoyed the company of British supporters, George Washington attacked and prevented Howe's army from ever setting out for Albany.
>
> Meanwhile, Burgoyne was clumsily moving his army through the woods. He had planned for his army to live off the land, but his troops were an easy target for local militias. As a result, his men suffered without food and supplies. As for St. Leger, he was only part way to Albany he was forced him to retreat.
>
> With only limited troop strength in New York, the British lost the Battle of Saratoga later that year. It was the turning point of the war.

Identify two errors or oversights and their consequences. Can you think of a chance occurrence that might have changed the outcome?

Error or Oversight	Consequence
1. General Howe decided to attack Philadelphia instead of marching on.	1. Howe's army never got to Albany to support Burgoyne and St. Legere.
2.	2.
3.	3

Framing Questions to Research

What is it? **Framing questions** to research means identifying specific information you would like to know about a topic. When you frame a question, you focus your search for answers.

How to do it. As you read, think about what information is not stated. What questions do you have? Write them down. Then choose one question to start your research. Write down any new questions that come to mind as you learn more. You may need to revise your original question. If your question seems too broad, reframe it to focus your research.

Too broad: *What was the role of city planning in 20th-century America?*

More focused: *How did city planning help San Francisco recover after the earthquake of 1906?*

Try it. Read the following passage.

> *Labor leader Mary Harris Jones, commonly known as Mother Jones, went to Pennsylvania in 1903. She was going to support a strike by 75,000 textile workers. To her surprise, she found that about 10,000 of the workers were children. Jones led a "March of the Mill Children" from Pennsylvania to Oyster Bay, New York. She petitioned President Theodore Roosevelt to support child labor laws.*
>
> *Mother Jones's march helped people across the country become aware of child labor. Reformers demanded an end to child labor. By 1909, 43 states had passed laws that outlawed the hiring of children.*

One question on the topic of child labor is suggested below. Frame three more questions for research on this topic. Which would be a good question to start researching?

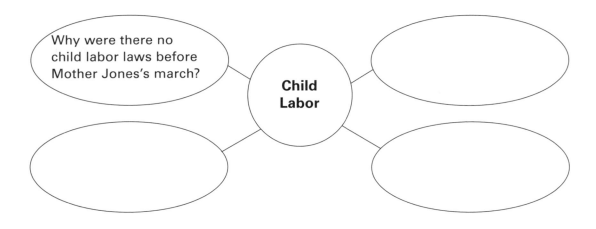

Distinguishing Fact from Opinion

What is it? Statements that can be proven to be true are **facts**. Statements that reflect someone's personal viewpoint are **opinions**. Recognizing the difference between fact and opinion will help you determine how reliable a source is.

How to do it. To recognize a fact, look for information that can be checked elsewhere. Often this type of text tells *who, what, where, when,* or *how much*. If you can find the same information in a reliable source, it's likely a fact.

To recognize opinions, look for words such as *think, feel,* or *believe*. Also look for words that carry a value judgment, such as *most, best, impressive,* or *wonderful*. An author's predictions may be an expression of opinion. For example, "With a little money, we could solve our town's pollution problem." That's the author's opinion.

Try it. As you read this passage, identify facts and opinions. List at least one of each and answer the questions. An example has been done for you.

> *The Chinese Emperor of Qin had the greatest and longest-lasting influence of all the emperors of China. He was born in 259 B.C.E. and became ruler at age 13. Sometimes called the Tiger of Qin, he was very ambitious. He used military might, spies, bribery, and alliances to conquer rival states. Soon he gained power over all of China. He proclaimed himself emperor in 221 B.C.E. During his reign, the emperor created a unified system of laws and writing. He also strengthened the empire against invasion. His tomb covers many square miles. The people of China will always remember him as the man who created a new world.*

Fact	How might you prove this fact?	Opinion	What suggests this is an opinion?
1. The emperor of Qin was born in 259 B.C.E. 2. 3.	Use a history book or encyclopedia	The emperor of Qin had the greatest influence of the Chinese emperors	The words *greatest* and *longest-lasting*

Selecting Useful Information

What is it? When you research a topic, you need to determine which information is useful and which isn't. Useful information is relevant, essential, and verifiable. Information is **relevant** if it is connected to your topic. Information is **essential** if you cannot answer your research question without it. Information is **verifiable** if you can find it in other reliable sources.

How to do it. Examine each piece of information in your reading. Does it help define, explain, or give details about your topic? Can you verify the information?

Try it. Suppose that you are researching this question: *What was daily life like for a Civil War soldier?* You have found firsthand information in letters from a Union soldier to his mother. In a chart, list information from the reading. Decide if it is relevant, essential, and verifiable for your topic. An example has been done for you.

> *For a few days . . . both armies are on very friendly terms. Well today I was out on the line and there was a lot of Rebs there and one of them invited me to go with him . . . Had a great chat. . . .*
>
> *Desertions from their army are quite numerous . . . I had on a pair of fine Gaiters and one of them asked me the price. I told him and he said they would cost in Petersburg $150. Common shoes cost 60 & 70 Dolls. Common letter paper 50 cts per sheet & mighty hard to get at that. They say themselves that they have had no coffee or sugar for 4 weeks.*
>
> *You need not be alarmed about my health for I have good heavy blanket and warm clothes. My boots was not very good but we have all drawed a good pair of government shoes. . . . There is about half a dozen men in our regiment that are sick. . . .*
>
> —*Papers of Tilton C. Reynolds, 1851–1963 Library of Congress: Manuscript Division.*

Information	Relevant?	Essential?	Verifiable?
Union soldier reports many desertions from the Confederate army	Yes, part of a soldier's daily life	maybe not, for the this topic	probably

Selecting Credible Sources: Primary Sources

What is it? A **primary source** is a record or an artifact from the past that was created by someone who witnessed an event or lived through an era. Examples are letters, diaries, interviews, photos, and things such as tools, clothing, or weapons.

How to do it. To select a primary source that is **credible,** or believable, you must ask questions about the source.

- Who created this source? What was its purpose?
- Is there any reason to think that the creator might exaggerate, leave out important information, or not tell the truth?

You might need to find out more about the source or its creator. You might also compare the source to other views of the same event.

Try it. Suppose that you are researching this question: *Who was to blame for the Boston Massacre?* "Boston Massacre" is the American name for a fight between British troops and a crowd of angry colonists in 1770. The colonists started a small riot, and British soldiers killed five of them. Consider the following primary sources, and answer the questions.

1. Trial testimony of Dr. John Jeffries, who treated a wounded colonist who later died
2. Trial testimony of one of the British soldiers who fired at the colonists
3. A flyer entitled "An account of a late military massacre at Boston," published in New York in 1770
4. An engraving that shows soldiers firing on unarmed citizens, created by Paul Revere, a silversmith living in Boston in 1770

Source	Credible or not credible?	Why?	What else would you like to know about the source?
1	Not very credible	It is unclear if Jeffries was an eyewitness or not.	Did Jeffries have political leanings toward either the Patriots or the British?
2			
3			
4			

Selecting Credible Sources: Secondary Sources

What is it? A **secondary source** is a record created by someone who did not personally experience the event described. Examples of secondary sources include encyclopedias, almanacs, biographies, and textbooks.

How to do it. To select a secondary source that is **credible,** or believable, you must ask questions about the source.

- Who is the author? What is the author's background? What else has the author written? Does the author belong to a group with a certain point of view?
- How recently was the source created or updated? If it was created long ago, where could you look for more recent sources?
- Why was the source created? Is it meant to give facts or to explain what happened? Does it try to persuade you to see things a certain way?

Try it. Suppose that you are researching this question: *What was everyday life like for enslaved Africans in the American colonies?* Consider the following secondary sources, and complete the table. Tell what you would like to know further about each source.

1. *Myths and Realities: Societies of the Colonial South,* by Carl Bridenbaugh, 1952. Bridenbaugh was a professor of American history at the University of California, Berkeley, and at Brown University.
2. *Resource Guide: Slavery,* on Digital History, a U.S. history Web site developed and maintained by the University of Houston, updated December 2005
3. *American Slavery As It Is: Testimony of a Thousand Witnesses,* published anonymously in 1839. Written by Theodore Dwight Weld, an antislavery activist.
4. *Slavery Defended: The Views of the Old South,* edited by Eric L. McKitrick, 1963. A collection of proslavery writings from the mid-1800s.

Source	Author	Date	Purpose	What else would you like to know about the source?
1	Bridenbaugh	1952	To explain and teach	What else has he written?
2				
3				
4				

Drawing Sound Conclusions

What is it? Sometimes writers state their conclusions directly. Other times it is up to you, the reader, to draw conclusions from the reading. A **sound conclusion** is based on solid evidence and your knowledge of the subject.

How to do it. First, read the passage. What facts are given? Looking at these facts together, what do they suggest to you that is not stated in the reading?

Try it. Read the following passage about ancient Greece.

> *In some city-states, aristocrats—wealthy men who had inherited large pieces of land—insisted that the king should be elected instead of inheriting his crown. Then they said the king could rule only for a certain number of years. Eventually, aristocrats in most city-states overthrew the monarchy. By 800 B.C.E., kings no longer ruled most Greek city-states.*

Identify two more facts from the passage. What conclusion could you draw from these facts? How could you test your conclusion to see if it is sound?

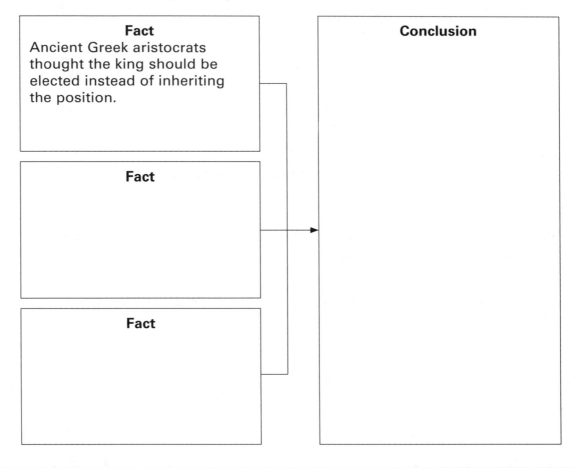

Fact
Ancient Greek aristocrats thought the king should be elected instead of inheriting the position.

Fact

Fact

Conclusion

Identifying Frame of Reference and Point of View

What is it? Someone's frame of reference includes all the things that influence how that person thinks and the way that person sees the world. Point of view is a person's individual opinion or perspective.

How to do it. First, identify everything you know about the writer of the passage. Consider background, age, culture, the historical period in which he or she lived, and beliefs. Next, look for expressions of the person's perspective. They may be stated directly—"I believe that…." Or they may be expressed in value judgments, such as "the worst ever…." How do you think this person's frame of reference might have influenced his or her point of view?

Try it. During the Civil War, the Union at first refused to enlist African American soldiers. Consider these two quotes from that time.

> *Do you know that this is a white man's government; that the white men are able to defend and protect it; and that to enlist a Negro soldier would be to drive every white man out of the service?*
>
> — Ohio Governor David Todd,
> in response to a group of African Americans who asked to form a regiment

> *Why does the government reject the Negro? Is he not a man? Can he not wield a sword, fire a gun, march and countermarch, and obey orders like any other? . . . Men in earnest don't fight with one hand, when they might fight with two, and a man drowning would not refuse to be saved even by a colored hand.*
>
> — African American anti-slavery leader Frederick Douglass

Identify the point of view and frame of reference of each man. How do you think frame of reference might have shaped each man's perspective?

	David Todd	**Frederick Douglass**
Point of View		
Frame of Reference		

Identifying Bias, Stereotyping, and Propaganda

What is it? **Bias** is a one-sided or slanted view. A **stereotype** is an oversimplified image of a group or an idea. **Propaganda** means the spreading of one-sided views to influence people's opinions or actions. To evaluate historical evidence, you must be able to recognize bias, stereotyping, and propaganda.

How to do it. To identify bias, look for exaggerations and emotionally charged images or words. Are opinions stated as if they were facts? What information is left out? In what way does the piece focus on one side of an issue?

To recognize a stereotype, look for exaggerations and for overly negative or positive statements or images.

To recognize propaganda, ask yourself: Does the piece present only one side of the story? Does the piece appeal to people's desire to belong or be part of a group? Does it connect the cause to a respected group or symbol?

Try it. In World War I, the British were at war with the Germans. This poster was created during that war. Answer the questions below.

1. What is the bias of this poster? What emotionally charged words and images does it use?

2. What stereotype of the Germans does this poster present?

3. What stereotype of the British does this poster present?

4. What is the propaganda message of this poster?

Conducting a Cost-Benefit Analysis

What is it? One way to make decisions is to conduct a **cost-benefit analysis** of your options. In this process, you compare the **costs** (disadvantages) of choosing a certain course of action with the **benefits** (advantages) of choosing that course.

How to do it. Identify the option you are considering. Make a list of all the costs of pursuing that option, and another list of the benefits. Compare the two lists. Are there more costs than benefits? Does any one cost weigh too heavily? Are the benefits guaranteed outcomes, or is there a chance they won't happen?

Finally, make the decision. Based on your analysis of the costs and benefits, which choice makes the most sense?

Try it. Suppose that you are a young man living in China in 1852. You are trying to decide whether to immigrate to California. You have heard stories of "Gold Mountain"—of great wealth, fine homes, and plenty of food. You have also talked to one man who returned empty-handed. He told you that he was badly treated in California. Meanwhile, your village in China has fallen on hard times. War, poor economic conditions, and overcrowded farms have forced your family into poverty. You have barely enough to eat. You will need to leave your family behind if you go to California.

Conduct a cost-benefit analysis of your option of immigrating to California.

Costs	Benefits
Might be badly treated in California	Could make lots of money in California

Put a star by any costs or benefits that are guaranteed.
Do you consider any of the costs too great?
What choice do you make? Why?

Interpreting Political Cartoons

What is it? Political cartoons appear on the editorial pages of newspapers. They may be funny, but their purpose is to carry a message or opinion. Cartoonists use characters and symbols—animals, people, or objects—to communicate their point. **Interpreting a political cartoon** means figuring out the cartoonist's message.

How to do it. Identify the symbols and characters in the cartoon. What does each one stand for? Are there labels or captions to give you clues? Are the characters and symbols simplified or exaggerated to make a point? What details are emphasized? What action is taking place in the cartoon? Fit these pieces of information together to determine the message of the cartoon.

Try it. Interpret this political cartoon by answering the questions below.

1. What are the characters and symbols in the cartoon, and what does each one represent?

2. How do the words help you identify the cartoonist's intention?

3. What action is taking place in the cartoon?

4. What opinion is the cartoonist expressing?

To the Teacher

Students encounter maps every day inside and outside their classes—in books and on handheld devices, computers, or television screens. Whether they're navigating cities and continents or exploring the world by way of an atlas, students will use map skills throughout their lives.

This Map Skill Toolkit provides support for learning and reviewing the basic skills of reading and interpreting maps of all kinds. It includes handouts for the following:

- oceans and continents
- latitude and longitude
- the global grid
- hemispheres
- compass rose
- map scale
- map titles and symbols

Oceans and Continents

What is it? In order to locate places on our planet, we need to name its largest features. Water covers nearly three-fourths of Earth's surface. The largest bodies of water are **oceans.** The large land areas that cover the rest of the earth are the **continents.**

How to do it. Find the oceans on the map below. This is really just one big body of water, but geographers usually divide it into four oceans. They are the Atlantic, Pacific, Indian, and Arctic oceans.

Now find the continents. Geographers identify seven continents. From largest to smallest, they are Asia, Africa, North America, South America, Antarctica, Europe and Australia. Europe and Asia are actually parts of one huge landmass that is sometimes called Eurasia. But geographers usually think of Europe and Asia as two continents because they have different cultures and histories.

Oceans and Continents

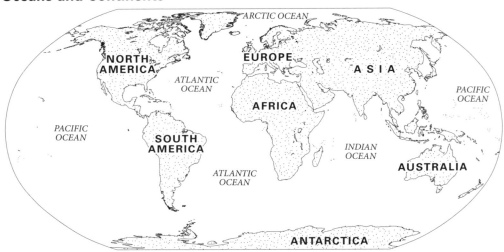

Try it. Use this map to answer the following questions.
1. Which is the most northern ocean on earth?
2. Which is the most southern continent on earth?
3. Which continents border the Atlantic Ocean?

4. Which ocean touches three continents? What are they?

5. Which ocean do you think is the largest? Why?

Latitude and Longitude

What is it? Mapmakers draw horizontal and vertical lines around the globe to help us locate places on Earth. The horizontal lines are **parallels of latitude.** The verticals are **meridians of longitude.** Both are measured in degrees.

How to do it. The globe on the left shows how parallels of latitude ring the globe horizontally. Find the equator. It is 0°. Now find the South Pole. It is 90° south latitude, written as 90°S. All of the parallels south of the equator are South latitude. Similarly, the North Pole is 90° north latitude, or 90°N, and all parallels north of the equator are North latitude.

The globe on the right shows how meridians of longitude divide the globe in vertical sections between the North and South poles. Find the Prime Meridian. It is 0° longitude. On the opposite side of the globe is the meridian of 180°. East and west of the Prime Meridian are 179° of longitude.

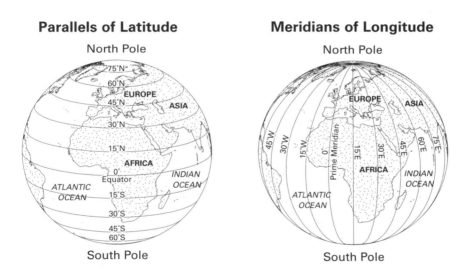

Parallels of Latitude

Meridians of Longitude

Try it. Use these illustrations to help you answer the following questions.

1. Locate the continent of Europe. Which parallels of latitude run through Europe?

2. Locate the prime meridian. Through which continents does it run?

3. Find 30° west longitude. It runs through which ocean?

4. Find the Indian Ocean. Name three meridians of longitude that cross it.

The Global Grid

What is it? The **global grid** shows both lines of latitude and of longitude. You can locate the "global address" or *absolute location* of any place on earth by finding where its degrees of latitude and longitude cross. For example, the location of Rio De Janeiro, Brazil is 23°S, 44°W. These numbers are called **coordinates.** Latitude always comes first.

How to do it. To find the coordinates of a place, first locate it on a map. Next look up and down to find the degree of latitude. You may have to estimate if the place is between two parallels on a map. Then look left and right to find the degree of longitude. Again, you may need to estimate if the place is between two meridians.

The Global Grid

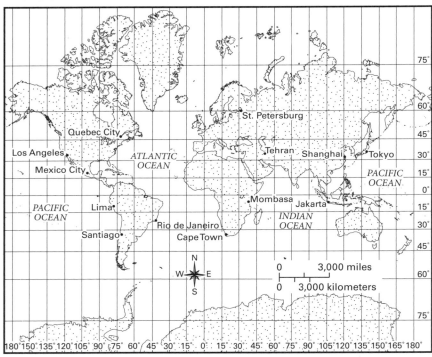

Try it. Use the grid on this map to locate cities around the world.

1. What are the coordinates of St. Petersburg?

2. Which city is located at 47°N, 71°W?

3. What are the coordinates of Shanghai?

4. Estimate the coordinates of Mexico City.

5. Which city is located at 33°N, 118°W?

The Hemispheres

What is it? A **hemisphere** is half of a globe or sphere. In geography, a hemisphere is half of planet Earth. Geographers recognize two sets of hemispheres on Earth. One set is the Northern Hemisphere and the Southern Hemisphere. The other set is the Eastern Hemisphere and the Western Hemisphere.

How to do it. Find the equator on the globe below. The equator divides Earth into the Northern and Southern Hemispheres. North of the equator lies the Northern Hemisphere. South of the equator lies the Southern Hemisphere.

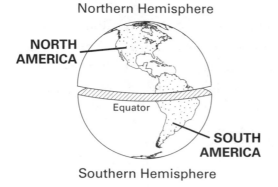

Now find the prime meridian on the second globe. It separates the Eastern and Western Hemispheres. To the east of the prime meridian lies the Eastern Hemisphere, while the Western Hemisphere lies to the west of the prime meridian.

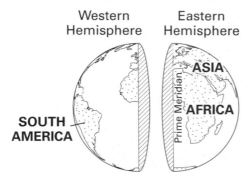

Try it. Answer the following questions, based on the information on these globes.

1. In which hemisphere, Northern or Southern, is the United States?

2. In which hemisphere, Eastern or Western, is Asia?

3. In which two hemispheres is Africa?

4. In which two hemispheres is South America?

Compass Rose

What is it? Mapmakers use a diagram called a **compass rose** to show directions on a map. A simple compass rose has two short lines that cross at right angles. The ends of the lines are labeled N for north, S for south, E for east, and W for west. These are the **cardinal directions**. A more complex compass rose has lines between the cardinal points to show intermediate directions. These lines are labeled NE for northeast, SE for southeast, SW for southwest, and NW for northwest.

How to do it. Use the compass rose to tell where one place is in relation to another. Find Colorado (CO) and Wyoming (WY) on the map below. The compass rose tells you that Colorado is south of Wyoming. This is one way to state its **relative location**. Now find Wisconsin (WI). From the compass rose, you can see that Minnesota (MN) is west of Wisconsin. You can also see that Indiana (IN) is southeast of Wisconsin.

Continental United States

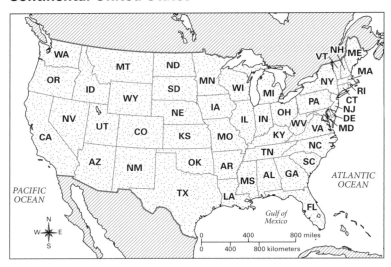

Try it. Use this map to answer the following questions.
1. Which state borders Oregon (OR) on the east? The north?
2. If you traveled from Georgia (GA) to Missouri (MO), in which direction would you go?
3. Find Colorado (CO) and Nebraska (NE). Where is Nebraska in relation to Colorado?
4. Suppose you go north from Texas (TX) to the next state. Then you go to the state to the west. Where would you be?

Map Scale

What is it? Mapmakers include a **scale** to show the relationship between a unit of measure on a map and the actual distance in the real world. The scale tells you how to read the distances on the map. For instance, an inch on a map might equal 10 miles on earth. A map scale usually has two short lines with notches on them. One line measures distance in miles, the other in kilometers.

How to do it. The easiest way to use a map scale is to make a map strip. Find the scale on the map below. Place a strip of paper under the map scale. Mark the scale's notches on the paper, and label the marks with the number of miles or kilometers. Use a ruler to help you extend the notches on your strip. Then place the strip with the "0" mark at one point on the map. Line up the strip with a second point. Now read the closest number on your strip to this second point. You have just figured out the actual distance between two places.

Continental United States

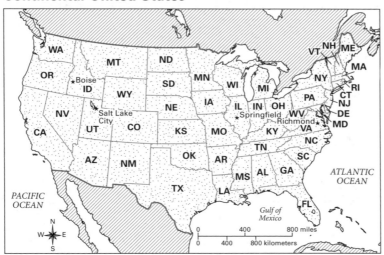

Try it. Practice reading distances using the scale on this map. Then answer the questions below.

1. What does one inch equal on this map?
2. About how many miles is it between Springfield, Illinois, and Richmond, Virginia?
3. If you start at Boise, Idaho, and go southeast, how many miles is it to Salt Lake City?
4. Plan a trip of 1,000 miles that goes through at least three states. Where would you start? Where would you end? Which states would you pass through?

Map Titles and Symbols

What is it? The **title** tells you the subject of a map. **Symbols** on a map represent different types of information. Symbols include shapes, colors, and lines. Shapes such as stars can stand for capital cities. Lines can represent borders, highways, and rivers. Areas of colors symbolize regions, such as green for forests. A **legend** lists the symbols on a map in a box and explains what they mean. A map legend is also called a **map key**.

How to do it. Read the map title first. Ask yourself what part of the world the map shows. The title should also tell what type of information the map shows, such as time period, routes, products, population, or climate.

Now look at the map itself. Match up each symbol with its explanation in the legend. Then look at the map as a whole. In your own words, summarize the information that the map presents.

Ancient Greek Trading Routes, About 500 B.C.E.

Try it. Use the map title and legend to answer the following questions.
1. What is the subject of this map? What period of time does it show?
2. What do the heavy solid lines on the map stand for?
3. What do the shaded areas represent?
4. Which product came from both Egypt and Tyras?
5. Which product came only from Persia?

Chapter 2
10: Mary Leaky, in Marguerite Holloway, "Mary Leaky: Unearthing History," *Scientific American,* October 1994.

Chapter 16
125: Sariputta, "Maha-hattipadopama Sutta: The Great Elephant Footprint Simile," trans. Thanissaro Bhikkhu, at www. online-dharma.net.

Chapter 21
194: Confucius, at www.quotation-spage.com. Laozi, at www.thetao. org. Hanfeizi, at www.academic. brooklyn.cuny.edu.

Chapter 23
205: Confucius, *The Analects of Confucius,* trans. Arthur Waley (New York: Vintage Books, 1989).

Chapter 27
246: Herodotos, "Demaratus on the Spartan Way of Living," at www. history-world.org.

Chapter 28
249: Aeschylus, *Four Plays of Aeschylus,* trans. G. M. Cookson (Oxford: Basil Blackwell, 1922).

Chapter 29
268: Sophocles, *Antigone,* trans., Ian Johnston (Arlington, VA: Richer Resources Pub., 2007). **270:** Socrates, at www.quotationspage. com. **271:** Socrates, at www.quo-tationspage.com. **272:** Socrates, at www.quotationspage.com.

Chapter 36
333: Scripture taken from the New Century Version. Copyright ©2005 by Thomas Nelson, Inc. Used by permission. All rights reserved. **334:** Ibid. **335:** Ibid.

Photographs

Cover: Ian Mckinnell/Getty Images

Title page: Ian Mckinnell/Getty Images

3 David L. Brill **29T:** ©Trustees of The British Museum, London **29M:** ©Trustees of The British Museum, London **29B:** ©Trustees of The British Museum, London **38TL:** Wikimedia Commons/Wikimedia **38TR:** Wikimedia Commons **38BL:** RF/Fotosearch **38BR:** Wikimedia **39TL:** Wikimedia Commons **39TR:** Wikimedia Commons **39BL:** Wikimedia Commons **39BR:** Wikimedia Commons **40TL:** Wikimedia Commons **40BR:** Wikimedia Commons **40TR:** RF/PHOTOS.COM **55:** RF/Steve Estvanik/Corbis **69:** © Erich Lessing/Art Resource, NY **80:** © Bettmann/CORBIS **87:** © David H. Wells/CORBIS **90TL:** RF/Photos.com **90TR:** RF/Photos.com **90BL:** Wikimedia **90BR:** RF/Photos.com **91TL:** RF/Photos.com **91TR:** RF/Photos.com **91BL:** Wikimedia Commons Wikimedia **91BR:** RF/Photos.com **92TR:** Wikimedia Commons./Wikimedia **92TL:** Wikimedia Commons **113:** © Borromeo/Art Resource, NY **115B:** Robert Harding **115:** © CORBIS **155:** © Adam Woolfitt/Woodfin Camp & Assoc. **157R:** © SEF /Art Resource, NY **158TL:** RF/Photos.com **158TR:** Mamoon Mengal/Wikimedia Commons/Wikimedia **158BL:** Wikimedia Commons/Wikimedia **158BR:** Wikimedia Commons/Wikimedia **159TR:** Per Honor et Gloria/Wikimedia Commons/Wikimedia **159BL:** RF/Ella/123RF **159TL:** PHGCOM/Wikimedia Commons/Wikimedia **159BR:** RF/Photos.com **160TL:** Wikimedia **160TR:** Wikimedia Commons/ Wikimedia **160BL:** RF/Lev Viktorov/123RF.com **160BR:** Wikimedia Commons **230TL:** Wikimedia Commons/Wikimedia **230TR:** Dr.Meierhofer/ Wikimedia Commons/Wikimedia **230BL:** WIKIMEDIA COMMONS/Wikimedia **230BR:** RF/K-PHOTOS /Alamy **231TR:** Imaginechina **231TL:** RF/Lawrence Wee/123RF **231BL:** RF/Kian Khoon Tan/123RF **231BR:** © RF/Panorama Media (Beijing) Ltd./Alamy **232TL:** RF/Holger Mette/123RF **232TR:** RF/Pascal Rateau/123RF **232BL:** RF/Ewan Chesser/123RF **232BR:** RF/Feng Yu/123RF **292:** RF/Gary Blakeley/Shutterstock **295TL:** RF/123RF **295TR:** Wikimedia Commons/Wikimedia **295BR:** RF/Vladimir Mucibabic/123RF **295BL:** RF/123RF **296TL:** RF/whitekrechet/123RF **296TR:** RF/Photos.com **296BL:** Angelo Vianello/123RF **296BR:** Karel Miragaya/123RF **297TL:** Wikimedia Commons/Wikimedia **297TR:** RF/Photos.com **297BL:** Fenia Labropoulou/123RF **297BR:** RF/Photos.com **352TL:** RF/Alexandr Tkachuk/123RF **352TR:** Massimo Merlini/RF/Alamy **352BL:** RF/Ivy Close Images/Alamy **352BR:** RF/A v.d. Wolde/Shutterstock **353TL:** RF/Iñigo Quintanilla/123RF **353TR:** RF/Hongqi Zhang/123RF **353BL:** ©RF/Itechno/Dreamstime.com **353BR:** RF/123RF **354TL:** RF/Richard Kane/123RF **354TR:** RF/Attila Jandi/123RF **354BL:** RF/Javarman Javarman/123RF **354BR:** RF/Pavle Marjanovic/123RF

Art

Chapter 1
4: Doug Roy

Chapter 3
14: Doug Roy **16:** Doug Roy

Chapter 5
28: Doug Roy

Chapter 6
37: Katy Haun

Chapter 8
45: Susan Jaekel **27:** Doug Roy **49:** DJ Simison **53:** DJ Simison

Chapter 9
70: Doug Roy

Chapter 10:
73: Doug Roy

Chapter 11:
77: Doug Roy

Chapter 12:
83: Doug Roy **89:** Doug Roy

Chapter 14
108–111: Doug Roy

Chapter 15
118: Doug Roy

Chapter 16
121–122: Doug Roy **126:** Doug Roy

Chapter 17
128–137: Doug Roy

Chapter 18
152: Susan Jaekel **153:** Susan Jaekel

Chapter 20
183–184: Len Ebert **187:** Doug Roy

Chapter 22
200: Len Ebert **202:** Doug Roy

Chapter 23
211: DJ Simison **216:** DJ Simison

Chapter 24
217–221: Doug Roy **224:** Doug Roy

Chapter 25
233: Doug Roy

Chapter 27
241: Doug Roy **243:** Doug Roy.

Chapter 29
263: Doug Roy **265–266:** Renate Lohmann **270–272:** Susan Jaekel. **276–277:** Renate Lohmann.

Chapter 34
312–313: Doug Roy

Chapter 35
327–328: Susan Jaekel

Chapter 37
342: Doug Roy

Chapter 38
345: Doug Roy